THE REAPER

JOHN FLETCHER STEWARD.

THE REAPER

*A HISTORY OF THE EFFORTS OF
THOSE WHO JUSTLY MAY BE
SAID TO HAVE MADE
BREAD CHEAP*

By JOHN F. STEWARD

*Author of
"Retrospective Exhibit of the Development of
Harvesting Machinery, Paris, 1900."
"Lost Maramech and Earliest Chicago"*

*Member of Jury of Awards at the Louisiana Pur-
chase Exposition in 1904, Assistant Geologist of the
Colorado River Exploring Expedition (1871), Hon-
orary Member of the Chicago Historical Society,
Late Member of the American Society of Mechanical
Engineers, Life Member of the Wisconsin Historical
Society, Late Member of the American Historical
Society, Member of the Illinois Historical Society,
Member of the Chicago Academy of Sciences, Late
Member of the Patent Committee of American
Society of Vehicle and Implement Mfg. Association,
Knight of one of the most Honorable Orders of
the Crown of Siam.*

❧

NEW YORK

GREENBERG: PUBLISHER

MANUFACTURED IN THE UNITED STATES OF AMERICA
BY H. WOLFF, NEW YORK, N. Y.

EDITOR'S FOREWORD

JOHN FLETCHER STEWARD, the author of this thorough study of the evolution of harvesting machinery, was born in the family homestead in Little Rock Township, Kendall county, Illinois, on June 23, 1841. It was new prairie country then, rich alike in soil fertility and the optimistic industry of its pioneers, poor in purse, and intensely idealistic and democratic. In all directions stretched rolling lands of vast potential wealth, cheap because men were scarce. Near at hand lay Chicago, the natural capital of the Prairie Empire. The trading post already had become a village whose strategic position at the foot of Lake Michigan marked it as the chief mart of the new country. It would become, inevitably, the greatest railroad center in the nation, once Stephenson's iron horse came west.

The town nearest the Steward homestead was Plano. There Steward's maternal uncle, John Fletcher Hollister, a Connecticut Yankee of the true inventive breed, located a workshop which eventually became a farm implement factory. Every little town in the vicinity had its experimenters of the same hopeful nature, men who in tiny shops after the day's work was done, kept everlastingly at the improvement of bread-winning tools. This sort of endeavor was the swift answer of a gifted people to the outstanding challenge of their environment. Since there were not men enough to till all these rich acres, multiply man power by machinery. This social and economic imperative, dominated the talent of that time and place as the Law of God dominated the Hebrew Prophets. It became, indeed, somewhat mixed with religion. Men like Hollister, sternly puritanical, thought of themselves as following the will of God in bringing wheat cheaply to market. If they could have perceived that overflowing wheat bins meant, among other things, swollen cities less mindful of religion than the countryside, and the consequent decline of the countryside in influence, perhaps they would have been less keen on the religious aspects of their inventing. Even so, they would have gone on, because there was money in it for the lucky ones, and immense fortunes for those who really hit pay dirt either in invention or manufacture. No one need worry about progress as long as progress pays but it is equally sure that each of these developers of harvesting machines were idealists in the sense that they felt sure their products would ease human labor and benefit humanity.

Give the white man of the Teutonic strain elbow-room and he becomes a go-getter. Well, here was elbow room at last. For hundreds of centuries this gifted branch of the Caucasian family had been stalled in sterile territory or cramped quarters. It had stumbled out of drying Mid-Asia in the dim ages of the long ago into that extension of Asia which we call Europe, only to find the best parts of Europe in the hands of a more cultured race, with better discipline, better weapons. Thin Baltic shore, fogs of Scandinavia, marshes of Jutland—from these poor homelands went forth Norse, Saxon, Angle, Jute. They took England—a tiny isle compared to the boundless dreams and immense vitality of its conquerors. Normandy was an outpost, and Sicily hardly more than a showroom for their qualities. On to America they came, but it was the America of sandy littoral or stern and rock-bound coast. Even so, worth conquering; the Indians were disposed of by battle, disease and rum; the country possessed laboriously by fast-arriving children. Eventually, the Appalachian mountain barrier was passed in the South and the valiant Six Nations of the Iroquois subdued in the North. A new Nation, with no feudal harness to hinder its strides, took hold of the interior of America, the empire of the Mississippi and the Great Lakes. Here, at long last, was land enough to satisfy the land hunger of the most energetic race on the planet, abundance of deep stoneless soil waiting for the multitudes. But in the meantime, there were no multitudes, so the relatively few humans on the scene must have machines.

The plow, of course, is the symbol of Man's triumph over Earth. Remember, in "The Covered Wagon" how the pioneers took the plow along with them over the Oregon Trail. The steel plow, with its renewable ploughshare, has made its share of American history. But the Prairie Empire needed not only to break land and cultivate; it needed also to harvest the crop. A man and a team can plow far more land than they can harvest. At plowing time there is not much else to do; at harvest time everything must be done at a rush. In the old countries the labor reserves were drawn on at harvest—but here, at the start, there were no reserves available. In a sense the grain problem of the prairies was to make a man and a team as efficient harvesters as they were plowers. Whoever had ideas along that line was likely to come to the Chicago country. Thither came Cyrus McCormick from Virginia, William Deering from Maine and Marcus Steward and John Fletcher Hollister from Connecticut.

The two latter were brothers-in-law, Marcus Steward having married Ursula Hollister in June, 1822. Where they were married does not appear in the Hollister family geneaology compiled by Lafayette Wallace Case, M. D., and published by the Fergus Printing Company in 1886; but it was probably in Hollisterville, Wayne County, Pa., into which wilderness Ursula's father had led a migration from East Glastonbury, Connecticut. In those days of slow travel, a family usually required two hops from New England to the Mississippi valley, the Massachusetts migrants settling first in western New York and their sons and daughters moving on West; the Connecticut folk frequently taking root in Pennsylvania.

Marcus and Ursula Steward probably stayed in Pennsylvania some years after their marriage, because the record shows them arriving on the homestead near Plano in 1838. A bustling journey it must have been, as they were accompanied by seven or eight children who, standing in line, made a neat "stair" at the standard two year interval favored in pioneer life. In the next three years were two more arrivals, the last being our author, John Fletcher Steward.

Whatever else young John F. did in his boyhood he read as widely as circumstances would permit. Curiosity raged in him all his life. He had a passion for geology, and a love of history almost as marked as his zeal in mechanics. These bore fruit in due time; but as a boy he first attracted attention by his uncanny skill in repairing and regulating balky time-pieces. At fourteen he was the "Mr. Fixit" of that unspecialized rustic community; and it was foreordained that he would do some of the exceedingly close work with precision tools and instruments which remained to be done in outfitting the farmer with harvest implements.

This development, however, was broken into by the Civil War. In 1861, young Steward was twenty, just the right age to save the Union when Father Abraham called for volunteers. He enlisted in Company F, 127th Illinois Volunteers, one of the regiments which Grant led South to cut the Confederacy in two along the Mississippi line. He was at the slogging siege of Vicksburg, suffering strains and exposures there from which he never fully recovered. Invalided home, he spent some time in Plano and then joined up again, this time with the Veteran Reserve Corps. When the war ended his unit was in camp at Pontiac, Michigan, and he was discharged July 4, 1865, at Detroit. Veteran Steward took home with him from the wars a bride in the lovely person of Sarah Louise Chandler, daughter of one of Pontiac's first families, which had entered that territory some time earlier from Vermont, via New York.

After the war the American spirit expanded gloriously in the direction of homesteads, State-making, and railroad building. Chicago began to hum, and Plano with it. Steward's father and uncle had rebuilt the Adolph Pressure Reaper, and Marsh Brothers were just constructing the first unit of a factory which made history. Casting his lot with Marsh Brothers, our author rose from workman to foreman in the Gammon & Deering establishment, and when William Deering took his factory to Chicago, John F. Steward went along as Superintendent.

The steady grind, however, was broken by one long and adventurous vacation, an experience so novel that millions of Americans envied him his opportunity, which came to him chiefly because of his geologic knowledge. In 1871 he became a member of the second government party to run the gauntlet of Colorado Canyon. Major John Wesley Powell had led a party through the Canyon the preceding year; the descent was repeated to gather additional data. Steward, then just thirty years of age, went along as assistant

geologist, serving without pay. References to his part in the expedition will be found in official publications and also in Fred S. Dellenbaugh's two books, "Romance of the Colorado River" (1903) and
"A Canyon Voyage" (1908). With his chief, Professor Thompson, Steward made several very arduous side expeditions to identify
the rocks of distant formations. His health broke under these
strains. Dellenbaugh says, on page 146 of the "Voyage":

"Meanwhile Steward's illness had increased, and I spent most of
the night trying to relieve his pain. The air was cold, and he was
most uncomfortable, the only shelter being of boughs we had built to
protect him from the sun. We had opium pills in our medicine chest,
and I had the little flask of brandy referred to. With several of the
pills and my brandy which I at last persuaded him to take as medicine
(he despised alcoholic drinks) his suffering was somewhat relieved
and he was able to lie still on his bed of willows. . . . The exposure
had brought on a trouble of the back originally developed during the
Civil War."

Since wintering in the Canyon with the rest of the party was out
of the question, Steward left the expedition on November 11,
hobbling painfully through the wilderness for many miles until he
could obtain a conveyance, because his lame back made it impossible
for him to sit a horse for any length of time. He had been with the
expedition since March (it entered the Canyon, May 11) meeting
severe tests with fortitude for five months.

After going to Chicago with William Deering, Steward was given
charge of the Company's patent matters. This association with
Mr. Deering, one of the great figures in the development of farm
machinery, lasted for many years. In William Deering, Steward
found an ideal employer for a man of inventive genius. Deering
honored invention, and was willing to wait patiently while Steward's ideas were germinating. Mr. Deering, who was born in Maine
in 1826, entered the field of implement manufacture in the early
seventies and from that time until the merger of his firm into the
International Harvester Company in 1902, exercised a dominant
influence over developments in the art of machine reaping and
harvesting. Under him, Mr. Steward brought out scores of patents,

the *Kendall County News* placing the number at 130, when, in 1915, it recorded his death and achievements. Mr. Deering had died two years previously.

After the consolidation of the harvesting companies in 1902, Mr. Steward continued in charge of patent matters for that company, remaining active until his last illness. His service with the I. H. C. and its predecessors covered almost fifty years.

Mr. Steward brought to this heavy historical task not only a detailed special knowledge, but also a keen interest in history for its own sake. His "Lost Maramech and Earliest Chicago: a History of the Foxes and of their Downfall near the Great Village of Maramech" is a model of what local history writing should be and so often is not. It reflects not only the point of view of the shrewd antiquarian, but also the humanitarianism of a man profoundly moved by the sufferings of a vanquished race. One will find in those pages the work of a kindly soul, and a man above price who will make no concessions in presenting the forthright truth as he knows it.

That sterling quality appears even more strongly in this work. While this history will appeal to future investigators by reason of its exact information rather than because of its partisanship in assigning credit for the many inventions which make up the modern reaper, nevertheless it is probable that the former would not have been forthcoming except for the stimulus of the latter. It required, I fancy, a stern hatred of presumption and deceit to rouse a busy man like Steward, in the autumn of his life, to a long labor of this exacting character. In its very nature, the work could have no economic reward; but it could add to the store of human knowledge, and it would set some things right which, in the sorry business conscience of the time, had gone sadly astray. That was enough for John Fletcher Steward, and it is enough, I feel sure, to win for him the respect of those who read his book. The labor of many years, it was completed in 1910 when Mr. Steward was a resident of Chicago. Its dating necessarily precludes the development of the "combine" which did not come into existence until later. Some reference is made, however, in the last chapter to some of the first developments in powered form machines.

My part has been relatively unimportant—to smooth, rough places, eliminate a few repetitions, and tone down certain parts of the text in which the author's strong feeling ran away with him.   The manuscript came to me with one page missing, and rather than guess at its contents, I have attempted no substitution, letting that particular chapter end in the air, so to speak.   The reader with a background of mechanical knowledge will be able to supply the omission.

ARTHUR POUND
Editor
Author of "The Iron Man in Industry"
"Johnson of the Mohawks"
"The Telephone Idea"
Co-Editor of "They Told Barron"

New Scotland, N. Y.,
April 30, 1930

PREFACE

THE AUTHOR, during more than the allotted term of life, has been in active touch with agricultural lines. The gaps in the shakeroof of a pioneer's log cabin beside a wheat field just in bloom, first gave him light. When yet a mere child it was his delight to ride upon the home-made reaper, his companion in the fields until after his teens were past.

Not many years elapsed before the boy had "found himself." With borrowed pocket-knives miniature water mills were built, whenever rains gave birth to roadside rivulets; and simple wood and tin windmills (the latter ever keeping the secret of the cause that so often required the application to the grindstone of his mother's shears) whirled on the gables. The few books at hand devoted to mechanical lines were devoured, and their contents to no little extent digested, while in his older boyhood he ran the saw-mill on the farm and often aided in the other mill, the rumbling of whose stones to him was music. Early manhood found him free from his military trappings, worn through the war for the Union, when an exceedingly active life in and study of the great art of which he writes began, and which continued for half a century. During the last two of the three revolutions that have been wrought in harvesting methods he has done his share, as the records of the Patent Offices show, and, as well, he noted all the steps taken by others.

It has been said by many that no other man has had half the opportunities to know the art, both practical and theoretical, as far as concerns inventions and general development. If half so said be true, who, more than he, should feel the duty to prepare this record; and from whom, less than from him, should apologetic words for the self appointed task be expected? Since early manhood he has "camped on the trail" of the false history of this great art.

xiii

His ordeal has been that of the fire of activity, but the passing away of the callous of brain and hand prompted the retracting, in softer lines, of many phrases of his manuscript as earliest written; but in so redrawing he has not minced words. All those forged in the heat of battle have been cast aside as unfitted for calm history. In stating important facts, however, he has not been mealy mouthed.

The very culmination of a long series of years of fiction are the two volumes; the "Romance of the Reaper" and "Cyrus Hall McCormick, His Life and Work" from the pen of Herbert N. Casson,[1] in both of which the author attempts to make the hero becomingly wear an unearned and misfit halo. When first organized, the International Harvester Company, the successor of five of the twelve of the then existing manufacturers of harvesting machinery, Cyrus H. McCormick, President, was popularly thought to be a combination in restraint of trade. In view of this, it was sought, by the management, to have a history written directed largely to showing the progress an ultimate development of the art, but directed particularly to showing the chaotic condition of the trade which led to the formation of the new company and the purchase of the several factories and good will in the trade. The present author, then head of the Department of Patents, was asked to open to Mr. Casson his store of records and general information which form the substance of this work. The early pages of the manuscript of this volume, books, law reports, Patent Office Documents, and hundreds of other documents were turned over to Casson, in my library. In addition to all this, the stories of the successes and failures of inventors and manufacturers were listened to by Mr. Casson, from the lips of the late William N. Whitely, the late William Deering, Charles W. Marsh, Ralph Emerson, the author, and many others grown gray in the business. The manuscript of the "Romance of the Reaper" was soon, in part, submitted to me, and it was then said by Mr. Casson, after my many criticisms, that he had decided not to attempt a history but would call it the "Romance of the Reaper."

[1] See Who's Who in America, Vol. XII. Later London correspondent for Wall Street Journal, etc.

CONTENTS

CHAPTER   PAGE

      EDITOR'S FOREWORD v

      PREFACE xiii

  I. THE INCENTIVE 3

  II. EARLY MACHINES 16

  III. OBED HUSSEY'S CONTRIBUTION 56

  IV. ROBERT McCORMICK AND HIS SONS 82

  V. REFUTING CERTAIN CLAIMS 96

  VI. PATENT HISTORY AND HEARINGS 103

  VII. THE McCORMICK TESTIMONY 114

  VIII. ENGLISH FIELD TRIALS 149

  IX. SELF-RAKING REAPERS—PRELIMINARY STAGES ... 186

  X. EXPERT REVIEW OF THE 1847 PATENT 194

  XI. THE ARRIVAL OF THE SELF-RAKING REAPER 219

  XII. THE BINDERS RIDE 228

  XIII. THE STORY OF THE MARSH HARVESTER 237

  XIV. HEADERS AND STRIPPERS 257

  XV. GRAIN BINDERS 265

  XVI. KNOT-TYING MACHINES 276

  XVII. THE APPLEBY PATENTS 289

  XVIII. WILLIAM DEERING AND THE BINDER 303

  XIX. GORHAM AND SPAULDING CLAIMS 308

  XX. JOHN F. APPLEBY'S STORY 319

  XXI. TWINE DEVELOPMENTS 344

  XXII. A LEGEND ANALYZED 346

  XXIII. BLOCKING THE GREAT PRETENSION 356

  XXIV. SOME DEERING CONTRIBUTIONS DISPLAYED 368

LIST OF ILLUSTRATIONS

PAGE

John Fletcher Steward ....*Frontispiece*

Machine Used in Ancient Gaul 17

Cut from Woodcroft's Specifications of English Patents 19

   "   "   "   "   "   "   " 21

   "   "   "   "   "   "   " 22

   "   "   "   "   "   "   " 23

Rev. Patrick Bell 37

Bells Reaper with Swathing Conveyor Removed 38

Side Elevation of Bell's Improved Machine 43

Randall 1833 51

Obed Hussey 56

Hussey's Reaping and Mowing Machine 57

Hussey's Reaping Machine 63

Edward Stabler 69

Josiah Hill Farms 78

Drawing of McCormick Reaper of 1834 83

Anvil Block 85

McCormick Cutting Device 93

Original McCormick Reaper of 1831 116

Testing First Reaper Near Steele's Tavern 117

Same Scene Redrawn 119

Photo Engraving of McCormick Advertising Poster 121

Cut Found in Cyrus H. McCormick His Life and Work.. 123

Still Another View of Fred Runger's Windmill 125

Manny's Report 141

John H. Manny 142

McCormick 1849 143

Hussey's Reaper in England 150

McCormick's American Reaper 154

Hussey's American Reaper 156

PAGE

McCormick's Reaper 175

Drawing of McCormick Patent 181

McCormick's Reaping Machine 183

Reaper of Woodward-Schnebley Type Seat of McCormick
  1842 Patent 191

Whitenack's Self Raking Reaping Machine 223

Dorsey's Reaping Machine 222

Drawing of Reaper 229

Drawing of Reaper 232

Marsh Harvester, 1858 239

Marsh Harvester, 1858 243

Marsh Harvester in Operation 250

Aultman and Miller Patent 261

Danford's Mowing Machine 262

John H. Gordon Packer Binder 272

Twisting, Holding and Cutting Device 274

Withington Wire Binder 277

Deering Wire Binder 278

Locke Binder 279

Spaulding's Unpatented Binder 284

Drawing 314

Gorham's Packer and Appleby's Packing Device 316

Appleby 320

Drawing 326

Twine Binder 1900 340

Deering Marsh Harvester 341

Minneapolis Appleby Binder 341

First McCormick Copy of Deering Minn. Binder 342

Picture of Various Inventors 367

Deering Auto Mower 370

Deering Auto Mower 374

THE REAPER

CHAPTER I.

The Incentive

Any complete history of the western prairies of America echoes the story of harvesting by means of machines. The history of one cannot be told without including the development of the other; for in this great field the struggles of the latter for recognition took place, and each of a horde of inventors here strove to establish the supremacy of the result of his labors.

Father Marquette, the companion of Joliet, left the record of his travels in 1673 through territory which has proved to be the great wheat center of the agricultural world. Joutel, who visited the Mississippi valley in 1687, spent that winter at Fort St. Louis, on what is now known as Starved Rock, in La Salle County, Illinois, and hunted along Fox River, visiting the Indian towns there located as far as Kane County. Of these scenes he says: "In regard to the country, it could not be more beautiful, and I can say that the country of the Illinois is perfect and that one there would be able to have all things necessary to support life; for with the beauty with which it is adorned is joined fertility."

Reports like these, more frequent as the years passed, drew population irresistibly into the Great West as soon as the savage tribes were removed. In the wake of those who came to seek farm homes followed others, mechanics, designers, and manufacturers, who were ready to undertake to produce the labor-saving machinery whose crying need was indicated by the abundance of arable land and the shortage of labor.

My earliest home was in the midst of the almost boundless prairies which include Kendall County and adjoining counties of Illinois. There, more than elsewhere, one could sympathize with the efforts on the part of inventors to relieve the laboring classes from the

3

stings of the stubble field and the scorching rays of the harvest sun.

Now that the capabilities of the Mississippi valley, from an agricultural point of view, are appreciated, we do not marvel when we read the records of the early explorers and those of the Jesuit fathers, written more than two hundred years ago, which speak of the great fertility of the soil, its natural productiveness and its great future. The Indian tribes, always friendly to the French, supplied the latter with provisions, as their needs demanded, furnishing corn that was even then often cultivated in rows, about three and one-half feet apart. The plants were ridged and hilled precisely as now by the most accomplished growers, and the yield was so great as to demonstrate to the explorers the possibilities of the western prairies as a wheat growing region. The French introduced seed wheat wherever they settled. In order to convey a full idea of the fertility of the soil we are told by them that with only crude implements amazing crops of corn were raised, the fields of a single village sometimes aggregating hundreds of acres. Pumpkins, watermelons, sunflowers and artichokes were abundant. From the seed wheat they brought and sowed and distributed among the Indians, rich returns were reaped. Millions of acres were covered with grass, in places as high as the backs of the buffalo, which in herds lazily grazed over the well-watered, treeless, prairies. The explorers carried the information to France and there with unbounded enthusiasm told that it was only necessary to put the plow to the sod in order to prepare for a crop, thereby accomplishing in one season what would require the labor of ten in France, because of the trees, shrubbery, stumps, and rocks to be cleared away. Later the people of New England, Pennsylvania, and Virginia listened to the stories told by trappers and hunters of their own blood.

Leaving his eastern home with the melting of the snows, the pioneer was led on and on, tempted by easy travel over prairies carpeted with blue grass. Land at $1.25 per acre, and land which required little labor to prepare it for seed! The first settlers of the prairies ignored the collection of wigwams and few houses that formed the village at the southern end of Lake Michigan. The village had not increased in population for two hundred years—from the time first visited by Joliet and Marquette who, by the way, spelled the name by which it was known C-h-i-c-a-g-o-u. The future of, this village held out to the first white American Settler no promises equal to those of the farm home. The earlier comers located their dwellings in the groves along the streams, but their holdings were as large as they could afford. Few were satisfied with an area of prairie land less than that which the eyesight could circumscribe. Lumber for buildings, fuel and fencing, was drawn from the groves that gemmed the prairies and lined the streams.

Since breaking plow and harrow were the only implements necessary in a stoneless and almost stumpless land, tillage required so little effort that each new-comer was led into the mistake of sowing more than he could reap. Eventually he became so pressed that he might well have exclaimed, "The harvest truly is plenteous, but the laborers are few." Trained midst the rocky New England hills, to long days of labor and to the necessity of employing every moment of fair weather for a useful purpose, his crops frequently outstripped his ability to harvest them.

The cry for something more than mere physical labor first found listening ears among the inventors and mechanics of the Eastern States. Those who responded undertook a difficult task, although one that, now accomplished, looks simple compared with the later triumphs of engineering design. Those who turned their inventive talents to agricultural tools found the rocky hillsides of the Eastern states unfavorable to their efforts and naturally directed their thoughts to the West, in search of field-conditions more favorable, and where great difficulties still remained to be overcome.

The earliest harvesting machines for use in this country established their practicability in the section I have described. Here the reaping machine first became a most important fact, and here, as in the struggle for existence in nature, the fittest survived. This struggle forms the subject matter of this story. On these broad prairies lie, in rust, the failures, now only known in names seldom spoken; and in the United States Patent Office is found little more than what may be considered faint memories unnecessary to recall except for the sake of doing exact justice to all who participated in this epoch-making advance.

With wheat often less than fifty cents per bushel, and oats half that price, even though hauled over almost impassable roads fifty miles or more, still the prairie farms paid for themselves and the necessary machinery. The crude reaper of the earlier days shared in producing the earnings to no mean extent. The possibilities once apparent, many a farmer turned his moments of newly won leisure and his New England ingenuity to curing the defects of the agricultural machinery of this early period, and often added a word to the great accumulations in the United States Patent Office. These include more than one hundred thousand patents covering all sorts of alleged and real improvements in agricultural machines and tools.

As early as the forties factories were found on the far-reaching prairies, turning out reaping machines as well as other tools to meet the great demands. Within a circle of one hundred miles drawn with Kendall County, Illinois, as a center are located a score of towns and villages where busy brains and hands did more towards the development of modern harvesting machinery than all outside that small area.

At Sun Prairie, Walworth County, Wisconsin, Esterly produced his first machine. At Ottawa, Illinois, Rugg manufactured operative machines. There were three factories in Kendall County, and in Kane as many more. Rockford earned the name Reaper City, and in DeKalb County many important steps were taken. To this region in 1835 Obed Hussey trundled his reapers into their third harvest, practical successes from the first. Here McCormick came ten years later with his nearly successful machines, and in 1847 built a modest factory that helped to form the nucleus of one of Chicago's wonderful industries. As time passed many of the little factories fell by the wayside, and others grew to immense proportions. Few there were who could then foresee, among the shifting scenes, any hint as to the final result; but in a retrospective view we realize that no other result was possible than that the great Mississippi valley must necessarily come to be the heart and center of the great group of manufacturing institutions, the smoke of which now mocks the clouds.

Of the limited number of early harvesting machines manufactured beyond the confines of the Mississippi valley, nearly all found their way thither where ideal conditions of operation prevailed. The

self-binding harvester there developed and by many considered
to be one of the modern wonders, has long since crept into the hilly
sections of our country, and even into the smaller grain fields of
Europe, winning its way against ancient custom and cheap labor.

Though America is the leading nation in this development, others
contributed largely. English inventors taught us, in particular, the
valuable lesson that the "shear cut" was as necessary for cutting
straws and grasses as to cut fibrous substances.

In the western harvest fields, while the fields were as yet cut with
the cradle, farm wives and children went into the fields, and cut
with scissors the standing straws which with nimble fingers they
braided and put into various hat forms. Yet the scissors-cut was a
long time getting into practical use on a large scale; while the
great essential in a reaping machine is, of course, to *cut* the straws
or grass blades, the final choice of methods was reached comparatively late. The usual mowing and reaping devices, the scythe and
cradle, suggested other methods of severing grain stalks by mechanical means, and hence it is natural to find, among the very earliest
efforts, attempts to imitate the action of the scythe and reaping
cradle, by giving motion to a rotating series of blades, or rapidly
moving sharp edged discs. However, it was soon discovered that no
cutting edge which depended solely upon rapidity of movement could
stand the test. However keen the scythe's edge, grasses are only
pushed away when it is moved slowly.

For untold generations grass had been laid with cutting blades.
Not until the trodden path had been departed from—not until
common shears were imitated, was grass or grain successfully cut
by other than manual power. With the adoption of the shear principle, the combined action of an edge and a co-operating resistant,
came the first harvesting machinery that could be dignified by that
name. No fibre is too delicate to be severed by shears. The coars-
est straws and grass blades, the human hair and the finest silken
fabrics are severed with an equal degree of perfection. We may,
then, treat the adoption of perfected cutting apparatus as embodying the foundation principle of the reaper. Once that basic fact
stood revealed, all that has since happened in mechanical harvesting became possible.

Before the settlers of America were "out of the woods," before the treeless West permitted the cultivation of large fields, the efforts made in England and Scotland to lighten the labors of the harvest field seemed distinctly promising. Both grass and grain were experimentally cut there by machinery during the last few years of the eighteenth century, but still the cry for relief from the tortures of the harvest field, first heard, long before the beginning of the Christian Era, echoed down the years.

In the British Museum, red with rust, are exhibited two smooth-edged Egyptian reaping hooks of iron. While the mere form of the sickle and scythe do not differ greatly, a distinction must be drawn, for the cutting principle exemplified in the smooth edge and that in the serrated edge are as widely different as can well be imagined. The ancients, and, in fact, people not so ancient after all, used the smooth-edged tool in cutting grass, the serrated edge for cutting grain. Grasses being usually short, it was found difficult to gather their tops in the left hand and thus hold them while the blade was forcibly drawn to sever them, as was the custom in reaping grain; and hence this work was done by a quick, glancing stroke of a keen blade. The quickness of the stroke required depended largely upon the keenness of the cutting edge.

Modern mowing machines are successful partly because of this chopping action, but to a greater extent they succeed because of the adoption of the shear cutting principle. As grasses needed to be spread to the sun, there is no necessity for careful bunching; in fact, the avoidance of bunching is necessary; but economy early dictated quite another method for grain harvesting. The heads of the grain being precious, only sufficient straw was left therewith to enable the proper handling of bundles when formed. The curved sickle blade was passed into the standing grain and the heads brought by its curvature into a close bunch. By a movement of the left hand the heads thus bunched were grasped and held, while the sickle was drawn quickly so as to sever all of the straws thus held. The handful carefully laid, the operation was repeated. The serrated edge of the blade was found superior, largely because of the fact that its delicate teeth were self-sharpening.

Limiting our investigations, for the moment, to the severing of ripened grain straws, I am prompted to say that the invention of the

"Sickle Edge" ranks among the major inventions of husbandry. What other tool has man ever produced having a self-sharpening edge? What object in nature suggested to man the possibility of such an edge? Did early man first take the strong, keenly armed blades of the various agaves and with quick drawing strokes harvest his grain? Or did he early learn that a keen edge, nicked by accident, worked better than a perfectly aligned tool. A little experience may have taught him to nick the edge with care, and reflection have influenced him to place the nicks so closely together as to leave needlelike points standing between them and to incline all these points in one direction. If we pass a needle through a substance its point penetrates easily, but the pressure upon its sides is likely to wear it away and make it smaller beyond its point. The principle involved in thus reducing the size of the needle is precisely that which, carried into effect, makes a "Sickle-edge" a self-sharpening one. If the fine teeth of the edge are so formed that the points pass through the grain straws, as a needle would pass through them, then the points are not materially dulled; but the metal becomes worn away from their sides. The teeth of the sickled-edge, so formed as to be substantially parallel with the direction of movement of the blade in cutting, split the straws into splinters which, being pressed into spaces between them wear spaces deeper. I have seen the serrated edges of harvester cutters so worn back by long use as to quadruple the original length of the needle-like points. The straws of fully ripe grain are easily severed, and, although the sickled edge has a tearing action as well as that of actual severing, it serves its purpose better than the plain edge. I shall have occasion to treat of this matter again, in detailing early attempts to utilize the principle made effective by the serrated edge, and in discussing the difference between the mode of operation of the mowing machine proper and the reaper.

Rees's Encyclopedia, edition of 1820, informs us that in England, at the beginning of the nineteenth century, three men with sickles could cut and bind two acres of wheat per day. As binding this amount required, comparatively, only a small part of the time, I judge that no English laborer could cut and bind more than an acre of grain per day. This fact was sufficient incentive to prompt the

"Society of Arts" of England, as early as 1780, to offer a prize of thirty pounds for an effective reaping machine and to continue such offer for a period of thirty-six years.

The following quotations taken from "Woodcroft's Appendix to the specifications of English patents for reaping machines," London 1853, explains the Society's offer: "For a machine, to answer the purpose of mowing and reaping wheat, rye, barley, oats, or beans, by which it may be done more expeditiously and cheaper, than by any method now practised—provided that it does not shed the corn or pulse more than the methods in common practice and that it lays the straws in such a manner as may be easily gathered up for binding—the gold medal, or thirty pounds." It was required that the "machine with certificates that at least three acres have been cut by it," be delivered to the Society on or before the second Tuesday in December, 1783. (See also Appendix of Society of Arts, Vol. 1, p. 107.)

The scythe, as an agricultural tool, so soon took the place of the smooth-edged hook in the hay fields, and the "cradle" that of the hand sickle in the harvest fields, that the demand for a reaping machine ceased to be as great as when the offer was first made. In the small fields of England, in consequence of this, efforts toward machine harvesting almost ceased. Nevertheless, the first reaping machine which actually met the requirements of the Society was produced in Great Britain, but, unfortunately for its maker, not within the required thirty-six years, which ended in 1816. It is probable that most of the machines produced during the period mentioned could not have cut three acres of grain in a fully successful manner, but that some of them promised well is clear from contemporaneous publications. The hard sickle was never much used in America after the Colonial days, but the grain cradle and scythe proved to be as inadequate to the demand of the great prairies as the reaping hook had been to the small fields of England.

A retrospect of the days of the scythe and cradle now seems more like a poetic flight of fancy than the prosaic stern reality so many years endured. With the dawn went to the field, a gang of men. In the log-cabin the early breakfast-work was hardly over before time for preparation of the necessary mid-morning "lunch" was at hand. By half-past nine the younger boys of the farm tugged a large basket of food to the field, and a pail of water. The writer was so young when these services began that he did not quite understand when told that the water for harvest hands, to be cool, "must be drawn from the northwest corner of the well." If the water did not reach the workmen in a cool state the boys were charged with negligence in not following the instructions or dallying on the way. A half hour of rest gave sufficient time to empty the basket. This field lunch was no sooner over than it was time to prepare dinner. The hour from twelve to one was given to eating and rest. Mid-day dinner dishes out of the way, the preparation of the afternoon "lunch" was at once undertaken. The half hour for rest and refreshments of the forenoon was repeated between three and four in the afternoon. At sundown the gang of workmen, every one again "as hungry as a hired man," trooped in to supper. This over, the evening work, practically that of a boarding-house, remained. Late at night, the worn women of the household sought rest. The labor and expense incident to boarding so many harvest hands added another stimulant to inventive geniuses in the agricultural field.

In America, by 1833, the cradle and scythe were used almost exclusively in saving grass and grain. A man with a scythe could mow but few acres of grass per day, and a boy with fork carefully spread it to the sun to cure. With a cradle a strong man could cut about three acres of good standing grain in a day. Another man equally able was required to rake and bind it.

Before going into the details of the history of harvesting machinery proper, it is well to consider, very carefully, the conditions that the inventor had to encounter. All that was actually necessary to be done in order to overcome the difficulties can soon be told, but the labor involved was shared by hundreds of inventors and mechanics for half a century.

The first requisite was to impart uninterrupted motion to the cutting apparatus and such other parts as were to be given movement by the action of the traction wheel or wheels. Unfortunately the condition of soil most favorable to the growth of grain was found to be unfavorable to traction, and it was soon learned that a driving wheel must be armed with spade-like projections, more or less high, adapted to enter the soil and thus better cling thereto. Even on ground fairly hard it was found that a driving wheel needed to be armed with these "lugs" because of the creeping action that constantly took place, due to the yielding of the soil in advance of the tread of the wheel. Stated otherwise, the labor required of the wheel in giving motion to the various parts is a constant resistant and the surface of the soil instead of rotating the wheel to the fullest extent, partly yields under it. The necessity for reducing to a minimum the resistance to the rotation of the driving wheel has become so apparent in automatic binders of late years, that elaborate perfect anti-friction methods and devices have been perfected.

Some grasses are tall, large and easy to cut; but others are short, wiry and hard. Timothy grass stands well; clover is usually prostrated and tangled. The taller grains sway in the wind and incline away from the advancing machine, or laterally, as often as they lean toward the cutting edge. Grain fields are weedy and sometimes difficult grasses are encountered in them. Rye is tall and wheat comparatively short. Both become tangled, lodged, and straw-broken at times. Rusted wheat is difficult to handle. "Lodging" is the rule with heavy oats. Over-ripe grain becomes so "fluffy" that good work cannot be done in harvesting it. Fractious teams and ignorant labor, with which they had to contend, should be added to the unfavorable conditions confronting early inventors. How to surmount all these difficulties by mechanisms adapted to perform well in one condition and not badly in another, and so to harmonize all of the parts essential to success that both the individual functions and the function of the parts when combined should be properly performed, long remained serious problems. All these problems now seem to be easy tasks; but the slow growth toward present efficient machines amply proves the contrary to have been true.

A team of horses might give motion to a machine by pulling it when hitched at one side of the work to be performed, or be so hitched as to push it ahead of them; but for years able men debated which hook-up was the better, and even now both systems are in use. Yet the method of direct draft that has so far shown itself to be the most practical was one embodied in the first *fully* successful reaping machine, early in the thirties of the nineteenth century.

Means for laying the swath and for accumulating the gavels, in grain cutting, were from the first recognized as necessary, and both manual and automatic devices were tested for receiving the cut grain and delivering it in gavel form to the ground.

One of the essentials was that of supporting, or poising, the machine upon its wheels. All of the working parts of a reaper or harvesting machine located upon the frame are, in reality, suspended from the axes of the supporting wheels, and movement is imparted to those parts directly from one or more of such supporting wheels. Resistance, due to the labor required of the traction of the wheels, tends to prevent the wheels from rotating, as they pass over the ground. Whatever the amount of such resistance, to that extent is the effort of the team directed to tip the machine over forward. This will be clearly understood if we suppose two supporting wheels abreast, a little distance apart, and the framework and gearing of the machines mainly between, as in the modern self-binding harvester. With the load exactly balanced on these wheels, the least possible amount of resistance, even a little friction, tends to cause the load to roll over forward at every attempt to advance; particularly if pushed from behind this is true. Experimenters found that more than ordinary attention must be paid to placing the load suitably upon the wheels and to locating properly the point of draft. Some placed a supplemental supporting wheel forward of the main supporting wheels and others did likewise behind, for the purpose of sustaining the preponderance of weight. The time soon came, however, when it was demonstrated that a draft tongue or thills could be used upon a carefully balanced machine, so that the proper working position could be maintained by the shoulders of the team without overburdening the horses. The difficulty of poising the machine properly is here dwelt upon mainly to prepare the reader to more fully understand the various attempts to produce a reaper and more clearly understand the causes of failure of machines hereafter to be mentioned.

The tendency of the early forms of cutting apparatus to force the grass blades or grain straws away from them rendered the seemingly easy task of cutting grain in fact a difficult one; and hence means were early provided for forcing the standing grain against the cutting devices and holding it here, until severed. The more defective the cutting devices the more necessary were extraneous means for making them effective. What is known in the trade as a "reel," was among the earliest mechanism applied to this end, with various ingenious adaptations for raising or lowering it, at will, to adjust it to the heights required by various lengths of standing grain to be cut, and to move it forward or back relative to the cutting apparatus. Such was the simple reaper.

The founders of our government foresaw the public benefits of protecting inventors. The operation of patent laws has now been reduced to a science and their interpretation has all to do with the matter under consideration. Because of this fact I shall often have occasion to refer to suits at law resorted to by patentees in attempting to establish and maintain their rights. The interpretation of these laws has occupied a large part of the time of the Supreme Court of the United States for the last half century, and as a result all features thereof have been made reasonably clear.

What is called as "the state of the art," at the time of granting any patent in controversy, is considered upon in every effort to determine an inventor's actual rights; and although the conceptive thought may have been original with him, he is not entitled to be considered the inventor of a device or machine, if what he did had been accomplished before. Not only this, he must have conceived and must also have accomplished practical results. The true inventor, then, is he who makes public, for the first time, not merely a new idea, but a practical exemplification of the principles involved in the device, machine, or process. We naturally give credit for inventive talent and good judgment in constructing a new machine, but even so the constructor is not entitled to a monopoly for a period of years unless he is *first in the field* with that particular device. If this were otherwise, whatever Tom, Dick, or Harry might make could be patented as many times over as new constructors might undertake the same task. The records of the patent offices and contemporaneous magazines tell and show what earlier inventors did, but they do not always point out every new feature presented in the machines made by the various experimenters.

For our purposes the nineteenth century may be divided into three epochs, each overlapping the other. That ending in 1832, which may be considered as the year practically closing the experimental epoch of the reaper; that between 1833 and 1870 as the epoch of the practical reaper, and that from 1870 to the close of the century as that of the harvesting machine, of which the automatic binding attachment has now become an essential part. During the first period of time many voyages, so to speak, were made which resulted only in discovery. In the second period the successful reaper had reached maturity and became standardized to a considerable degree, but its good works live in the perfected mowing machine and the self-binding harvester.

During the last epoch the modern twine binder was borne into the harvest fields on the shoulders of the Marsh harvester, which had proved its merits during the second period.

CHAPTER II

EARLY MACHINES

In discussing the experimental period, first consideration must be given to English inventors.

I quote from the report of the jury of the great London Exhibition in 1851:

"At the opening of this century it was thought that a successful reaping machine had been invented; and a reward was voted by Parliament to its author. The machines were employed here, and abroad, but from its intricacy, fell into disuse."

"Of this and the Australian machine," Mr. Woodcroft tells us in his Appendix to the specifications of English Patents for Reaping machines, London, 1853, "the writer could not obtain full information after numerous inquiries."

Probably there were other machines that escaped all search of historians. The "intricacy," spoken of by the London jury, may not have been the sole cause of the machine having "fallen into disuse," for Mr. Woodcroft mentions a sufficient cause when he says:

"It will be a matter of surprise to many that in this age and country, when machinery is made to perform the simplest and heaviest tasks, as well as the most intricate and delicate, there should still be little grain mechanically reaped. This result may be traced to many causes. Farmers generally are regardless of the new mechanical aids and in some cases even hostile to them."

As the present work is to be more a history of practical accomplishments than of trivial and fruitless efforts, I quickly pass over the devices of the ancient Gauls at the beginning of the first century, as recorded by Pliny and Palladius because, technically considered, those devices were in no sense machines, but, on the contrary, mere

16

agricultural tools. In fact they were probably of very little practical value. The "strippers" now used in Australia are no proof that the Gallic machines were practical, for the Australian strippers are, in fact, machines—machines depending upon power transmitted from a traction wheel to make them effective. The Gallic tool consisted of a large box having supporting wheels at each side and rearwardly extending thills between which an ox was yoked. At the front edge of the box was a comb, consisting of a series of closely placed teeth precisely like those forming the toilet article. This box was pushed forward and the heads of the grain pulled from the straws. In order to prevent the comb from clogging a workman walked beside the card and, with a paddle or a hoe-like scraper, pulled the heads backward into the box.

Machine used in ancient Gaul at the time of the birth of Christ.

One of the most interesting European adaptations of this idea is described by the Hon. Charles W. Marsh (one of the joint inventors of the Marsh Harvester) in a history of harvesting machinery written by him, and published in the "Farm Implement News," of Chicago, Ill. He says:

"In the summer of 1870 I spent several pleasant days at an agricultural college in Ungarisch Altenburg, a little town situated upon an arm of the Danube, which puts out from the main river not far below Vienne, and returns to it at Raab. While there I was shown a model of a primitive reaper in the college museum, built somewhat after the style of the Kerr machine made in 1811. It has a revolving perpendicular drum, carrying a projecting circular knife at its base, and a rim at the top notched so as to catch and carry the heads of the cut grain, and, in connection with the knife, operating on the butts as the drum revolved, to deliver in a swath outside of the line of the cut. This drum with its knife and notched rim was revolved, as I remember, by a crossed belt on a system of pulleys from the axle, between the two wheels, which supported the drum, suspended before them to a pulley on an upright spindle through the center of the drum. It had shafts reaching back for the animal which pushed it forward, and it was altogether a simple contrivance which might work fairly well. The professors told me that this model was a reconstruction from an engraving on a stone found in this vicinity (the country here is level, exceedingly fertile, and was colonized by fugitive Cathaginians during the third Punic war, about 150 B. C.), and that this stone has been verified by similar lines of figures found engraved among the ruins of Carthage. It may be said that the Cathaginians were an exceedingly enterprising, ingenious and practical people, noted for trade and manufactures. It was of them the old Romans said that their only aim in life was 'to buy cheap and sell dear.' They were infinitely more advanced than the Gauls, who used the stripping harvester or header not so very long after, and they might have produced either."

In Vol. 3 of the "Annals of Agriculture," 1787, page 161, is a drawing of a reaping machine, with a description written by William Pitt, of Pendeford, England. Mr. Pitt states that he was prompted to undertake such a machine after reading a translation from Pliny and Palladius of the description of the Gallic machine. The machine was something more than an improvement on the Gallic contrivance. It consisted of a box supported upon wheels at its sides and provided with thills so that it might be pushed by a horse traveling in the rear. Forward of this box was located a large cylinder or drum of length nearly equal to the width of the machine so connected to the supporting wheel as to be suitably rotated and having its entire surface armed with what may be considered combs. These teeth were practically tangential to the surface of the drum and extended some distance therefrom. The cylinder or drum was very similar to that of an ordinary wool carding machine. It was connected by a belt to one of the supporting wheels and adapted to revolve in such a direction that its teeth would pass forwardly and upwardly, and, seizing the heads from below throw them over backward into a small box. In the rear of the box referred to, was the large one into which the accumulated heads of grain were transferred from time to time. The action of the "rippling cylinder," as the inventor called the gathering device, would have a tendency to pull its forward end toward the ground and the resistance to the free turning of the supporting wheels would add materially to that tendency. The draft of the animal, being but a push in effect, would increase this difficulty by lifting the thills and tipping the machine forward. That such a machine would be of little use is hinted by the inventor's own words, as the standing straw left by the machine would still require cutting:

"The grain thus collected in a short time of the most favorable weather, the straw may be cut and collected at leisure, and with less regard to rain or showers than is necessarily the case in the common mode of harvesting."

In Walker's Philosophy, published in 1799, is a drawing and description of a reaping machine, whose maker is unknown to me. The drawing shows that the machine was pushed by a horse in thills and provided with cutting apparatus consisting of a disc armed with a number of scythe-blades adapted to be rotated upon a horizontal plane by suitable gearing. Stationary fingers were provided in advance to pass into the standing grain and hold the straws from being broken down instead of being cut by the blades. In this is found the first provision for preventing the machine from tipping forward, under the stresses incident to the effort of the horse that pushed, and the effort of the traction wheel to impart motion to the cutting apparatus. This provision consisted of a small wheel, well forward of the supporting wheels, beneath a forwardly extending arm that served as a divider.

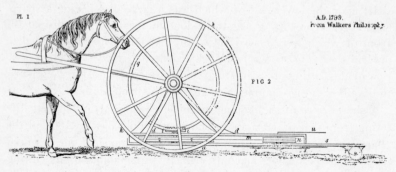

Cut from Woodcroft's Specifications of English Patents.

August 23, 1805, an English patent was granted to James Pluck-nett, of Deptford, for a reaping machine. The drawings reveal it was adapted to be pushed and to do its cutting by means of a large hori-zontal disc, well sharpened, placed close to the ground and so geared to the supporting wheel axle as to receive rapid rotation. Upon each side of the disc are forwardly extending projections that may be considered to be a foreshadow, if nothing more, of the modern grain divider.

In 1806 a Mr. Gladstone produced a reaper having an arrange-ment of parts for gathering, cutting and delivering the grain. This machine deserves more than a passing notice, for in it we find the following six features which, slightly modified so as to enable their present day counterparts to perform added functions, are embodied in modern harvesting machines. First, it is supported upon two wheels only; second, the placement of the horse in advance thereof so that the animal walked beside the grain operated upon; third, side delivery of the grain or grass cut; and, fourth, the machine so bal-anced that a slight preponderance of its weight remained forward of the axis of the supporting wheels; fifth, we find forwardly extend-ing fingers that serve, in a measure, to protect the edge of the cutting device. These last may be considered as an improvement on those of the Plucknett machine, and as true forerunners of the guard fingers of modern machines, although they performed only one of the three essential functions of those now used. Sixth, the support-ing wheels were placed abreast, with the framework of the machine and its gearing could be sustained between them.

Motion was imparted from the supporting wheels to a vertical shaft upon the lower end of which was a large disc having a sharp-ened edge. The cutting was to be done by means of this disc at the front of which were placed forwardly extending fingers adapted to prevent the grain straws from being deflected sidewise. The opera-tion of the cutting apparatus may be considered, in a large measure, to have been a mere imitation of that of the hand scythe.

A short notice of the reaping machine made by Mr. Plucknett dif-fering from that of 1805 above shown was published in 1807 in the "Farmers' Dictionary." In it is found another one of the essential elements of the reaping machine, namely: Adaptability of its cutting apparatus to cut grain or grass at various heights from the ground,

FL. III.
(1 Sheet)

Plan View

Side Elevation. (one wheel being removed.)

End Elevation

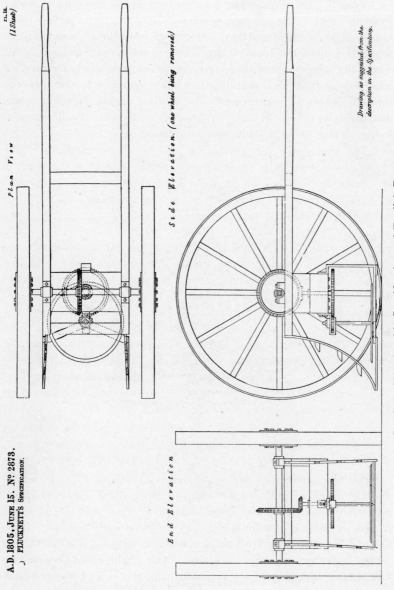

Drawing as suggested from the
description in the Specification.

Cut from Woodcroft's Specifications of English Patents.

by tilting the gearing carriage and cutting device upward or downward in front. The machine is shown as having been drawn by a horse. The cutting apparatus, a disc with sword-like projections, is supported upon the main frame and geared from the main axle. The thills are so jointed to the gearing frame that the latter may be rocked on the axle and secured in any chosen position by pins passing through perforated segments. The cutting apparatus being some distance forward of the axle, up and down adjustment with respect to the surface of the ground was not difficult.

A.D. 1807.   PL. V
PLUCKNETT.

J R Jobbins

Cut from Woodcroft's Specifications of English Patents.

Upon the same plate in the "Farmers' Dictionary" is shown a reaping machine produced by Salmon, dated 1807. The machine was narrow and evidently designed to be pushed, or, at least, controlled by hand if drawn, for it was provided with handles. It is the first machine of record in which the shearing action of blades jointed together was made available. The cutting devices were, in fact, a close imitation of the common hand shears and so connected to suitable gearing as to be moved quite rapidly. If this machine were ever used, it seems probable that it did little work on account

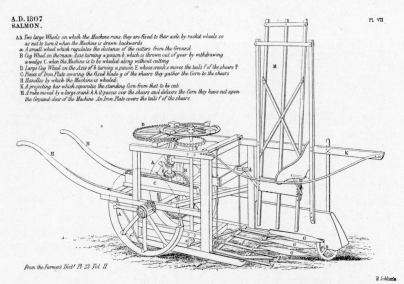

A A *Two large Wheels on which the Machine runs, they are fixed to thar axle by rackit wheels so*
  as not to turn it when the Machine is drawn backwards
a *A small wheel which regulates the distance of the cutters from the Ground*
B *Cog Wheel on the main Axis turning a pinion b, which is thrown out of gear by withdrawing*
  a wedge C, when the Machine is to be wheeled along without cutting
D *Large Cog Wheel on the Axis of b turning a pinion E whose crank e moves the tails f of the shears F*
G *Pieces of Iron Plate covering the fixed blade g of the shears they gather the Corn to the shears*
H *Handles by which the Machine is wheeled.*
K *A projecting bar which separates the standing Corn from that to be cut.*
M *A rake moved by a large crank h h it passes over the shears and delivers the Corn they have cut upon*
  the Ground clear of the Machine. An Iron Plate covers the tails f of the shears.

From the Farmer's Dict Pl 23 Vol II

PL. VII

E Jobbins

Cut from Woodcroft's Specifications of English Patents.

of the fact that *vibrating* shears unaccompanied by means for holding the grain to them, have always proved troublesome. It is, also,
one of the first machines shown provided with anything closely
approaching a grain divider. A little in advance of the grain end of
the cutting apparatus (that part which extends toward the standing
grain) was placed a small supporting wheel, suitably housed to prevent entanglement with the standing grain, and having above it a
forwardly extended arm with a laterally curved rod. This last is
referred to in the specification as "A projecting bar which separates
the standing corn from that to be cut." Although the forwardly
extending bar is shown at some height, and there is left an opportunity for leaning grain to be trodden on by the little wheel beneath,
the acumen of this inventor must not be waived aside. Whatever
the practicability of Salmon's machine, his divider served as an object
lesson to those following him.

The primary office of a grain divider is to part a way in the grain
field a little distance forward of the cutting apparatus to turn those
grain straws which are to be cut slightly to one side, and permitting
those which are to be left to pass outside of itself, as a man might
walk through a flock of sheep turning some to the right into another

field and some to the left. The length of the divider is unimportant, a *long* point not being required, in mowing machines. In grain however, which sometimes grows high and with interlocking heads, the divider must act as a wedge and force the heads asunder before cutting takes place. If entangled heads were not drawn apart by the divider *before* the act of cutting is accomplished, part of the cut straws would be drawn off the machine by the straws left standing at the side. In that class of machines in which mechanisms are provided for taking the grain from the platform, means exist for pulling the cut grain from entanglement with that left standing. This is an exceedingly important matter.

Obviously, this Salmon machine combines the grain divider, *"which separates the standing corn* (grain) *from that to be cut,"* at each passage of the machine, and means of pulling clear any cut grain away entangled with that to be left standing. This would be considered in patent law an operative combination; that is, a combination of mechanical elements. In view of this, no inventor later than Salmon could be entitled to a broad claim covering a grain platform, a grain divider and means co-operating therewith for keeping the divider clear, be the means either manual or automatic. Salmon's combination of these two elements, the rake and divider, is now exclusively used in the "reel-rake" reaping machine, the ordinary horizontal reel having been found less competent to keep the divider clear. Still another thing to consider is the fact that Salmon has left a valuable combination of mechanical elements in his grain receiving platform and rake, for the two co-operating are adapted to deliver the grain in *gavels* upon the ground. His rake moved orbitally in a vertical plane, the lower portion of its orbit conforming closely to the surface of the grain-receiving platform. The platform, not shown in the drawings, consisted of a sheet of iron lying immediately over the lever-portions of the shears. The cutting apparatus will receive further attention, as its principles were embodied in some of the earliest and, later, in successful reaping machines.

In 1811 two English machines were made public. One was produced by Kerr of Edinburgh, and one by Smith of Deanston. Both were operated in the harvest of that year. The description of one will, in a large measure, serve for the other. Both were pushed by horses. A large horizontal, sharp-edged disc was placed before the traction wheels and given rotation at a high rate of speed. Placed above the disc was a cylindrical shield somewhat smaller and of considerable height. This prevented the cut grain from falling backward; it also carried the swath stubbleward. The drawings show no provision for preventing either machine from tipping over forward as likely to occur, under the stress of what may be termed pushing-draft and the resistance due to the labor required of the supporting wheels. Smith, however, provided his horses with pad-saddles and placed a bar across their backs, and to it secured the push-tongue by some means not shown. Notwithstanding this plainly ridiculous resort to preserve the horizontal position of the machine, Smith deserves credit for having done one thing well worth being copied, namely: he was first to regulate the height of cut by raising the cutting apparatus independently of the gearing carriage. From the description found in the Encyclopedia Edinensis we learn as follows: "By a particular apparatus he can raise or lower the cutter when an obstacle comes in the way or from going from one field to another," the "he" referring, of course, to the attendant. Tests proved this machine to be able to cut one acre per hour. Experiments were continued several years and a set of silver plate, valued at 50 guineas, was presented to Mr. Smith by the Highland Society of Scotland.

Another important British contribution is that of Dobbs.

"The machine of the English patent to Dobbs, in 1814, had dividers of wood or metal. The outer diverging-rod rose as it extended backward and diverged laterally from the point, to raise the stalks of grain inclining inwards, and to turn them off from the other parts of the machines." (See U. S. Supreme Court decision, McCormick v. Talcott et als.)

Dobbs says:

"The machine is intended to be applied to cut all kinds of grain, and also to gather it, if necessary; it is also intended to be used, with different cutters, on beans, Indian corn, rice, tobacco, sugar canes, and whatever other produce of the earth the purchaser may think it proper to work it upon."*** At each side of every pair of feeders is fixed an instrument I call dividers, made of wood or metal, &c., its intention is to enter the straw before the feeders come near it, to assist in drawing the straw to the feeders, and bearing the straw that is not to be cut from the machine. These dividers are sharp at the point, and become gradually wider against the feeders. The dividers are extended to nearly the top or above the rollers if necessary, to divide straw that is most entangled."*** I have the "dividers, which first enter the corn (grain) near the bottom, and divide it into parts; they are carried near to the top of the rollers c, c, the more effectually to assist the other parts of the machine in its operations."

Alexander Scott, of Ormiston, Haddingtonshire, Scotland, produced a reaper in 1815, fully described in the *Edinburgh Encyclopedia,* which also possessed a number of new features. The machine, mounted upon two wheels, was adapted to be drawn forward by a team so attached as to travel beside the standing grain and permit the cutting apparatus to take its swath and the delivering apparatus to carry the latter stubbleward behind the team. The only features that have survived, however, are those having to do with the cutting apparatus and the dividing of the grain. The cutter proper, which consisted of a large horizontally placed disc was, no doubt, defective, like all others of its kind. Combined with it, however, is shown a series of stationary forwardly projecting fingers adapted to shield the cutting edge from stumps, stones and other obstructions. These fingers were sufficiently far apart to permit the standing straws or grass to pass between them and also serve to prevent the straws from being swept aside by the cutting edge and thus escape the edge. The cutting blades consisted of a series of serrated sections made of thin steel and adapted to move *over* the projecting fingers. As the cutters are shown to move in but one direction, I judge that the cutting apparatus fell far short of accomplishing the best results for, as will later appear, such devices, operating to cut only in one direction, have always choked badly.

One very important feature must not escape attention. At either side of the machine, in such position as to properly serve its purposes, is a forwardly extending finger; that on one side is adapted to act as a grain divider, while the other guides any grain that might otherwise escape the cutting apparatus at the stubble side of the machine. This may be considered the genesis of the "inside (stubble side) gatherer" used in modern machines. Its purpose was to gather a little wider than the width of cut, so that, should the driver fail to rein his team correctly, no straws would be left standing. This machine was adapted to cut upon the right-hand side of the team, a little in rear of the same, and there was fixed on the long, right-hand prong a sheet of thin plate-iron, kneed to the same acute angle to the prong, and of the same height with the drum, for the purpose of *"dividing the standing corn from that to be cut."* This "drum" was similar to some already mentioned and, like them, consisted of a sheet metal affair of considerable height adapted, by means of teeth pivoted to it, to seize the grain straws cut and carry them delivery-ward. Here is a mechanical element co-operating with the divider, one function of which was to divide "the standing corn from that to be cut." (In all these English specifications it will be noticed we find the word "corn" used instead of "grain.") We have, in this machine, a divider of good height and length, and means for pulling the grain away therefrom, namely, the swath delivering apparatus. The divider thus becomes effective, as in Salmon's machine. Notwithstanding these three anticipations, efforts were made several years later to monopolize the use of the grain divider shown in a later patent, soon to be considered, when combined with mechanical elements (or a hand rake) necessary to make it effective in separating off the grain to be cut.

In 1820, Joseph Mann, of Raby, England, experimented with a machine which was described in the *Quarterly Journal of Agriculture* and accompanied by a drawing. Here is shown a machine adapted to travel beside the grain to be cut, with a large cutting disc close to the ground adapted to rotate on a horizontal plane. Immediately there-above is seen a series of orbitally moving teeth adapted to push the cut straws stubbleward. This machine is said to have "performed in a tolerably satisfactory manner."

"The corn was fairly cut, and it was considered by those who had seen other reaping machines at work, to lay the swath more regularly at right angles with the line of direction than had been observed of previous machines."

Only one feature of this machine is worthy of notice, but it is a highly important one. Its gearing carriage, or framework, was so supported upon its wheels as to be capable of adjustment to any desired height for cutting long or short grain. "For this purpose, the axles of both wheels of the carriage are supported in sliding bars with guide rods*** and by means of levers, one only of which is shown at O, the director has the power at any time of altering the inclination of the cutters with reference to the horizon, in transverse direction of the machine." Some of the parts described have partly to do with that now known as "tilt"; that is, with giving the plane of the cutting apparatus an incline or a decline, as Plucknett had accomplished by other means, in 1807. The supporting wheels were journaled upon stationary axles which by means of slides secured to them were adapted to permit the frame to be raised or lowered relative thereto and be resecured by bolts. This feature should be borne in mind as it was crudely shown and later claimed in an American patent soon to receive attention.

The next machine worthy of consideration was described in the *Mechanics' Magazine,* Vol. V. Its significance arises from the fact that the arrangement of its parts corresponds so nearly with that of the operative parts of the earliest successful reaping machines. As there has been an effort by later inventors to belittle this machine, I will quote from the description before me. (See Woodcroft's Specifications of English Patents, 1853, from which the accounts of all the early English machines herein given are taken.)

"In 1822, Mr. Henry Ogle, of Renington, near Alnwick, invented a machine for reaping corn, to which, in the same year, an apparatus for collecting the corn into sheaves was added by Messrs. Thomas and Joseph Brown, of Alnwick.***

"Sir:—In the year 1822, I made a small model of a machine for reaping corn; but not being a workman in that business myself, and being on very friendly terms with one Thomas Brown, a founder, in Alnwick, and his son, Joseph Brown, I presented it to them. They made a better model of it than I had made, of iron, and presented it to the public many market days at Alnwick, thinking to carry it into execution by subscription, but were disappointed,—the farmers considered it an impossibility. Thomas and Joseph Brown then made the machine at their own expense, and tried it first near Alnwick; it did not, however, altogether answer, the teeth of the frame*** where the knife cut upon (as hereafter described) were too long, and collected the dirt among the corn too much. They then made the teeth shorter, and tried it again at a place called South Sidem, near Warkworth, in a field of wheat; it then cut to great perfection, but still, not laying the corn into sheaves, the farmer did not think that it lessened the expense much. Mr. Brown took it home again, and added the part for collecting the corn into a sheaf*** when he tried it again

at Alnwick, in a field of barley, which it cut and laid out in sheaves
extremely well.   Messrs. Brown then advertised at the beginning of
the year 1823 that they would furnish machines of this sort complete for sheaving corn at the beginning of harvest, but found none
of the farmers that would go to the expense, though the machine was
seen even to cut the lying corn where it was not bound down with new
rising green corn.   Some working people at last threatened to kill Mr.
Brown if he persevered any further in it, and it has never been tried
more.   It was estimated, from what was tried, that it would cut at
an easy rate fourteen acres per day."

The drawings in Woodcroft, show a machine supported upon two
wheels having draft thills for a horse, a cutting device extended
laterally from immediately behind the right-hand supporting wheel,
a grain-receiving platform hinged at the rear of the cutting apparatus, and a reel for leaning the grain backwardly.   This feature not
only properly presents the grain to the cutting apparatus, but at the
same time, causes it to fall properly upon the receiving platform. The
description of the machine is very meagre, but it seems that the
cutting apparatus consisted of a knife adapted to be rapidly reciprocated immediately *above* a series of teeth extending about three
inches, more or less, from the supporting bar in a forward direction.   The mechanism for reciprocating the knife consisted of a series
of cams upon the main supporting wheels, adapted to act alternately
upon a lever connected to the cutter.   This cutter is referred to as
a knife, and it is believed to have been merely a straight knife; but I
am informed that a son of Mr. Brown, who came to America after
the Ogle reaper had been made, once stated to the Hon. C. W.
Marsh that a cutter consisting of a series of knives riveted to a
straight bar and adapted to reciprocate over the forwardly projecting fingers, above referred to, was used.   In the Ogle machine is
clearly a combination of a reel, grain-receiving platform, and cutting apparatus, all of the parts arranged substantially as now extensively used.   Only the grain divider, so essential in cutting bad conditions of grain, was wanting, and this might have been taken from
the prior art.

A Mr. Pidgeon, whose given name is not divulged by Woodcroft,
gave an account to the Society of Arts, years ago, of Ogle's machines, as well as others.   He was acquainted with Ogle, who was a
schoolmaster in the same town.   Pidgeon tells us that the machine

came out under immense difficulties. So little did the circumstances of that time encourage attempts to make reapers, that Ogle and one John Common, a mechanic at Denwick, had to conduct their experiments by moonlight in order to save their machines from being broken to pieces, and themselves from injury. Common and Ogle, began their work as early as 1812, but it seems that Common departed somewhat from the principles shown in the Ogle reaper, or, very likely, Ogle departed from the plans that he and Common had worked upon together. It is said that Common aimed high and sought the prize offered by the Society of Arts. His patron, the Duke of Northumberland, aided his moonlight experiments, after Common and Ogle had parted company. Mr. Pidgeon, at a meeting of the Farmers' Club, in London, 1887, stated that the reaper made by Mr. Common "was a perfect anticipation of Bell's and Crosskill's reaper or the swath-delivering machine." The Bell reaper, next to be considered, was manufactured by Crosskill for many years, hence the association of the name of Bell and Crosskill. Mr. Pidgeon continuing said: "The story which I told some years back, at the Society of Arts about its emigration to America, and how it fell into McCormick's hands, is interesting, and I may perhaps venture to repeat it here. Common had a friend named Brown, a mechanic living at Alnwick, to whom he was obliged to go for some of his work, and all his patterns were in Brown's hands. Brown emigrated in 1830 to Canada and took his patterns with him. Later on, he left Canada and went to Sterling in New York state, where he died in 1850."

Brown, while experimenting with Ogle's machine, used a fork, and oftentimes raked the accumulation of grain from the platform stubbleward so as to leave a path for the travel of the team in making the next round. (The dropping platform, which proved to be one of the most perfect features of Ogle's machine, was extensively used in America from 1860 to 1875, on that class of machines known as "Droppers.") Common, Brown, and Ogle all enriched the art to a considerable extent. Brown's hand-raking arrangement was like that first used in America. Ogle's machine has received many unjust criticisms, though the cutting apparatus may have been defective, and the use of cams for giving movement to the cutting apparatus of harvesting machines has always proved defective, and that the receiving platform, not being made of slats, may have failed to discharge its load neatly when let fall, but Ogle's reel was a success from the start because it cooperated with the cutting apparatus and the grain-receiving platform.

The presence of a reel, however, may be considered as evidence of defective cutting apparatus, as is quite likely true in this instance. The cutting apparatus of the modern mowing machine reaches the highest degree of perfection yet attained, and the machine has no reel, which fact, in a measure, corroborates the point of view. If its cutting apparatus were defective, it would push the grass before it, and a reel would be required to force the grass into position to be cut, and there hold it until severed. We must credit Ogle with having foreseen the most suitable general arrangement of the essential parts of a practical machine, and it ill behooves moderns to deny indebtedness to him for this general arrangement because his machine, as a whole, was not practical enough to survive. Particularly is this true if such a course be an attempt to waive him away in order to remove an anticipation of our own devices. The width of cut of this machine is not stated, but if it is true (as claimed) that it could harvest at the rate of fourteen acres per day, the cutting apparatus must have been at least five feet in length, from which I estimate the diameter of the reel to have been about four feet, and hence only a foot smaller than many of those at present in use. A reel of that size was no doubt efficient in a measure since its speed of rotation seems to have been substantially correct.

The first reaping machine that was to any considerable extent practical was that of the Rev. Patrick Bell. Although it may have been imperfect in many of its details, it was made in some numbers, and was in constant use for twenty-five or thirty years in England and Scotland.

The following account is taken from the *North British Agriculturist,* published in Edinburgh, Scotland, and dated July 19, 1893. From the same paper I quote a communication which is also self-explanatory. These articles are of so recent a date, particularly the later one, that, in order to substantiate them, we may turn to Woodcroft and quote from the article taken from Loudon's *Encyclopedia of Agriculture* as there found.

Mr. George K. Fuller, of Chittenango, Madison County, N. Y., stated in a letter to the *Scientific American* that one of the Rev. Patrick Bell's reaping machines was imported by John B. Yates, of that place, in 1834, and put in operation in his (Fuller's) presence, superintended by Mr. Bell himself, who visited this country in that year. It reaped a level field of wheat at about the rate of an acre per hour. (Sci. Am. Vol. VIII, p. 54.)

Mr. Marsh says, in his "History of Harvesting Machinery," "it is claimed that another was imported into Virginia at an early date, but of that we have no certainty."

Publication of the *North British Agriculturist's* article on Bell and his work called forth years afterward the following rejoinder:

FROM THE *NATIONAL MAGAZINE* FOR SEPTEMBER, 1892.

"In the face of continued successes, a Scotch paper, known as the "North British Agriculturist," claimed the honor of invention for a Scotch creature named Bell, and with the most brazen effrontery urged Scotchmen in Canada to discredit the American.

"In 1863 this claimant and his journalistic friends were cornered by the "Marklain Express," of London, England, which denied their story and declared it to be concocted out of whole cloth. Such language from such a journal as the "Express," cleared up doubts, and the canny Scots were forced to cast away their claims, which national vanity had upheld for a season.

"More serious claims made before that of Bell, led one to wonder that imitators in America and Europe did not push such claims to the extent of robbing the true inventor of all his patents and crushing his business."

The evidence offered in this controversy seems to be covered by the following quotations from the North British Agriculturist:

"On account of the immense change effected in our agricultural practice through the invention of the reaping machine, we have devoted a good deal of space in this, our Jubilee number, to an account of "The Evolution of the Reaper." The Rev. Patrick Bell, the inventor of the reaping machine, was born at Auchterhouse, near Dundee, and was educated at the University of St. Andrews, whose Senatus conferred upon him, in after years, the degree of LL.D. It was in the course of his student days that he worked out his great idea. After being licensed as a minister, he was appointed to the charge of Carmyllie Parish, Forfarshire, where he lived and worked all the rest of his life. In 1868 he was presented with a testimonial of £1000, subscribed by the members of the Highland Society and other agriculturists, as a tangible recognition of the incalculable service he had rendered to the country through his great invention. He died at a ripe old age on the 22nd April, 1869. The present editor of the N. B. Agriculturist was a parishioner of Dr. Bell's, and he cherishes many pleasant memories of the worthy minister who invented the reaping machine.

"On being informed only a few days ago that a Bell's reaper, as originally designed by its inventor, had been in regular use on the farm of Thurston, Innerwick, up till a comparatively recent date, we wrote to Mr. Hunter, proprietor of Thurston, on the subject, and in reply received the following communication, which is very interesting as showing the quality of the work done by the Bell's reaper :—

"Sir,—Richard Hunter, Esq., of Thurston, desires me to write you in reply to your letter of the 8th inst. regarding the Rev. Patrick Bell's reaper. I must tell you that it was not the present proprietor that had the experience of the reaper. It was his uncle, James W. Hunter, who died in 1879. He farmed over 2000 acres of his own estate, and kept twenty pair of horses on three large farms, with a manager on each. The farms were all worked on the five-course rotation—that is, two years' grass, one white crop, one green crop, and one white crop with seeds. He kept six of Bell's reapers, and cut all the crop on the three farms with them, working them eight hours a day with the same horses and men.

"I myself had a long experience with the reaper, and must say after all the improvements we have seen, self-binders and the rest, that is was a wonderful machine, and did its work very well. It had its drawbacks no doubt. One of these was its heavy draught. Another was that it laid down the grain in swath instead of in sheaf, which of course caused more outlay of manual labor. There was one particular advantage it possessed, namely, it worked with a revolving canvas, and the grain could be put either to one side or another, and in a standing crop you could cut both ways, the grain was laid to the side, and the horses had plenty of open ground to

walk on clear of the uncut grain and the swath from the reaper.
And in fine weather, by allowing the grain to lie in swath for a
couple of days before putting it in sheaf and stook, it was ready
for the stacks.—I am, &c.,

pro RICHARD HUNTER, Esq.,
ALEXANDER WIGHT.

Thurston, Innerwick, 10th July 1893."

"THE EVOLUTION OF THE REAPER."

"At the annual meeting, in 1867, of the British Association for the
Promotion of Science, which was held that year in Dundee, under
the presidency of the Duke of Buccleuch, the Rev. Patrick Bell read
a paper on reaping machines. At the outset of his paper, Mr. Bell
gave an account of the reaping machine in the various forms through
which it had passed in the course of its evolution. Noticing the two
sickles from Egypt in the British Museum, he said that they were
much like our own reaping hooks, with smooth-cutting edges; and
after remarking that, from the earliest times down to our own day,
there had been little, if any, alteration made upon the reaping-hook
since its invention, Mr. Bell described the ani-ani, a rude implement
used in Java for cutting corn, which was inferior to the reaping-
hook in point of execution, though the principle for cutting was that
of scissors, the same as in the reaping machine. The heads of the
grain only were cut off by the ani-ani. He then noticed the earliest
real machines constructed for reaping, describing the principle
adopted in each machine. He said that no fewer than thirty contrivances had been attempted to construct an efficient reaping machine upon the principle of a circular cutter, though he was not sure
that any of them ever reached maturity. Coming down to 1852, he
said that, in that year, no fewer than thirty patents were taken out
in this country for reaping machines. In America, from the beginning of this century to the end of 1851, no fewer than ninety-eight
contrivances were patented at Washington, embodying, like those in
this country, almost every conceivable principle. The reaper which
bore his (Mr. Bell's) name was invented in 1826, and used in the
field in 1827, and had been in successful operation every season since.
The most successful American reapers were upon his principle, and
were patented at Washington in 1833-34, seven or eight years after

his invention was known to the world, so that his neighbors in the
Far West had ample time to make up their minds whether they would
think for themselves or quietly take a hint from a brother.   Mr.
Bell concluded his paper with the following account of the difficulties
he experienced in completing his own invention:—

"Before I finally conclude, it may be expected of me to state in a
few sentences the rise and progress of the reaping machine known
by my name.   From my earliest years I had a liking and turn for the
study and practice of mechanics.   I am the son of a farmer, and was
accustomed from my early youth to witness all the operations of
the farm performed, and in most of them I engaged with my own
hands.   I was not a Presbyterian minister during the time in which
I invented the reaping machine, as is currently stated, but an alum-
nus of one of our national Universities—the University of St.
Andrews.   A farmer's son, in my days at least, although an aca-
demic, would not have been allowed to study undisturbed in his
sanctum, and was liable, especially in the harvest season, to be summoned to wield the fork or some other implement of toil.   At a very
early period of my life I was most painfully struck with the very
severe nature of the toil to which the harvest workers were subjected—a toil made doubly oppressive sometimes by the heat of the
weather, and always by the very awkward position in which they
were obliged to stoop when engaged in their work.   It may sound
as an empty sentimentalism, but it is nevertheless true, that a desire
to mitigate such excessive toil led me to inquire whether there might
not be a possibility of transferring part of it at least to beams of
wood and bars of iron, supplemented by the bones and sinews of the
horse.   Sure I am that I had no intention of taking the people's
bread from them; and had I been so taunted I believe that even
then I could have demonstrated that the multiplication and employment of machinery in agricultural work immediately promotes the
increase of the people's bread, and does not ultimately tend to dimin-
ish the means of the people to obtain that bread.   For years I had
thought of the matter, and had diligently searched for some principle; and, taking up one after another, I duly weighed the possibilities of their application to the object in view, and abandoned
them all as worthless.

"One evening after tea, while walking in my father's garden, my eyes caught a pair of gardener's shears sticking in the hedge. I seized them by the handles, which protruded, and I proceeded to snap at the twigs of the thorns. My mind was full of mechanics at the time, and many hours were spent in my workshop; and contemplating the shears attentively, I insensibly said to myself, 'Here is a principle, and is there any reason why it should not be applied to the cutting down of the corn?' Not altogether satisfied with my performance on the hedge, I brushed through it, with the shears in my hand, to a field of young oats adjoining, and commenced cutting them right and left. It was well that no neighbouring gossip saw me at the unwonted employment, else the rumor might have been readily circulated that the poor student had gone crazed. For weeks and for months, by night and by day, those shears were uppermost in my thoughts, and I searched anxiously and indefatigably for the mode in which they should be employed. Plan after plan presented itself to me, and were put upon paper. The merits of each, and the likelihood of its success, were carefully scrutinised and pondered, and eventually I fixed upon the plan now successfully in operation. This took place in the summer of 1827. The next step was to construct a model, and to ascertain how thoughts would look when transferred to steel and iron. This was done, and it was during the process of making the little wooden frame and my puny cutters that the idea of a sloping canvas for conveying the cut corn to the side occurred to me. My first idea was to place the canvas level with the ground, and it was merely because it was more conveniently situated in the model, and pleased the eye better, that the angular position was adopted, so that in reality the position and the angle of the canvas were more matters of accident than the result of consideration. Were the truth always known, I believe that much more important improvements in mechanical science would be found to have a similar origin. Having finished my model, and speculated as accurately and deeply as I was able upon the possibilities and probabilities of the actual results, I determined to have a machine constructed upon the large scale. For this purpose I had to pass out of my character of inventor into that of engineer and workman. The plan I took was this. After making my calculations as to size, &c., I joined a quantity of rough sticks together, and called them a frame. Then I made cutters of wood of every part that required to be made of iron and steel. I sent these piece by piece as I required them to the blacksmith, with the instructions to make a thing of iron as like the wooden ones sent as possible. When I got a few of the pieces from the smith, I finished them with the file, and secured each to its proper place. I remember the cutters gave me a world of trouble and vexation. When they came into my hands they were in a very rude state, and required much filing, grinding, and fitting. By dint of patient application I got the whole into a sufficiently perfect state, as I thought, for trial.

Rev. Patrick Bell, LL.D.
"Inventor of the First Practical Reaping Machine."

"It may amuse you, perhaps, if I give you some account of the first field I cut. That you may understand this, imagine an empty outhouse, rather long and narrow, having in one end a wright's bench, and in the other a rude looking piece of mechanism, an embryo reaping machine. For my subsequent operations I chose a quiet day, that is a day when there were few people about the place. On that day an eavesdropper might have seen me busily but stealthily engaged in conveying earth in a common wheelbarrow into the work-

Bell's Reaper, with Swathing Conveyor Removed in Order to Show the Arrangement of the Gearing.

shop. When the place between the bench and the rude but ambi-
tious candidate for the honours of the harvest field was covered to
the depth of some six inches, I proceeded to compress the loose
mould with my feet. I next went to an old stack that happened to
be in the barnyard, and drawing a sheaf of oats out of it, and carrying it to the workshop, I planted it stalk by stalk at about the same
thickness which I knew it would have grown in the field. This done,
I shut and barred the door, and then going behind the machine I
pushed it forward with all my might through my planted oats. As
soon as I recovered my breath, I anxiously examined how the work
had been done. I found that it had been all very well cut, but it was
lying higgeldy-piggeldy, in such a mess as would have utterly dis-
graced me in the harvest field. Upon the whole, however, I was not
discouraged, but rather encouraged by this first experiment. The
cutting was perfect, and that was the great point I then aimed at.

"Although by this experiment I had proved my new invention to
be a cutting machine, it certainly little deserved to be dignified with
the name of reaping machine and yet it was a reaping machine I
had set my heart upon constructing. Had I at this stage been content to summon a man with a rake to do the work of wheels and
pinions, my machine was complete; and, had I been contented with
a combination, I would have saved myself a host of trouble, and
what to me at the time was no small expenditure of money. My
workshop was again speedily cleared of earth and loam, and made
ready for the jack-plane and files. I proceeded forthwith to put
the canvas in order. One might naturally suppose that this would
be an easy matter, but I did not find it so. After the rollers were
put in position, the wheels for driving them adjusted, and the canvas stretched and fixed upon the rollers the proper tightness, I conceived in my simplicity that the work was done, and my object
secured. The result was otherwise; for, on pushing the machine
forward only the length of the house, I found that it twisted, and
would have been torn in pieces if it had proceeded many yards forward. I proceeded now to make grooves at the end of the rollers,
in which I placed a small rope. To these ropes, one at the top and
the other at the bottom of the rollers, I sewed the canvas, expect-
ing that the ropes and canvas would move together in uniformity,

and that my object would thus be obtained; but, upon trial I was a second time disappointed. The ropes, from inequality in the grooves, moved irregularly, and the canvas became twisted as before. For a time I was nonplussed and dispirited, but, plucking up courage, and ruminating over mechanical appliances, I thought of the pitched chains. Having made some 6 inches of such a chain out of a piece of old iron hoop, I sent the same as a pattern to a blacksmith, with an order to make for me so many feet of chain like the model sent. Having received the chains, and put them in their place, the canvas was speedily attached, and the machine was prepared to meet the third trial of its construction which had now been made. The wheelbarrow was again in requisition, and another visit made to the old stack in the barnyard, and the process of dibbling another sheaf gone through. The door was again shut, and, palpitating with expectation, I pushed the machine forward. To my unspeakable satisfaction the oats were not only nicely cut, but were lying almost unanimously by the side of the machine in one even continuous row, as I had confidently expected. You may smile, but I now complimented myself sensibly, I think on my success, being convinced that I had converted the implement from a cutting to a reaping-machine. All this took place in 1828. Until the crops were ripe nothing more could be done. I was in high excitement and hope, and I waited patiently for the ripening of the grain. In the meantime, I revolved in my mind, with anxious and provident hope, everything that was likely to happen when the actual trial in the open field should come to be made. I was fearful that there should happen to me what had happened to many an experimenter before who performs his experience to a wish in the laboratory or workshop, but who utterly fails when he actually adjourns to the actual domain of nature or of art. I had observed in my experiment upon the pigmy and artificial field in the workshop that while the oats upon the whole came to the canvas, and were regularly removed to its side, nevertheless some seeds straggled away capriciously in different and adverse directions. And yet I could not forget that in the workshop all was calm, and that I had the elements greatly under my own control, but that in the open field the blowing wind might multiply the capricious stragglers and fan the flame of disunion, and damage the success of the operation. It was an antici-

pation of this kind that induced me to think of the reel or collector. Having plenty of time before harvest, I constructed this
part of the implement, and laid it past to be used or not as the
emergencies of the field might require.

"The period now approached that was to decide the merits of the
machine. That night I will never forget. Before the corn was
perfectly ripe (I had not patience to wait for that), a younger
brother of mine and I resolved to have a quiet and unobserved
start by ourselves. That could not be got while the sun was in the
heavens, nor for a considerable time after he was set; and, accordingly, about eleven o'clock at night, in a dark autumn evening, when
every man, woman, and child were in their beds, the machine was
quietly taken from its quarters, and the good horse Jock was yoked
to it, and we trio wended our way through a field of lea to one of
standing wheat beyond it—my brother and I the meanwhile speaking to one another in whispers. We reached our destination, and the
machine was put in position right in the end of a ridge. My duty
was to look ahead, and my brother's to guide the horse. I gave the
word of command to go on, and on the implement went; but it had
not proceeded above 5 or 6 yards when I called upon my brother to
stop. Upon examining the work we found it far from satisfactory.
The wheat was well enough cut, but it was lying in a bundle before
the machine. For a moment we were both downcast; but, recollect-
ing myself, I had yet great hope, and said so, the whole of the
machine not being used, the reel or collector having been left behind.
I ran across the field and brought the reel and everything connected
with it upon my shoulders, and adjusted it as well as the darkness
of the night would permit, and we were soon ready for a second
start. Taking our positions respectively as before, the machine
moved forward, and now all was right. The wheat was lying by
the side of the machine as prettily as any that has been ever cut by it
since. After this we merely took it back again to the end of the
ridge, and made a cut with the open edge to ascertain how the
swathes would lie upon the stubble, with which being well pleased,
we, after some pardonable congratulations, moved the machine back
to its old quarters as quickly and quietly as possible."

In order that this matter, now so important, may be made clear
I reproduce the engraving illustrating the machine and quote some-

what from the description. This machine, from a practical point of view, is the culmination of British efforts, as it embodied so large a number of the essential elements of perfect reaping machines that were invented in England. In fact, we may say, as embodied by Bell, they were proved to be of practical value.

Early American makers borrowed much from English inventors and some of them have refused to give any credit whatever for what was actually accomplished. The Bell machine has been severely criticised in efforts to waive it away and out of consideration so that it should not stand as a barrier against the placement of credit where, in fact, no credit may be due. Viewed in the light of today, when all the grain of the civilized world is cut as by magic, with the cutting apparatus invented by Obed Hussey and patented only a few years later than Bell produced his machine, I am ready to admit that Bell's cutting apparatus, which consisted of a series of shears, was comparatively faulty.

I am qualified to speak upon this subject, from personal knowledge, for, upon the farm where I was raised, a machine was rebuilt in 1843 with shears and did its work for several years. The first harvest it cut 175 acres. The next year the machine was modified by having the width of cut reduced to 8 feet and 3 inches. These machines still depended upon shears to do the cutting. 330 acres of grain were laid low by it during that harvest, and about as many the following year. The cutting edges of the shear blades, when dulled, behaved, in damp grain, precisely as a dull pair of domestic shears act when operating upon wet paper. Only in so far as domestic shears are failures, so was this cutting device a failure. Therefore, it does not harmonize with common sense to say that Bell's cutting apparatus must have failed because it consisted of shears. In view of the many unfavorable conditions of grain, the cutting apparatus referred to as having been used on our home farm, gave trouble, and many were the stops to sharpen the shear blades and pull the unsevered shreds from between them. Little was then thought of what we can now see was a hardship, for the machine was earning good money at an exceedingly rapid rate.

One criticism of Bell's reel is that it was but 25 inches in diameter, and hence was so impractical that it should not stand in the way of later inventors, but the fact is that it was large; his judgment made it clear to him that it should be so made, and the Crosskill-Bell machines that followed were supplied with reels of ample diameter. Be all this as it may, patentability does not lie in principles of things, but in such adaptation of mechanical or chemical means as make the principles serviceable to man; nor does it lie in sizes of things, unless proportions modify functions.

Bell's machine closes the first of the three epochs into which we may divide the century which gave birth to the modern self-binding harvester. It was practically the last step leading to unquestioned success. I will here recapitulate and point out to what extent the first *fully* successful inventors were indebted to those whose efforts, largely unsuccessful, preceded theirs. Many American inventors were, no doubt, ignorant of what had been done, but it is true, nevertheless, that records containing all the foregoing information adorned the shelves of public and private libraries in America, so that he who ran could have read. The various encyclopedias did not serve as burying grounds, but, on the contrary, did serve the very purposes intended; and they shone forth then as now, ever accessible to the public. To them I refer the reader for details that would be wearisome here.

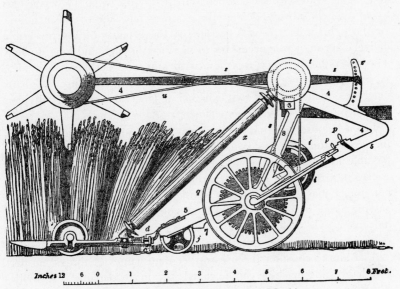

Side Elevation of Bell's Improved Machine.

Summary of Chapter I

In the Bell machine were devices that embodied the identical shear principle of cutting which, now modified by giving only one of the two series of blades a rapid reciprocating motion in a direct line, through "guards," is cutting the grain of the world. A reel was also provided, and that, too, capable of both forward and rearward adjustments and adjustment in height to conform to the requirements of the various conditions of grain to be operated upon. A self-delivering, grain-receiving platform was also provided, and by its means the swath was carried to the side of the machine. By a truly ingenious arrangement the movement of the endless grain-delivering device was reversible so that the swath might be laid to the right or to the left. By this means the necessity of driving around a field was avoided. The action of the endless conveyor was such as to tend to draw the cut grain from entanglement with that left standing. In the small fields of England it is quite apparent that it would be worth while not to be obliged to mow around them. Mr. Bell did not think it worth while, all things considered, to apply Mr. Salmon's or Mr. Scott's form of grain divider, for a long and high divider would compel him to do just what he wished to avoid, namely, always deliver the grain at one side of the machine. In short, in order to avail himself of the benefits of his reversible delivery apron, it was necessary to sacrifice the high and long divider. The reversible delivery was new with him, and perhaps a pet idea. A record of more than twenty-five years' constant use of many machines, made it plain that whether long divider or short divider, the machine was no mere experiment.

Let it be observed that the reel was sustained by forwardly reaching arms and that, in consequence, the reel support formed no possible lodgement for entangled masses of straw. Who has seen a snag in a river and a rapid current of water passing by it, without noticing a mass of debris lodged thereon? Now, a grain divider, passing along in a harvest field is not unlike the apparent up-stream movement of a snag through the water of a river, and the accumulation of grain on any obstruction, as the divider of a reaper, is similar.

As I aim to consider the uses rather than names of things, no part of a harvesting machine can be called a grain divider unless it divides something; and no obstruction that forms merely a lodgement can

be considered a grain divider. All this is to impress upon the reader
the important fact that Bell and Ogle supported their reels in such
a way as not to interfere with separating the cut from the uncut
grain.

Bell supported his main frame upon the traction wheel and maintained its proper position relative to the ground by means of supplemental wheels placed well forward, so that the effort of the team
could not so tip it as to thrust its cutting apparatus into the ground.
In the modern reaper the team is driven beside the grain precisely
as Gladstone's was, and the delivery is also stubbleward. Mr.
Gladstone chose the stubbleward direction of delivery rather than
the grainward, as was sometimes practiced in England and is still
in common use on the Continent.

The modern reaper tilts in order that the cutting apparatus and
grain receiving platform may be inclined at will; let us thank
Plucknett and Mann for this.

No machine is now considered to be competent unless it can be
raised upon the supporting wheels without materially disturbing the
chosen position to which the grain-receiving platform is tilted.
Mann showed how this might be done.

Smith taught one way of raising and lowering the cutting apparatus at will, and nearly all of the early inventors showed means for
connecting and disconnecting the train of gearing from the traction
wheels.

Salmon used a leading wheel such as now is considered to be
important in some classes of mowers. Those English inventors who
placed the team in rear of the machine soon learned that the
pushing force was not favorable to the action of the team in its
efforts to regulate the direction of travel. They so provided, however, that the attendant could change the direction of movement at
will, thus regulating the width of cut.

As showing how long Bell's machine continued to be in use from
the first one in 1828, the following from James Todd, Esq., of
Castlemains, Dirleton, England, may be quoted. The machine was
purchased by Mr. Todd in 1853, having Bell's original shears:

"In the harvest of 1854 one of Bell's Improved Reapers, also made
by Crosskill of London, but fitted with the serrated knives and fingers,
was started on the same farm.

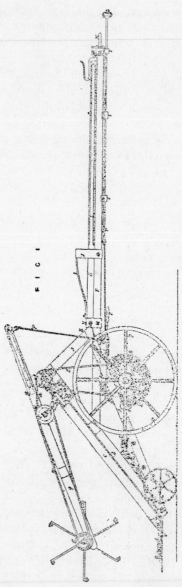

FIG.

"In the end of 1854 Mr. Todd improved the machine supplied in
1853, by removing the scissor cutting arrangement and having it
fitted with the serrated sickle arrangement. Mr. Todd also improved

the 1853 and 1854 machines by putting in a spur wheel to increase the speed of the knives. This improvement was a success as it enabled the horses to walk at a steadier pace. He also bent the reel arms and lengthened them, so that they were able to come within six inches of the ground, enabling the grain which lay away from the cutting bar to fall in a correct manner upon the revolving canvas. In addition to that he fitted both machines with new dividing irons made of spring steel, thus enabling the machines to make a much better separation in twisted grain.

"Mr. Wright of Hedderwick Hill near Dunbar, in the year 1851, bought Bell's Reaper, manufactured by Crosskill. This machine was shown at the Great Exhibition of 1851, and was purchased there. It was fitted with the scissor arrangement of cutting apparatus."

In my possession is a faded, defective photograph taken of one of Bell's machines in 1865 while undergoing repairs at a country workshop. On account of the condition of the photograph it cannot well be reproduced, but suffice it to say that it differs little from the cuts shown on previous pages, as far as principles are concerned. It is much lighter and neater in construction, however.

The latest improvements on the Bell machine are probably shown in a British patent to George Bell, dated 1857. The improvements, which may well be worth considering, are pointed out in the claims of the patent, which read:

"First the general arrangement and construction of reaping and mowing machines as hereinbefore described.

"Second the mechanical arrangements for communicating a rapid lateral reciprocatory motion to the cutter, as hereinbefore described, or any mere modification thereof.

"Third, the use and application of a moveable draught pole in addition to a fixed steerage or guiding pole, in order to give the driver a more effective control over the machine, as hereinbefore described.

"Fourth, the system or mode of regulating the height of the gathering reel from the cutter by means of the mechanical arrangement hereinbefore described, or any mere modification thereof."

Mr. Woodcroft evidently had not become aware of the fact that Bell's machine was in constant operation in large numbers for a long time before the publication of his "Appendix to English Patented Reaping Machines"; hence, the erroneous statement regarding thereto found in the following matter.

" 'The inconvenience to which agriculturists are subjected, in gathering in their cereal crops, from the want of an immediate and adequate supply of reapers when the weather is most favorable for their operation, has induced many ingenious men, during the present century, to turn their attention to the subject, with the view of substituting self-acting machinery for the sickle and the scythe. The most successful among the early attempts at reaping by mechanical means, seem to have been those of Mr. Smith, of Deanston (a man renowned in the annals of agriculture), and the Rev. Patrick Bell. A description of the machines invented by these gentlemen is published in Loudon's Encyclopedia of Agriculture; from which it appears, that the first trial of Mr. Smith's machine took place during the harvest of 1811, and that Mr. Bell's was publicly tested in 1828; but, although fair results were in each case obtained, they were, from some unexplained cause, abandoned by their inventors, and were, consequently, lost sight of by the public;—thus affording another instance, if such were wanted, of the utter inutility to the general public of the most valuable suggestions, unless thrust upon their notice by some party who is pecuniarly interested in introducing them in a practical form. That these machines contained the elements necessary for an efficient reaper there can be no doubt; and it is, perhaps, owing to this fact, that nothing was done by independent parties to bring them into use. But, however this may be, it is evident that neither the requirements of the farmer, nor the prospect of reward to agricultural implement makers, were sufficient to awaken public attention to the national importance of reaping by mechanical means. The credit of effecting this step in advance is undoubtedly due to our transatlantic brethren, whatever may be the ground for disputing the novelty of the two rival American reapers, which, from the practical illustrations of their efficiency, have of late excited so much interest in the agricultural world; and there is little doubt that, at the coming harvest, manual labor will be, in great part, superseded by this class of machinery.' "

The time was come when, if inventors in the art of reaping grain were ever to reap the harvest our patent laws had provided for, they must act. As no American reaping machine was sufficiently practical to safely be put on the market before 1833, little knowledge can be gained in regard to the earlier efforts of inventors in this country, outside of the Patent Office; and, in fact, but little enough from the records thereof for the reason that the requirements of the statutes were not strict and the applicant often did not prepare his specifications and drawings carefully. But few of the early American patents embodied any general principles, not already made known, upon which the successful harvesting machine was found alone to depend. Most of the early records perished when the

Patent Office burned in 1836, but the loss has been little felt. A few specifications and drawings, however, were reproduced. In 1825 James Ten Eyck, of Bridgewater, N. J., patented a machine for cutting grain not unlike modern lawn mowers. It had a reel which not only gathered to be cut, but formed, in fact, one of the elements of the cutting apparatus. That it proved practical is made evident by the fact that the cutting principle is now found to be embodied in all lawn mowers, and the further fact that the first successful "Heading" machines were provided with it. In this arrangement there were two co-operating elements, namely: a stationary cutting blade and means for forcing the grain or grasses there-against and thus cutting them. The fact that there was a perfect and successful co-operation of these two elements, such as to carry the straws back upon a platform and compel the cutting blade to do its work is self-evident to anyone after examining the action of an ordinary lawn mower. If it be said that Ten Eyck used a reel because his stationary blade could not cut without it, then I reply that is true, yet many inventors have resorted to that combination since, and have relied upon it for success. The point I am making will be appreciated further on. It does not matter whether Ten Eyck finally put his cutting blades on the reel and allowed them to shear against a fixed blade, or sharpened the fixed blade and permitted the bars of the reel to co-operate with it by forcing the grain straws there-against, for the principle remains the same.

On May 3, 1831, a patent was granted to William Manning of Plainfield, N. J., for improvement in grass and grain cutting machines. The machine he constructed demands our attention particularly because of its cutting apparatus. The drawings reveal a machine limited to the function of mowing. An axle is shown with a supporting wheel at each end, and to it, near its middle, two thills are attached. From each end of the long axle extends, forward and downward, a long and strong arm, and across these at their forward end is the finger bar. The horse traveled between the forwardly-reaching arms and behind the finger bar of the cutting apparatus. He pulled the gearing carriage, supported upon its wheels, and the cutting apparatus may be described as being pushed by the arms extending forward from the gearing carriage. A cam gave motion to the cutting devices. The finger bar was made so very narrow

that the cut grasses could fall over it, and remain prostrated upon
the stubble as evenly as it had stood. This is an exceedingly important matter for the machine at once became a *grass-cutting* and
spreading device. Grass-spreading, I say, because it so left the swath
cut that it required no man with fork to follow and spread the grass,
as when laid by a laborer using a scythe. Manning's actual cutting
blades were secured to a bar which reciprocated, and it was of
course necessary to provide something to prevent its blades from
moving the grasses sidewise instead of cutting them. From the
bar, just referred to, he extended a series of sled-runners like fingers
forwardly, suitably adapted to enter and extend well into the standing growth to be cut. These fingers being adapted to slide upon the
ground, it was not necessary to suspend his cutting apparatus, for it
was, as in modern mowing machines, adapted to slide over the
surface of the ground and be free to conform to the undulations
thereof. In detail the cutting instrument consisted of a series of
spear-point-shaped blades secured to a flat iron bar, suitably guided,
which supported upon the finger bar. I quote from the specification:

"A flat bar of iron lies along upon the cross bar, and the cutters
are to be attached to this upper bar. The cutters are spear-shaped, and
are sharpened on each of their edges. They may vary in their length
and width, but ordinarily they may be about six inches long, and three
or four wide at their bases. The grass or grain, which is held up by
the teeth, passes between these knives or cutters."

The reciprocating cutter was designed to be moved by a zig-zag
cam. Manning seems not to have appreciated his task, for, as shown
in his patent, he arranged to give the cutters a very slow stroke.
Besides, he tells us that he intended to some time give the cutters
a rotary motion by placing them upon the periphery of a wheel.
If he had done so his machine would no longer have been a mower,
nor would his cutting apparatus have cut without clogging. The
cutting apparatus must have been seriously inadequate. A slow
stroke of the cutter cannot be depended upon, particularly in cutting close to the ground where grass blades are almost invariably
damp, tough, and covered with the grit of the soil. Manning does not
tell us that he intended to have the cutting blades pass closely to the

teeth beneath them, but if he did so have them the device must have been defective for precisely the same reason that domestic shears are defective if the edges of the blades are not actually pressed ino contact. One element of the perfect cutting apparatus that now cuts the grain of the civilized world, soon to be mentioned, was lacking, namely, means for so resisting the action of the cutting blades as to prevent them from folding uncut straws between themselves and the fingers beneath.

A machine with a cutting apparatus thus faulty must have failed to serve any useful purpose, but in this patent we find two helpful suggestions; use of a bar narrow enough to permit the cut grass to fall backward thereover and be drawn therefrom; and a cutting apparatus free to conform to the undulatory surface of the ground passed over.

Abram Randall, of Oneida County, New York, put a machine into the harvest of 1833 which embodied all of the essential elements of the grain reaper, properly arranged and combined to do the work that it was intended to accomplish. Aside from the fact that its cutting apparatus was not of the form modernly approved, Randall's foreshadowed one of the successful forms of reaper in the matter of general arrangement.

From an old cut.

Randall 1833.

"This machine exhibited great ingenuity and judgment in its construction. The frame that contained the gearing was suspended between two wheels of two and a half feet diameter, whose axle revolved and from which motion was communicated to the reel and cutters. The platform for receiving the grain was attached to the rear end of this frame, and extended out one side a distance equal to the width of the swath to be cut by the machine. Cutters similar to Bell's were attached to the front edge of the platform, which was just in rear of the wheels. The team was attached in front of the machine, and traveled forward of the driving wheels. The grain was gathered up to the cutters; when cut it was thrown back upon the platform by means of a reel, the center of it placed a little in front of the cutters, which reel depended for motion upon a belt connecting it with the axle of the main driving wheel, in the same manner as the reels in all the various machines are moved. For the purpose of separating the grain to be cut from that to be left standing, a point on the side of the machine next the grain projected in front of the cutter. This projection was broad at the cutters, thus leaning the grain both inwards and outwards. Upon this projection was placed a broad board edgewise, sloping from back of the cutters down to the point in front. The board came close to the ends of the arms of the reel as they passed over the cutters. As at first constructed, the grain was raked from this machine by a man who rode upon the machine immediately in rear of the driving wheels at the side of the cutters, and nearly in range with them; with his back toward the team he raked the grain off at the side of the platform. Mr. Randall afterwards made some experiments with a self-raker."

This machine is found fully described in a remonstrance filed by the citizens of New York against the extension of letters patent granted to Cyrus H. McCormick, June 21, 1834, for improvement in Reaping Machines, and is also found described as quoted above in a pamphlet entitled "Memorial of Robert McCormick, being a brief history of the McCormick Reaper. Chicago, 1885." The illustration shows a grain-receiving platform and cutting apparatus, a grain divider extending not only to the rear of the platform, but also forwardly and terminating in a point. The reel is placed over the cutting apparatus so to gather and incline the grain to be cut as to permit it to fall upon the platform when severed. Also it brought tangled and leaning grain to the cutting apparatus, all parts of which were arranged nearly as in modern machines. The cutting apparatus was no doubt somewhat defective, as mechanically moved shears have always been. The addition of the reel not only rendered them fairly effective by forcing the straws against them, but it better fitted the machine to operate well in tangled conditions of grain. The platform seems to have been mounted upon a suitable gearing carriage; thereon a man could stand, and, with ordinary rake, draw the gavels therefrom to the ground, well out of the way of the machine on the next round. Preponderance of weight seems to have been behind the supporting wheels and hence a supplemental wheel was placed so as to maintain the machine in its horizontal position. At the rear of the platform is a vertically placed shield designed to prevent the reel from throwing or the wind scattering any severed stalks. The grain divider joins the shield. Observed that the grain end of the reel is supported by a forwardly projecting arm and not by a mere post extending upwardly from the *point* of the divider, such as would serve but as an obstruction.

Randall's machine, no doubt, would have found its way from factories to the fields, except that better cutting devices than double-acting shears were soon made available.

However, these early machines I have mentioned combined in one way or another the following basic elements of the modern reaper: a supporting carriage, a grain-receiving platform, a cutting device, means for imparting movement to the cutting apparatus, a reel and a divider. Many of the early machines which stood as "anticipations," in the way of later inventors, were somewhat faulty, both generally and in detail. In them were mechanical elements properly combined, but the elements were so faultily constructed as to render some of the machines little less than failures. They demonstrated the practicability of the combinations and arrangements, however, and those who invented them must be credited with having enriched the art, and left, with few exceptions, little more to be required than the skill of the mechanic. I am not discussing the most question as to Randall's property rights, but I desire to show that what he did must stand in the way of later inventors who seek to acquire property-rights in the same combinations. (During later litigation under Cyrus H. McCormick's patents, efforts to discredit Randall's dates failed.) Randall understood the functions necessary to be performed, and he provided means for performing them. Although his machine, as a whole, did not survive, his judgment was indeed far-reaching. Randall shows a combination of reel, cutting apparatus, grain platform and divider, all arranged in a practical way, and mounted upon a gearing carriage; hence, a subsequent inventor, using this combination of elements, but having a different cutting apparatus, for instance, could only be entitled to a patent covering his specific form of cutting apparatus, as an element of the combination, at best. If granted more, his grant would invade public right. In patent law it is considered that all belongs to the public which is not known to belong to the individual; but it is sometimes a difficult matter for an individual to show that what he claims to have newly accomplished does not already belong to the public.

Since the change in our patent laws, which now require a careful examination before the claims presented by an applicant can be allowed, the grant of the patent has become presumptive evidence that the alleged invention is in fact an invention. Before the change, however, each applicant was only required to put in writing what he supposed himself to be entitled to hold as a monopoly, for a period of years. Before the act of 1836, then, we may regard the *claims* of patents already granted as having had little weight. One effect, however, they have and still hold: namely, that of an admission, on the part of the applicant, that all *not* claimed by him was public property, or property of earlier inventors. What an inventor is entitled to cover is not always clear, but what he does not consider himself entitled to cover may be determined by examining his letters patent in the light of the prior art. This experimental, rather fumbling, period closed with the year 1832, for the next machine to be noticed brought with it the dawn of a new era.

Our patent laws grant a monopoly only after the conceptive thought is made available to the public by physical embodiment or at least by "constructive reduction to practice"; that is to say by means of drawings and specifications sufficiently clear to be followed by a mechanic versed in the art. Consequently, no American can waive aside, with good grace, the enrichment of the art of harvesting grass and grain, as recorded by our English cousins during the first third of the nineteenth century. Many of those told us what to do and showed several ways of accomplishing the desired result. All of the essential elements of the reaper, generically considered, were known through British publications in this country before the first fully successful American reaper was made. These include:

A divider (two in fact in Bell's, as the machine was adapted to deliver the swath to either right or left).

Side delivery.

Adjustment of the height of cut (whether the machines were moving or standing).

Adjustment of the height of reel.

Adjustment of the reel fore and aft.

Continuous side delivery by rakes.

Continuous side delivery by means of grain receiving conveyors.

Means for guiding the machine by use of controlling wheels (as shown in early illustrations).

Propelling by means of thrust tongue (Smith and others).

Clutching devices for disconnecting the gearing from the traction wheels while traveling idle.

Cutting apparatus.

All of these elements are now found in all of the headers and header binders put out by the thousand up to the present time. In some quarters it is stated that conveyors, the planes of which were so nearly vertical, as in Bell's machine, could not be made practical, yet the best work in harvesting and binding has been accomplished by machines with just such conveyors. The writer has seen acres of grain cut and bound by machines, some of which were patented to L. W. Noyes, the discharged bundles left standing squarely upon end.

CHAPTER III.

Obed Hussey's Contribution.

"Thrust in thy sickle, and reap; for the time is come for thee to reap; for the harvest of the earth is ripe." Rev. 14:15.

Obed Hussey and the workshop where his
first reaper was made.

During the harvest of 1833 Obed Hussey operated what must be considered the first fully successful reaper ever produced. With it

56

began the second epoch in the making of the history of harvesting machinery—that of practical field operations, improvements and perfection. A patent was granted to him on December 31, 1833. Turning the pages of the Patent Office records one finds a modest but clear sheet of drawings, and less than two pages of descriptive matter, but they are enough to set forth definitely an invention which proved to be practically a culmination of all the efforts of the many

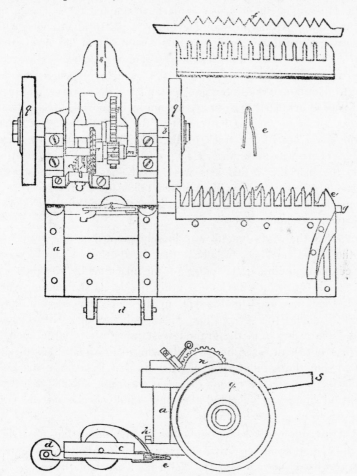

Hussey's reaping and mowing machine, patented December 21, 1833.

diligent workers who had wrought for nearly a half century. By this invention the reaper and the mowing machine became realities. The machine was adapted to be used both as a reaper and mower, at will, by the removal or placement of certain adjustable parts. The story of this machine is a long one, but nevertheless one which must be fully told, in order that the credit for producing the first *successful* reaping machine shall not be misplaced.

The Hussey patent describes a machine adapted to be drawn by a team walking beside the standing grain; a platform provided with the cutting apparatus of such superior design that it has now stood the test of more than eighty years' constant use, just as it left the hands of its designer, supporting wheels which compelled the machine to maintain its position, and a stand for the raker. The platform was so arranged that the gavels might be moved directly from the rear; or by a swinging movement of the rake, the operator could lay the gavel out of the track of the team when cutting the next swath. There was no hindrance to prevent the raker from trotting beside the machine, if his legs were good ones, and drawing the gavels off sidewise, as has been much talked of in reference to a later machine. The importance of this invention is such that I publish the drawings complete.

Note that the draft tongue was loosely pivoted to the frame so that there was no "neck weight"; that is, the horses' necks were relieved of maintaining the poise of the machine by sustaining a great weight upon their necks. A grain divider is shown somewhat shorter than that used by Randall, in the same harvest, but large enough to deflect the severed and fallen stalks to the platform and swing them away from the grain left standing; it is large enough for grass, but small for grain. The drawings show a machine of narrow cut, but the specifications instruct us that in a large machine the platform should be cut off between the right sill and the first guard and immediately behind the right-hand wheel, and the two parts secured together by hinges.

What invention a machine embodies is one thing, but its treatment by the applicant for a patent may be quite another, as shown by a careful consideration of the claim filed, particularly before the enactment of the amended law, which provided that the officials in the Patent Office should take a hand.

As no examination as to novelty was made until much later than the grant of the Hussey patent, the claims of this important matter must be examined in view of the state of the art at that time, in order to determine precisely what Hussey contributed. The first three claims are devoted to the cutting apparatus, the fourth to the general construction of the machine, and the fifth to the machine as a mower. It has long been the custom of the courts to respect every right of an inventor. In order to "save" valid claims badly drawn and protect the inventor of what he was entitled to, an interpretation was often placed upon them in court. Modern patent lawyers may smile at my treatment of this matter, but I speak here of the practice in that long bygone day of contemporaneous practices.

Such a construction saved Hussey's first claim for a patent on a straight, horizontal saw with teeth sharp on their two sides. It is possible that such a cutting device was used by Ogle, as Mr. Brown, one of the builders of Ogle's machine, is said to have stated. Clearly Manning's cutter consisted of a series of sharp blades. We have no knowledge, however, that a cutter like that of Hussey was ever so placed, relative to the guard fingers, as to form shears, in effect. We are not informed whether Manning's cutting blades were provided with edges beveled upon one side, or edges like that of an ordinary knife—that is, simply thinned by grinding metal away from both sides, nor do we know that Manning's cutters were so shaped as to have shear-like edges. The latter were more like mere rake teeth, as he says in his specification. That Manning intended his cutters and guard teeth to co-operate is plain, not merely because of their relative locations, but he so states specifically. Co-operation would take place in either case, for, whatever the shape of the rake-like teeth, they would still prevent the grass blades from being pushed away by the action of the moving cutters instead of being cut. As Hussey's drawings are difficult to analyze because of small scale, we may take the cutting apparatus of the modern mower to fully exemplify what he did, in fact, a complete carrying out of the inventions described and claimed. The face of the guard was made smooth. The edges of the teeth of his so-called "saw," are shown to have been beveled upon one side and carefully sharpened. Hussey's early experience taught him that for all kinds of work it was not best to have the edges of the blades beveled on only one side, and in a later patent showed the edges merely relieved on the underside, as found on nearly all reaping and harvesting machine "sickles" up to the present day. Given an extremely rapid movement, these cutters, when sharp, would sever the grain straws or grasses without the co-operation of a fellow edge, or its equivalent, but such effect would be little more than was accomplished by Ogle's knives and pins. In order to "save the claim" the guard, which is adapted to co-act as the fellow shear blade, should, I think, be included. So including the guard, we have a combination of two elements, namely, a cutting blade, having edges beveled upon one side, and a guard for this single shear-like blade to co-operate with. Beveled upon one side only, the actual cutting edge could lie very close to the co-operating edge of the guard. (In later practice the courts have shown little inclination to read an element into a claim to save it.) The devices covered by Hussey's second claim are most important, for the claim covers that feature which was, above all, a gift to the world—an apparatus which cut the most difficult grasses, whether sharp or somewhat dull, and that, too, with little tendency to clog. As later improved by Hussey, by cutting away a part of the upper portion of the guard, which was in no way functional, the device was rendered so perfect that it remains as it left his hands. The claim, it seems to me, should be considered as a combination of three elements, namely, a series of cutting sections, a series of projecting fingers lying immediately there-below and a part above, both adapted to co-operate with the blades. It may be treated, however, another way: The sharp edged saw teeth as the first element, and slotted guard into which the saw teeth move, and thus give a chopping blow to the doubly supported straws it operates upon, the parts above and below being considered as two elements. The guards may be said to be double edged, as well as the so-called saw teeth, and, consequently, as the result of the reciprocation of the cutters, a chopping blow can be struck while passing in either direction. Nowhere in the prior art is this arrangement found, and, I add that nowhere in the harvest fields of the civilized world do we fail to find it now.

Remove the portion of Hussey's guards that forms the upper limit of the slot and it would be necessary, in order to make the blades cut well when dull, to press the two shearing edges forcibly together, as the edges of ordinary scissors must be forced into contact. With

the upper portion of the guard present, however, the part Hussey
called a bearer, the straws cannot easily fold between the co-operating portions thereof, and hence, if not sheared off by keen edges
they are chopped off. The claim seems to be drawn clearly enough
for all, practical purposes, however; at any rate, like the inventions
covered by others, it received public acquiescence. Mr. Hussey "hit
the nail on the head" at the first effort. He made his cutting sections
three inches in width, which is the dimension now used. He told us
how to rivet them to a straight flat bar. Manufacturers still place
the back of the cutting sections upon the finger bar as he instructed.
Hundreds of experiments have been made by varying the widths of
the sections, all the way from an inch and a half to six inches, yet all
now follow his original proportions. His instructions as to the proportions of the guards are similarly valid. The slot in the guards
is still made very nearly the width he laid down. Surely it is no
coincidence that Hussey, in his instructions to the public, mapped so
accurately both construction and proportions that neither is materially
departed from today.

The fourth claim deals with general arrangements. It is necessary
for us to distinguish between what is new in his general arrangement
and what is old. The arrangement, by which the team can walk in
advance of the gearing-carriage portion of the machine, and beside
the grain, is old, but not *all* of Hussey's general arrangement was old
for it contains a raker's stand in combination with a grain-receiving
platform and, as well, a jointed platform, thereby adapting the machine to move over undulating ground, as in the modern mowing
machine.

The fifth claim, it is probable would never have stood the test as to
validity, unless by construction of court; in the light of modern
patent law and practices (except those of Germany—in a sense) the
claim more nearly covers the result accomplished than the means
for accomplishing the result; in short, it covers but the characteriza-
tion. Technically, the claim might be considered by a court to read
as if drawn to cover a platform so wide as to be adapted to receive
grain, but having a portion removable, thus, in turn, adapting the
machine for cutting grass. It might also have been so construed as to
be, in effect, for a combination of cutting apparatus and removable
grain-receiving platform, whereby the machine, by removal of such

part became adapted to the cutting and spreading of grass. Be this as it may, Hussey seems to have been entitled to all that he attempted to claim, if properly expressed. The Hussey machine was put into the harvest in 1833 and by it grain was first cut as it is now cut. The invention of the cutting apparatus proved every other element of his reaping machine, in which it was placed, to be of practical value; and not only that, proved that many things before invented and since applied to Hussey's machine, were valuable.

As a later patentee, who became a prominent manufacturer, claimed to have anticipated Hussey's inventions, the history of this great art has, in part, become so hidden and warped that the right of Hussey to wear his well-earned laurels is sometimes questioned—not questioned by those versed in the art, but popularly so. This matter will be treated at some length hereafter; it is sufficient for our immediate purpose to say that, as fast as moderate financial ability would permit, Hussey's machines were put on the market, the first after the machine operated in 1833, having been sold for the harvest of 1834 to fill orders given in 1833. The reaping machine having at last become a pronounced success, inventions in that field multiplied, and with each year, from 1850 to 1900, the number of patents granted in the United States covering details of the reaper has rapidly increased. As comparatively few of the devices patented have proved to be of practical value, however, I shall limit discussion to the consideration of those which cut some figure in the development of the modern machine or, though absurd, were made the foundation of claims to the contents of competitors' purses, and for notoriety.

Though the Hussey machine may be criticized as self-interest has done and may still do, yet the fact remains that its essential principles and the practical combination of mechanisms to make its principles effective, came to stay—at least to remain until the present time, and possibly, yes probably, to stay forever. If any one man can be said to have invented the reaper it was he whose inventions, were they little or great, enabled him to build the *first fully successful one* and set a model for his successors.

Before me is a book—"Valley of the Upper Wabash," by Henry William Ellsworth published in 1839. It speaks of the possibilities of the West, shows plans for dwellings, a machine for ditching and making on the great prairies what was known as "sod fence." It speaks of plows, but the author appreciated the fact that more labor was required in reaping than in sowing. He gives a table of expenses of raising hay and grain and the reduction in the cost of same because of the natural facilities; but he dwells considerably upon a matter of greater importance to agriculturists than any other ever before known. He foretells a revolution, dwells upon the reduction of the labor of the harvest field by half—a reduction of the terrors of harvest time to the housewife by one-half. Ellsworth mentions the reaping machine:

"Another material reduction of the expense attending the cultivation of hay and other crops will be found in the use of the mowing and reaping machine recently invented. A machine of this description, invented by Mr. Obed Hussey, of Cambridge, Maryland, has of late excited general admiration from the neatness and rapidity of its execu-

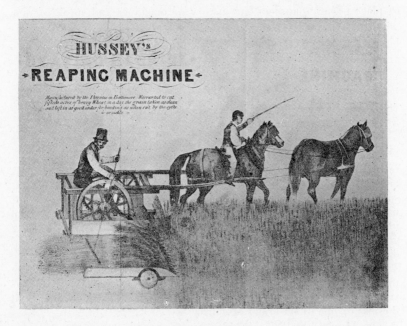

tion and the great amount of labor which its use will save. Its introduction, on large farms of the description we have mentioned, will undoubtedly be followed by remarkable results. These machines when in good order (and they seldom need repair) can cut from twelve to fifteen acres of grass and from fifteen to twenty acres of wheat daily."

Then follows a letter from Mr. John Stonebraker, dated August 15, 1837, from which I quote:

"I procured a reaping machine this summer of Mr. Hussey, the inventor, which I have used through my wheat harvest. It was in constant use every day and performed its work to my satisfaction, and far better than I had any expectation of when I first engaged it of Mr. Hussey. I can say one thing which to some may appear incredible, but it is not the less true; the cutters of my machine have not been sharpened since I have had it; nor have I yet seen any appearance of a need of it in the quality of its work. How many harvests a machine would cut without sharpening is hard to say; I propose sharpening mine once a year only."

It is human nature to desire to know all that can be learned of the characteristics of the benefactors of mankind, and hence it is not out of place to here pause in our history of machines and speak of one who, more than any others—yes, more than very many others combined, helped to increase the output of foodstuffs and lessen the labors and famines of mankind.

I am in receipt of a charming letter from Mrs. Eunice W. Lamberton, of Rochester, N. Y., formerly the wife of Obed Hussey, from which it would be injustice to one of the greatest benefactors of the agricultural world to fail to quote:

"Obed Hussey descended from the good old Quaker stock of Nantucket, Mass. He was a 'birthright' friend and lived up to his inheritance both in thought and deed. Extremely sensitive, modest and unassuming, generous almost to a fault, Mr. Hussey was withal, one of nature's noblemen. Of course a man of his sympathetic heart was often imposed upon by the thriftless and 'ne'er do well,' but he went on doing good just the same, his right hand never knowing what his left hand did.

"As an instance of his kindly bearing toward every one, allow me to mention here the manner of his death. It was the mere giving of 'a cup of cold water' that tells the tale, and that caused to the world the loss of one of its brightest spirits.

"On August 4th, 1860, Mr. Hussey and I, with our infant daughter were traveling from Boston to Portland, Maine. In those days there was often no water in the cars. When stopping at a station a child, an entire stranger, asked for a drink of water, when Mr. Hussey immediately stepped out to get it for her. On his return, as he attempted to re-enter, the cars started, he was thrown beneath the wheels and instantly killed. He was sixty-eight years of age.

"Mr. Hussey was highly educated, cultured and refined; a philosopher as well as a writer of both poetry and prose, of more than ordinary ability: and I assure you was anything but a 'common sailor.' Note * ("Near Hussey's little shop in Baltimore was a hardware dealer, a special friend. Across the street was an outdoor book stall, built against the wall of a large building. Hussey, being of a literary turn of mind, often visited the old Scotchman, and there also came his literary acquaintance, Edgar A. Poe." William Dinges, to the author, 1909).

"When young, like all Nantucket boys, he had a desire to go to sea, for in those days on that little island, it was considered the height of ambition to go 'round Cape Horn,' and it even passed into a proverb that 'no Nantucket girl would marry a man who had not struck a whale.'

"Mr. Hussey did make one if not two voyages in the whale ship, but whether he 'struck a whale' history failed to record, but I know he married when advanced in years, a young Nantucket girl, who is proud to boast of the same lineage, i. e., one that goes back more than two hundred years to the first settlers on that sandy shore.

"But pardon, I beg of you, this digression, for it is not my history that you care to know.

"Mr. Hussey was a skillful draughtsman and an incessant worker at his different inventions all his life. His steam plow, which was a success and for which he received a medal in the West, caused him much hard labor and expenditure of time, strength and money.

"I have heard him mention a machine of his invention for grinding out hooks and eyes, which he exhibited at the Maryland Institute, Baltimore, much to the amusement and astonishment of the sightseers.

"Mr. Hussey lived at Baltimore twenty-four years, and I am not sure but longer, quietly pursuing his inventions, making his own drawings and working with his own hands while directing a mill for grinding corn and cobs, also a husking machine run by horse power, both of which were extensively used.

"He also invented the 'iron finger bar,' but did not get it patented and allowed it to become public property.

"I remember of being with Mr. Hussey at Gen. Tench Tilghman's plantation, Talbot County, Maryland, when he (Mr. Hussey) was trying his invention for grinding sugar cane.

"I also saw him making artificial ice at Baltimore, but do not know whether he brought that invention to perfection. He invented a rubber block for tackle and said to me, that it would be a great success on shipboard.

"I am not absolutely certain where Mr. Hussey was born, whether Nantucket or near Biddeford, Maine. He had many relatives in both places and used to say, jokingly, that he belonged 'all along shore.'"

Whoever, by kindness and gentle manner, wins the heart of a child has always a friend to speak his praise. The love Obed Hussey won from the child, Sarah A. Shenoweth, whom I recently met, spoke to me through lips that do not tire in telling of his labors and his virtues, through lips which, though thinned by years, are yet as animate when speaking of the friend who won her little heart, as ever they were when her cheeks shared their bloom.

The child that "likes to see things made" watches every move; and we are assured that no interested child could have watched more closely the shaping of the pieces, and the test of the machine that to her seemed in part so much the result of her own efforts. This early friend of Mr. Hussey wrote saying:

"As a child, it seemed that I had always known Mr. Hussey. I saw him every day of my life, for he lived in a room, the use of which my grandfather, Richard B. Chenoweth, a manufacturer of agricultural implements in Baltimore City, had given him, at his factory. No grown person was allowed to enter, for in this room he spent most of his time making patterns for the perfecting of his reaper. I, unforbidden, was his constant visitor, and asked him numberless questions, one of which, I remember, was why he washed and dried his dishes with shavings. His reply, characteristic of himself, was, 'Shavings are clean.'

"At this time, I was about seven years of age, having been born in 1824. Although very poor at the time, he was a man of education, upright and honorable, and so very gentle in both speech and manner that I never knew fear or awe of him. I do not know for a certainty how long he remained there,—several years, at the least, I think, but of his connection with the reaper, I am *positive,* for it was talked of morning, noon and night. To this day, my brother bears on his finger a scar, made by receiving a cut from one of the teeth of the machine. When, finally, the model was completed, it was brought out into the yard of the factory for trial. This trial was made on a board, drilled with holes, and stuck full of rye straws. I helped to put those very straws in place. Mr. Hussey, with repressed excitement, stood watching, and when he saw the perfect success of his invention, he hastened to his room, too moved and agitated to speak. This scene is vividly impressed on my mind, as is also a remark made by a workman, that Mr. Hussey did not wish us to see tears in his eyes."

Well may here follow a letter from the brother, Mr. W. H. Chenoweth, which speaks for itself:

"Chicago, Nov. 25, 1893.

"CLARK LANE, ESQ.,
  ELKHART, IND.
"My dear sir:—

I notice in this morning's Inter Ocean your letter of 22nd in regard to the First Reaper and Obed Hussey; now I can say that the name of Obed Hussey called to my mind the best friend of my boyhood days, as he was in the habit of keeping me supplied with pennies when I was short, and taught me how to put iron on a wood sled, and helped me to make my first wagon as he turned the wheels for me. You are right with regard to the date of the fingers and shaped cutters for Reapers, as I saw and handled it, to my sorrow in 1833 or 34 before the machine was finished and nearly cut my fingers off. I have the whole thing photographed in my mind and can show the spot or within 10 feet of it where it lay on the floor. It was not possible to try it in Maryland, owing to the hilly nature of the ground, and was afterwards taken to Ohio for trial and was *rebuilt there,* or at least a part of it, but of that part (the rebuilding) I do not know for a certainty, but the bars, fingers and knives I do most positively remember, as I was a lad of some eight or nine years old with a mechanical turn of mind and was looking into what seemed strange to me, hence I cut my finger so bad that I carried the scar for a number of years. I very distinctly remember the incomplete reaper made by my old friend Obed Hussey, as it was made in my grandfather's shop in Baltimore, Maryland, who was at that time the leading plow-maker of the U. S. and that it was made either in 1833 or 34, as I would not have had a chance to see it if later than '34, as I was not at home until '38, when it had been sent, as I was told, to Ohio for trial and some parts had to be rebuilt.

"Please excuse the liberty I have taken in writing to you, but I could not resist the temptation to give my tribute to my old friend, O. Hussey.

Very respectfully yours,
(Signed) W. H. CHENOWETH."

In the *Mechanic's Magazine* of April, 1834, we find an illustration of "Hussey's Grain Cutter." This picture does not represent the model deposited in the Patent Office with his application, for it is very different in many essentials from the drawing of the patent, which, of course, followed the machine line for line. It has neither divider nor outer wheel, and the construction of the platform is different. Mr. Hussey had no occasion to make a model after that made for the Patent Office, for when his patent was granted he had already had a full-sized machine in the field. The picture in the

Mechanic's Magazine undoubtedly represents the half sized model made at the little shop in Baltimore before Mr. Hussey's departure therefrom late in 1832, or very early in 1833, the making of which was so keenly watched by little friends of the builder. Mr. Hussey's improved machine, practically that shown in his patent, was built at the factory of Jarvis Reynolds, who provided all necessary mechanical facilities. There it was he built his first full sized machine. Mr. Hussey made a drawing of his cutting apparatus and prepared a written description of it which he forwarded with a letter to Edwin G. Pratt, before the latter removed from Indiana, which occurred during 1833. The letter from Mr. Pratt I have before me, and in it is a sketch of the cutting apparatus corresponding with that of the drawing sent him by Mr. Hussey.

Edward Stabler was a personal friend of Obed Hussey—"a farmer and mechanic," as he termed himself, living at Sandy Hill, Maryland. His ability as a mechanic is evidenced by government seals cut by him; that for the Smithsonian Institution may be mentioned as well qualified to show his skill. Stabler was a postmaster from President Jackson's time to that of his own death. As Hussey's historian he has left very much valuable information in the form of letters, legal papers, etc., now in the library of the Chicago Historical Society. In 1854 and '55 he published "A Brief Narrative of the Invention of Reaping Machines," "Hussey's Reaping Machine in England" and "A Review of the Pamphlet of W. N. P. Fitzgerald in Opposition to the Extension of the Patent of Obed Hussey; and also of the Defense, of Evidence in Favor of said Extension," etc. These pamphlets have been reprinted in one volume, entitled "Overlooked Reaper History, Chicago, 1897." From these pamphlets I shall have occasion to quote, in efforts to place the reader in position to determine who the real inventor of the reaper was, if any one man is entitled to the honor. Hussey's machine was so successful from the first that it soon won its way into public favor without blustering advertisements. He was residing in Baltimore, Maryland, when his attention was first directed to reaping machines. Threshing machines were then being introduced and Mr. Hussey, overhearing a conversation in regard to such implements, asked if there were no machines to *reap* the grain. The reply was, "No, and whoever will invent one will make a fortune."

"Without any knowledge, as we believe," says our informant, "of what had been done by others,—and certainly his occupations had not been such as to make him familiar with the subject by reading, or otherwise, it claimed the attention of his leisure hours so far as to make a model. This satisfied him that the thing was practical, and he undertook an operating machine, which, although lightly made, was sufficient fully to test the principle." The paragraph just quoted was written by Hussey's historian several years before the death of the latter, and there seems no reason to doubt that the model referred to by the Chenoweths was made when and where they said it was.

Here follows material that has come to hand on Obed Hussey's character and industry amid the early trials so common to inventors. This letter written to his friend and champion, Edward Stabler, throws a white light:

Edward Stabler.

                              "Baltimore, March 12, 1854."
"My Esteemed Friend, Edward Stabler:—
   "I think the work goes bravely on. I am unable to express my estimation of thy disinterested efforts; I never before experienced anything of the kind; it seems entirely new to me to have any one go out of their way so much, to do so much for me. I am not so much surprised at the progress thee makes considering the man, as I am that any man could be found to do me such a service. I hope thee will not get weary;

I am sure thee will not. I hope the Committee will not act so unjustly
as to turn their backs on all cases because there is 'rascality' in some;
because there is rascality in some cases, why should a just cause
suffer? The facts in my case can be easily proved. I made no money
during the existence of my patent, or I might say I made less than I
would have made if I had held an under-clerk's position in the Patent
Office; I would have been better off at the end of the 14 years if I had
filled exactly such a station as my foreman holds, and got his pay, and
would not have had half the hard work nor a hundredth part of the
heart-aching. I never experienced half the fatigue in Rowing after a
whale in the Pacific Ocean (which I have often done) as I experienced
year after year for eighteen years in the harvest field, I might say
twenty years, for I worked as hard in England as I do at home, for
in the harvest, wherever I am, there is no rest for me. If I am guilty
of no rascality why should I not be compensated for toiling to introduce an invention which I thought to be of so much advantage to the
world? I know I was the *first* one who successfully accomplished the
cutting of grain and grass by machinery. If others tried to do it
before me it was not doing it; being the first who ever did it, why
should I be obliged to suffer and toil most, and get the least by it?
No man knows how much I have suffered in body and mind since 1833,
on account of this thing; the first year I operated in Balto. three years
after I cut the first crop I could not go to meeting for many weeks
for want of a *decent coat,* while for economy I made my own coffee
and eats, and slept in my shop, until I had sold machines enough to be
able to do better; there was no rascality in all that. My machines
then cost me nearly all I got for them when counting moderate wages
for my own labour. The quaker who lent me the ninety dollars ten
years afterward would not then (ten years before) trust me for
iron, one who was not a quaker did. There is one thing not generally
understood, thou will remember the trial at Lloyd's, thou remembers
also that I received the purse of 100 dollars, now what would the world
suppose I would do? Why that I would do like the flour holders, *keep
the prices up!* But it is a fact and can be proved, that after it was
announced to me that the verdict was in my favour I said to a gentleman *now I will reduce my price ten dollars,* on each machine, *and I did
it,* from that hour! and did not breathe my intention until after that
decision was announced to me! Where is the man who has done the
like under similar circumstances? There is no 'rascality' in that. Now
I do not believe that there is a reaper in the Country (which is good
for anything) at so low a price as mine, and not one on which so
little profit is made.

"I will inclose a pamphlet which I suppose thee has already seen,
it may be useful.

Thy friend,

(Signed) Obed Hussey."

Mr. Hussey having failed to apply for an extension of his 1833 patent early enough, a bill was introduced in Congress with an extension in view. In some correspondence between Mr. Hussey and the Hon. H. May an enclosure is found reading as follows:

"During the examination of my case in the Committee-room on the 21st inst. you asked me a question, and accompanied it with a remark to the effect 'Why could I not raise a company in Baltimore with sufficient capital and make as many machines as Howard & Co. and compete with them on equal ground?' The excitement of the occasion disqualified me for giving a full reply to your question and remarks. I was at the time so impressed with the injustice and the great hardship of being compelled to compete with the world for what of right belonged to myself exclusively that I had not the words to express my feelings. Could any gentleman look back twenty-one years and see me combating the prejudices of the farmers, and exerting the most intense labor of body and mind, and continuing to do so from year to year, at the very door of poverty, and also look back on those New York parties through the same period, accumulating wealth by the usual course of business, and perhaps watching my progress, and waiting for the proper moment to step in with their money-power and grasp the lion's share of the prize, which justly belonged to myself. If they could look back on the circumstances and comprehend the case in all its reality and truth, I should have no fear of a just decision by the Committee in the House of Representatives. The Government which can tolerate and uphold such a state of things, would appear to me to be a hard Government.

"The end, and design of the Patent Laws was to reward the inventor for a valuable invention by giving him the exclusive right to make and vend the article which he had invented and fourteen years was deemed a sufficient time in which to secure that reward. The telegraph was perfect on its first trial. It required no improvement. On the contrary, half the wire was dispensed with. The Government was at the cost of trying the experiment and has since heaped wealth on the inventor. My fourteen years were required in perfecting my invention without any return for time and labor. (The finishing touch to his cutting apparatus is, no doubt, here referred to, and shown in his patent of 1847).

"Public opinion on the subject of valuable inventions is liberal until an obscure individual appears in the community claiming the reward for a valuable invention; the disposition then seems to be to let him shrink into a corner. The world has got the advantage of his labors and has no further use for him; every unreasonable man in the community, will at once claim an equal right with the inventor of the device and one not content to urge their claims by misrepresentation but must heap abuse on the poor inventor whom they have in a great measure pushed out of their way. The idea that a wise Government, of an enlightened country, can not only look on and suffer such injustice but will actually encourage it by disregarding the prayers of the poor inventor is a mystery to those who build their hopes on the dogma that *'Truth is mighty and will prevail.'* I hope the Committee will not pass lightly over my case but duly consider as I believe they will to whom the advantages of this invention belongs whether to me or to the parties in New York. My chief aim in addressing this to you is to endeavor to draw a parallel between myself, and the parties in New York, and thereby secure your good opinion in my favor."

In this mass of correspondence we find a letter written by Mr. Edward Stabler to the Hon. Mr. May speaking of his having prepared for his friend, Mr. Hussey, pamphlets giving the history, etc., of Mr. Hussey's early efforts. The following extracts from various letters are interesting:

Edward Stabler, January 11, 1854, to Hon. Henry May:

"As requested I have examined the petitions of the 450 farmers who advocate the extension of Hussey's patent and from a personal acquaintance or by character with much the larger portion in Delaware, Maryland, Virginia and North Caroline, and on reliable information of those from New York—234 in number—I am satisfied that they are wheat-growers to an amount of not less than from four to 500,000 bushels annually.*** They use Hussey's reaper, and some of them three and four, or more of these great labor-saving implements."

Edward Stabler writes to Hon. Henry May under date March 19, 1854.

"The most that I fear is that Hussey's interests,—(which all appear willing to admit is a meritorious case)—may suffer in the contests that I am satisfied will take place with regard to Moore & Haskells and McCormick's extensions. I should be greatly pleased, and have stronger hopes if Hussey's case could be acted on promptly and before that contest begins.

"On the ground of its having been so long and so favorably reported on, by the Senate's Committee in '48—six years next May, possibly it could be called up at an early date— the sooner the better, to avoid competition from interested parties, and which I certainly anticipate if long delayed in either House or Congress. Honestly believing the cause just and right, for no fee, however large, could tempt me to advocate what I thought unjust or wrong—I shall persevere as long as there is ground for hope. If we fail I shall have the pleasing reflection, doing unto others as you would that they under similar circumstances should do unto you."

Edward Stabler, February 5, 1854, to J. A. Pierce, member of one of the Committees.

"I will, however, preface my remarks by saying that I have no connection whatever with his business operations nor pecuniary interest in his affairs; but being well acquainted with him I am free to say, that I have known no man on whose word I placed more implicit reliance, no one more honestly entitled to what he asks for.

"He has faithfully devoted the prime of his life, and no small portion of it either, in the invention and the perfecting of the reaping and mowing machine; and his untiring perseverance has certainly been crowned with success so far as to confer a signal and lasting benefit on his country, but unfortunately he has derived no corresponding advantage for himself, and from no fault on his part.

"While C. H. McCormick has literally fattened on the agricultural public by the sale of his inferior and cheaply made machines—for such I do really consider them, both from my own observations and the report to me by those who had been induced to purchase them—Hussey has been pirated on from all quarters, and others reaping the reward of his labors. And I perceive by the papers on file, and accompanying the printed report (No. 16) that this same C. H. McCormick has actually petitioned against the renewal of Hussey's patent. It is really a very hard case; that a poor man and one of the most deserving in the community, in every sense of the term, should thus fail of a just reward when he has done so much to benefit others.*** Believing as I do that the extension is no more than sheer justice to Obed Hussey,—quite equal in merit to any that has been granted,—as one of the *most meritorious* in the language of the Committee, I do most earnestly solicit thy kind aid and influence to get it through the Senate.*** He was then (and still is) a comparatively poor man; without the means from his limited sales to extend his business in a profitable manner or to protect his known and acknowledged rights from the depredations of others. His shops,—and I speak from personal knowledge—are for the most part dilapidated sheds,—too confined and cramped up to do any part of his work to the best advantage, and from a personal knowledge speaking as a practical machinist of some 25 years experience I do know that his profits are far less than some other machine makers—not the half of what is usually supposed.

A postscript is added, which reads:

"I should have made no allusion to C. H. McCormick or to his machines, had he not volunteered by petition to injure his rival—in my opinion a most worthy, reliable and deserving man—and I would add that in my estimation the two machines differ just about as widely as the two men."

Hussey must have begun on his large machine late in 1832, or early in 1833, at latest. During the early part of the harvest of 1833 he was in the field. "The machine was started," Stabler tells us, "but owing to some part giving way, or some slight defect not apparent until then, it at first failed to work satisfactorily. One burly fellow present picked up a reaping cradle and, swinging it with an air of great exultation, exclaimed, 'this is the machine to cut the wheat!'" Another account charges the breakage to a fractious team.

"After the jeers and merriment of the crowd had somewhat subsided, the inventor remedied the defect, and assisted by the laborers present—the horses having been removed—pulled the machine to the top of an adjacent hill; when, alone, he drew the machine down the hill and through the standing grain, when it cut every head clean in its track. The same machine was directly afterwards exhibited before the Hamilton County Agricultural Society near Carthage, on the 2nd day of July, 1833."

The secretary of the Society wrote an exceedingly favorable report. The group of spectators present at this trial drew up a warm testimonial. On July 2nd, 1833, then, the evidence shows that the problem, which had so long exercised the minds of inventors, was solved.

Obed Hussey who was not as easily discouraged as many stands revealed in this incident as a sanguine man. He, no doubt, felt chagrined that his machine had broken down, but had the pluck then and there to close the hooting mouths by another effort. In 1834 other Hussey machines were marketed. The *Genesee Farmer,* of Dec. 6, 1834, reports that Mr. Hussey, the inventor of a machine for harvesting wheat, had left in the village one of his machines for the purpose of giving the farmers an opportunity to test its value. During the harvest of 1834 it was operated in the presence of hundreds of farmers with most satisfactory results. On July 6, 1835, Mr. Hussey was at Palmyra, Mo., with two of his machines, at the farm of his old friend,

Edwin G. Pratt. The machine "excited much attention, and its . performance was highly satisfactory." The results of the trials were published in the *Missouri Courier* in August or September of 1835. The machines were sold for $150.00 each. A Mr. Muldrow paid $500 for another kind of machine, however, in which the cutting was done by a "whirling wheel." (This was probably one of those put out in the state of New York about that time, following early English types, which soon became obsolete in this country.)

In 1836 Mr. Hussey was back in Maryland, at the written solicitation of the Board of Trustees of the Maryland Agricultural Society. The machine was operated at Oxford, Talbot County, on July 1, in the presence of the Board and a considerable number of other gentlemen. Its performance was perfect, as it cut every spear of grain, collected it in bunches of the proper size for sheaves and laid it straight and even for the binder. On July 12, a public exhibition was made at Easton, under the direction of the Board; several hundred persons, principally farmers, being present. This same machine was sold to Mr. Tench Tilghman, for whom it cut 180 acres of wheat, oats and barley, during that season. The report of the Board of Trustees of the Maryland Agricultural Society stated that "three mules of medium size worked in it constantly with as much ease as in a drag harrow. They moved with equal facility in a walk or trot." In 1837 Hussey machines were sold in various parts of Maryland—one at Hornewood, one at West River, and several others throughout the state. One of the machines sold in 1838, to the St. George's and Appoquinomick Ag. Society, cut several hundred acres of grain, up to 1845, and was then reported in good repair. In these seven the cost of its repairs was only 1¼¢ per acre. The popularity of the machine became so pronounced that other inventors gained courage, and those who before had failed picked up their work or began on other lines of innovation.

In 1843 one of Hussey's machines was entered in a field-contest with one brought in by Cyrus H. McCormick of Rockbridge County, Va. I say brought in, because the claim that it was in fact invented and made by Robert McCormick seems to be well founded, as I shall presently show. The contest took place on the farm of a Mr. Hutchinson, about four miles from the city of Richmond. Mr. Hussey had, for a number of years, been building two sizes of machines, and at the first day's trial was obliged to use a small one because his only large machine within reach was elsewhere occupied. The majority of the self-appointed committee of by-standers reported in favor of McCormick's machine, but Mr. Roane, one of them, who signed very reluctantly, later bought a Hussey machine. A few days after, at a contest at Tree Hill, Mr. Hussey was present with his large machine.

The "American Farmer" published soon after this event a letter from Mr. Roane to Mr. Hussey, dated January 23, 1844, in which he says:

"Averse as I am to having my name in print on *this,* or any other occasion, I cannot with propriety decline a response to your inquiry. I had never seen or formed an idea of a reaping machine until I went to Hutchinson's. I was surprised and delighted with the performance of each of them, and fully resolved to own one of them by the *next* harvest, but their performance that day left me in a state of doubt which I should select. The report spoke in terms of high praise of each machine, and I consented to its award, that on the whole Mr. McCormick's was preferable, merely because being the cheapest, and requiring but two horses, it would best suit the majority of our farm-ers, who make small crops of wheat on *weak land,* for I doubted its capacity in *heavy* grain. After this report was made I heard your complaint that you did not have a fair trial, because being unable to bring into the field your large improved reaper, which was up the river, you were compelled to comply with your *engagement* for the day, with a *small* and *inferior* machine, drawn by an indifferent and untutored team. Mr. Hutchinson's wheat was badly rusted, and there-fore light. I had ready for the scythe, a low ground field of heavy and well matured grain; partly to expedite my harvest work, and partly to renew the trial, that I might solve my doubts as to the merits of these machines, I succeeded in engaging them to be at Tree Hill on a named day. They both came agreeable to appointment, Mr. McCor-mick bringing the machine he used at Hutchinson's and you bringing the one you could not on that occasion bring down the river. The day was fine, and both machines did their best, and had a very fair trial. My doubts were fully removed, and my mind convinced that in the heavy wheat we raise on our river low grounds, rich bottoms, etc., *your* machine is superior to Mr. McCormick's of which I still think highly. I accordingly ordered one of yours to be made for the approaching harvest.

"I wish you all possible success in cutting hemp in the 'Great West.'

It must be very desirable to cut that valuable plant instead of pulling it up by the roots, and I cannot doubt that your reaper has ample *power* for the purpose."

No one will claim that Mr. Hussey was a good business man; like most inventors, his mind was on the many things he sought to accomplish rather than on the hoarding of wealth. We have already quoted from correspondence that passed between him and his friends, when attempting to get his 1833 patent extended.

"Mr. Hussey's early machines were made by Jarvis Reynolds of Cincinnati, Ohio," we are informed by Mr. William N. Whitely, who early became familiar with the facts, he having opposed Hussey's extension application, "in a shop on the river front, beginning in 1831 or '32. After making that operated in 1833 he built several others during two or three years or more. Some of the early ones were taken to Glendale, Ohio, to the farm of Algernon Foster."

"The first machine taken there had a reel on it, but after using it a short time the reel was laid aside. On the same machine was an extra platform, attached to the rear, so that the raker could deliver the grain to one side. The machines were intended for both reaping and mowing." Mr. Whitely states that he saw two of the machines still on Mr. Foster's farm in 1860, that had been there since, probably, 1835.

The machines were at first bought by farmers who did cutting for the neighbors as well as themselves, and under the circumstances were anxious to prostrate as many acres of grain per day as possible; in order to accomplish this, they applied four horses and moved on a "jog trot." At this pace the reel was found of little service because the rapidly moving machine passed under the cut grain and caused it to fall backward on the platform so that the raker had little to do but to remove it, except where it was badly lodged; in such cases he manipulated his rake as it is now used on all reelless reaping machines.

After building the machines for Algernon Foster, Mr. Hussey undertook the manufacture of two or more machines for the harvest of 1835. From a recent letter received from John Lane, I quote:

" 'Old Judge Foster' was a well known jurist and judge of court in Hamilton County, Ohio, having his country home (a farm)

3 ½ miles near due east from my father's place of business, and it was he who introduced Obed Hussey to John Lane as being a mechanic who could and would make for him the reaper he was at that time seeking to have made in Cincinnati.   Also it was agreed between said Hussey and Foster that when said reaper had been made and tested to their satisfaction in the standing grains, his sons, Algernon and brother (whose name I do not remember) would pay all costs of making said reaper and put the same in use to best of their ability."

Mr. Lane goes on to say that one of the machines was taken to Laporte, Indiana, and there put to work.   Another was sent to Illinois.   Of this "little country smith shop, where this Obed Hussey Reaper, having the first, the last, and the only successful cutting device that has ever made any reaping machine a success the world over," to Mr. Lane's words, I present a picture taken from photographs forwarded to me.   Shrubbery has grown round the little shop which was later turned into a dwelling, and to the right is

Josiah Hills Farms, where Henry Rogers and others
made Hussey reapers in 1835.

the "cleared land," exactly the spot where the reaper was tested in the standing grain, and whence it went to larger fields.

The turning and fitting for these machines was done at the mill of Henry Rogers, about 500 yards away from the little shop. In the following copy of a recent affidavit, date not given, these facts are sufficiently substantiated:

"Who invented the reaper? The full, honest answer is that Obed Hussey invented the Reaper.

"Between April and July, 1835, John Lane and Henry Rogers (with Isaac and Clark Lane assisting in the work) at their respective places of business one mile north of Mt. Healthy, Hamilton County, Ohio, made to order of Obed Hussey one Reaping Machine for S. F. and Algernon Foster, then of the same County and State. Said Reaper was made to conform to or with drawings and patterns made and furnished by the said Obed Hussey, who also superintended the work of making the machine, and witnessed its trial in the field near the middle of June, 1835, in presence of many farmers, mechanics and others near by where the same was made; and when and where it was delivered to the Messrs. Fosters, who took this same reaper to La Porte County, Indiana, for the reaping season of the same year.

"For the iron and steel work done as aforesaid books in my possession show that fifty three and 69/100 dollars was paid by Messrs. Fosters, July 6th, 1835, to John Lane and by him receipted for in full, etc., etc.

"The cutting device we then made for this machine evidently was the invention of Obed Hussey; and it was as near exactly the same in all material parts to the cutting device now universally in use, as the hand made sickle could then or now be made. The sections of sickle were forged steel blades V shaped, having serrated or sickle cut edges, and riveted to vibrating bar passing through slotted fingers, substantially riveted to the apron or table upon which the cut grain fell in position to be raked, or 'forked off.'

"This Obed Hussey machine cutting in a good average stand of barley June, 1835, was light draught for two horses and left as clean and as evenly cut stubble behind it as the best of machines now do the same work. But one fault, if any, with this reaper was *the lack of one or more cogs* in the driving wheel that gave motion to the sickle, which required the team to walk a bit too fast for teams of habitual, or slow, motion.

(Signed) Clark Lane."

The above was duly executed before L. J. Smith, Notary Public, for Hamilton County, Ohio.

Many little factories over the country began manufacturing the Hussey machines during the thirties, and Mr. Whitely mentions particularly Mintern & Allen, of Urbana, Ohio, near his old home, as having built the Hussey machines for a number of years.   They were, however, comparatively late in taking hold of it, beginning about the year 1845.

Mr. Whitely further informs me that: "The inspiration given by Hussey's reaping machines started a brother of Algernon Foster to improving, and he took out a patent in the forties for a reaping machine and made a great variety of cutting apparatuses, and, in fact, the home of the Fosters, near Glendale, became a veritable reaping and mowing machine shop, commencing with the advent of Hussey there and continuing for many years thereafter."

These facts, perhaps, more than anything else, led Robert McCormick and his two sons to seek that then famous region to find builders for their machines, there to reach the fairly practical stage, where arrangements were made with A. C. Brown and John Magness for the harvest of 1846.   The success of small makers farther west later paved the way for Cyrus McCormick to the young city of Chicago, where and when his career and that of his brother Leander as successful manufacturers began.

In the West, Hussey combined reapers and mowers soon became extensively used.   We hear from them in Kane County, DeKalb County, Kendall County, La Salle County, Sangamon County, Green County, Carroll County, and elsewhere in Illinois, and in fact all over the upper Mississippi valley.   I shall have occasion to refer to this matter again, but, for the time being, leaving the machines singing the new harvest song, I return to June 14, 1834, when a patent was granted to Barnard Jackson.   The machine was evidently of no practical value for the cutting apparatus consisted merely of scythes, adapted to rotate upon a horizontal plane.   The patent is referred to only because the machine shown was provided with traction wheels having their peripheries "made rough, to take hold of the ground."   Wheels so armed with spade-like projections had been used for hundreds of purposes but here we find them, possibly for the first time in America, upon a reaping machine.

In the following chapter matters are to be presented that will require careful consideration from a Patent Law point of view, in consequence of which it is not here out of place to digress so far as to make a short statement of what is required by an applicant for a patent, in order to secure to him a monopoly for the period provided, and also make clear what shall become public property after expiration of the patent. Our first Patent Laws were enacted in 1790, and they required that the applicant should file "a specification in writing, containing a description, accompanied with drafts or models, and explanations and models * * * of the thing or things, by him or them invented or discovered, and described as aforesaid, in the said patent; which specification shall be so particular, and said models so exact, as not only to distinguish the invention or discovery from any other things before known and used, but also to enable a workman or other person skilled in the art of manufacture, whereof it is a branch, or wherewith it may be nearest connected, to make, construct, or use the same to the end that the public may have the full benefit thereof, after the expiration of the patent term," etc.

It was held as early as 1817 in Gray v. James, "the description should be accommodated to the comprehension of any practical mechanic, without taxing his genius or inventive powers."

The object of this provision was said to be twofold:

1. "That when the term was expired, and the invention becomes public property such means of information may be accessible through the Patent Office as will enable others to avail themselves of its benefits; and 2. that while the patent is in force others may be informed of the precise claim of the patentee and not ignorantly infringe his exclusive right."

This was the construction put upon the section of the law, in part quoted by Judge McLean in an important case, soon to be referred to, and it may be considered as the interpretation that the law had been given from the beginning.

I shall labor under many disadvantages, as will the reader, if he attempts to analyze the next patent to be considered, when it comes to the details of construction, and it seems to me quite probable that if the patent had not been finally adjudged invalid for want of novelty, it would have been declared invalid because of an "insufficient specification."

CHAPTER IV.

ROBERT McCORMICK AND HIS SONS.

"We, the descendants of *Robert McCormick* claim that by his great contribution to the art and crafts in the contest for human honor he has won the golden chalice, gaining the victor's crown, and earned a place immortal in the Hall of Fame." ("Robert McCormick, Inventor," by Robert Hall McCormick and James Hall Shields.)

The model and drawings were restored after the destruction of the Patent Office in 1836.

The absurdity of this lay-out, published in 1912, is apparent. Why should anyone pound out a reaper on a cobblestone anvil on a farm of 1800 acres, having already a workshop where hemp brakes, plows and bellows were made for the market, and several skilled workmen constantly employed? A claim is made that Cyrus H. McCormick constructed the fine model that we find in the Patent Office, and yet, according to this cobblestone legend, he seems to have lacked common tools. As a matter of fact the McCormick model was destroyed by the fire of 1836, and the model later reproduced was no doubt made by one of the many model makers that then abounded in Washington, at the expense of the Government, which undertook to replace drawings and models for all patentees who made application.

The house of McCormick has been divided against itself almost from the beginning of the McCormick efforts in the field of agricultural machinery, certainly since 1848. Leander McCormick, the second son of the family, published a book entitled "Memorial of Robert McCormick," crediting all of the reaper inventions and many more to his father. In 1910 a book was published by Robert Hall McCormick and James Hall Shields, both grandchildren of Robert McCormick, the father of Cyrus Hall McCormick, the eldest son, in whose name, contrary to our then and now patent

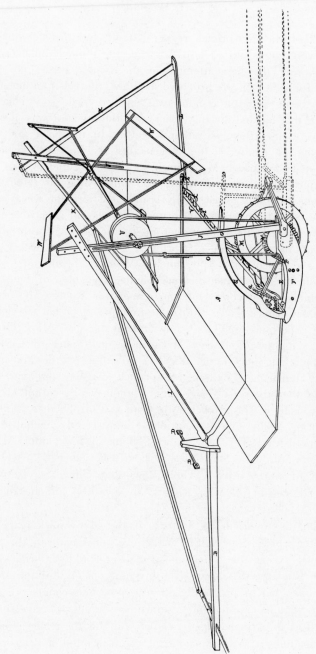

Drawing of the McCormick Reaper, Patent of 1834.

laws, all of the McCormick reaper patents and the side-hill plow patent were taken out. The patent covering the side-hill plow, and that covering the first attempt on the reaper, were, no doubt, applied for by Cyrus, as proposed assignee, the belief of the father and son being that the assignee was entitled to do so. The claim of Cyrus that he, and not his father, was the inventor was not made until five years after his father's death. In the book are sworn statements of many of the descendants of Robert McCormick. We first find Robert McCormick, a nephew; then Cyrus Hall McCormick, the alleged inventor, who admits that his father made a machine that was tested in 1831 and "cut straight wheat well"; next we have Leander J. McCormick, the second son, who credits the entire invention to his father up to the death of the latter in 1846; we have William McCormick, a nephew of Robert, who credits the invention to his uncle; William Steele McCormick asserts similar alleged facts; Henry Shultz, a neighbor of the McCormick family, who worked on the reaper for Robert McCormick; C. R. McCormick gives similar testimony; S. Ellen McCormick Ranney makes precisely the same statements; also Mary Caroline Shields, daughter of Robert McCormick, and sister of Cyrus H. who claims that her father was the inventor of the McCormick reaper; Henrietta Hamilton McCormick corroborates the statements of the others; so do Horatio Thompson, Zachariah McChesney, a cousin of Mrs. Robert McCormick, Col. Thomas Paxton, a neighboring millwright and farmer, John H. B. Schultz, who also worked for Robert McCormick, Thomas H. McGuffin, A. Horace Henry, William Steele, John H. Rush, James E. A. Gibbs, inventor of the Wilcox & Gibbs sewing machine, Serena M. C. Hogshead, cousin of Mrs. Robert McCormick, Joseph Anderson and N. M. Hitt.

Nothing is found in the history of the McCormick reaper disputing the words, nearly all of which are under oath, of the people mentioned except the statement of Cyrus Hall McCormick, first made in England, that he was the inventor not only of the *McCormick reaper,* but of practically all reapers. This claim once made, it seems that his family and his business successors have directed every effort to perpetuating the claim. Of this the reader, for himself, must judge. With this amazing claim in mind, it is in order to

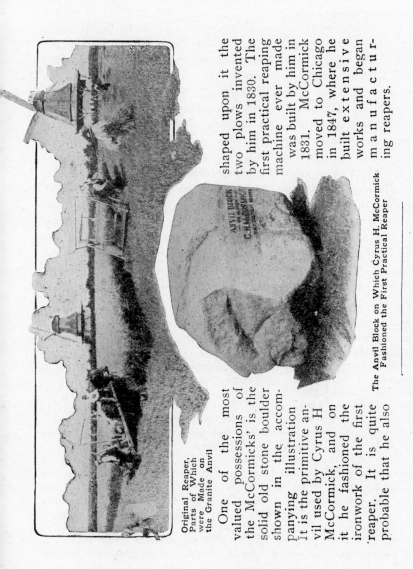

Original Reaper, Parts of Which were Made on the Granite Anvil

The Anvil Block on Which Cyrus H. McCormick Fashioned the First Practical Reaper

One of the most valued possessions of the McCormicks' is the solid old stone boulder shown in the accompanying illustration It is the primitive anvil used by Cyrus H McCormick, and on it he fashioned the ironwork of the first reaper. It is quite probable that he also shaped upon it the two plows invented by him in 1830. The first practical reaping machine ever made was built by him in 1831. McCormick moved to Chicago in 1847, where he built extensive works and began manufacturing reapers.

ANVIL BLOCK USED BY McCORMICK

follow the work done on the McCormick farm, even though courts have frequently judged that work to be of slight value. It is alleged that Robert McCormick began his efforts as early as 1816. From the description, and also because he had an ample library I judge, he followed Hobbs and other English inventors, as he had every right to do. All of the inventing in the McCormick family appears to have been done by Robert McCormick, the father, and Leander, the son. All who know Cyrus agree that he did not possess an inventive mind; neither then nor later did he originate anything of paramount importance in the mechanical field; his talents were those of the business man.

The patent was granted, however, to Cyrus H. McCormick, June 21, 1834. It is one over which more noise has been raised, probably, than over all others within the confines of the art we are considering. Its very feature is in rust; it would remain covered with dust and cobwebs in the Patent Office but for the statements made in regard to it in latter days. Cyrus H. McCormick never claimed to have invented the McCormick reaper, as already stated, until five years after his father's death. The claims of the 1834 patent read:

"My claim is to the arrangement of the several parts so as to constitute the machine as shown in the drawing. And I particularly claim the cutting by means of a vibrating blade operated by a crank having the edge either smooth, or with teeth, either with stationary wires, or pieces, above and below, and projecting before it, for the purpose of staying or supporting the grain whilst cutting; or the using a double crank and another blade or vibrating bar, as before described, having projections before the blade or cutter, on the upper side,—both working in contrary directions, thereby lessening the friction and liability to wear by dividing the motion necessary to one between the two.

"I also claim the method of gathering and bringing the grain back to the cutter and delivering it on the apron or platform by means of a reel, as described above, movable to any height required to suit the grain, and the platform to hold the grain until a sufficient quantity shall have been collected for a sheaf, more or less. Likewise the mode of changing the machine for cutting either high or low, as described above; also the method of dividing and keeping separate the grain to be cut from that to be left standing, and the method of attaching the tongue, when behind, to the breast of the horse, to enable him to guide the machine with accuracy."

It will be observed that this claim particularly covers the specific apparatus shown and, as a secondary matter, although stated first, the "arrangement" of the several parts so as to constitute the machine as shown in the drawing.

At the grain end of the platform is what was designed to serve as a divider. The letters of reference shown on the drawing are not used in the specification and as it is somewhat difficult to follow the description, I omit it. The sketch shows a platform, a main supporting and traction wheel, provided with lugs at the stubble side thereof, and a smaller wheel at its grain end. At the rear of the platform an upwardly deflected shield is shown.

A reel is supported at both its ends over the cutting apparatus, and is adapted to be raised or lowered as required by various heights of grain, (the reel-driving belt being lengthened or shortened accordingly) and to be moved forwardly and rearwardly only while the machine is still. The cutting apparatus is given movement from the master wheel by suitable gearing. Here, then, is a machine with a platform supported by a wheel at each end, cutting apparatus, a reel, and a so-called grain divider. The only difference noticeable between these parts and those of Randall is that the divider is intended to extend forwardly more than twice as far as that of the latter. The reel, like that of Bell, is so arranged as to be given vertical adjustments, not however, by means like Bell's permitting movement without lengthening or shortening the belt for driving. As a combination of elements so far considered was not new with C. H. McCormick, it only remains to consider those things in the design which were in fact new. Bearing in mind my analysis of previous machines, consideration reveals that the new principles embodied in the parts making up the McCormick machine of 1834 were not well qualified for the work to be accomplished.

Although our patent laws required that the claims should for a specific statement of that which the inventor believed himself to be entitled to monopolize for the term of the patent, we find the claims of this patent faulty and difficult to comprehend. In the light of present patent law practice, they are so ambiguous as to mean nothing. The claims presented, like those of many patents of that date, can be considered no more than mere attempts to comply with the requirements of the statutes. As drawn, these are for aggregations. In modern practice only the association of mechanical parts in such a manner that they co-operate lends patentability, if new.

Group the elements of the machine in what I conceive to be proper combinations; let us consider whether such combinations were in fact new in 1834.

1st: In the machine is a reel adapted to be moved to any position required to suit the height of grain operated upon, a cutting device and a grain platform, these parts adapted to cut and hold the grain until a sufficient quantity shall have been collected for a sheaf, all co-operating for the specific purpose.

2nd: Means whereby the machine is adapted to be changed for cutting high or low.

3rd: Cutting apparatus, the receiving platform, the reel and means for dividing and keeping separate the grain to be cut from that to be left standing.

4th: Gearing carriage, the cutting apparatus, reel and other essential parts and means for attaching the tongue to the breast of the horses to enable them to guide the machine.

As any claim in almost any patent may be the rock on which experts split, in interpreting it, the grouping of parts above suggested as the subject matter of possible claims may be criticised, but of one thing I feel sure: As the claims are drawn in the patent they are ambiguous, functional, and for aggregations, and hence, for these reasons, if not for others, are invalid. As associations of mechanical elements producing no mutual modifications of functions or any new change in the material operated upon, they are not now allowable as claims, and never were. I leave each reader to construe the claims of the patent as he pleases, however, and proceed to consider the mechanical devices embodied and the effort to make the principles effective.

It is but justice to most of those to whom a patent was granted prior to 1836 to say that the applicant was left in the dark as to what he was entitled to claim when he filed his application. There was no examination in the Patent Office in the early days, and many an inventor believed himself entitled to cover much more than, even then, could have been considered patentable. Before it became the practice to make examinations, in order to determine the question of novelty, the applicant was permitted to claim whatever he believed himself entitled to, but the mere fact that he claimed it gave him no guarantee whatever, in the invention as claimed. Whatever property right he might be entitled to was left for after consideration,— in short, the questions of novelty and patentability were left wholly to be determined at such time as the question might be raised in a suit for infringement, following the early English law. During the term of this McCormick patent, and that of many before and after it, the laws were so changed as to require an examination in the Patent Office, and when, in 1848, an effort was made to extend this patent, the question of novelty for the first time was taken up, and an examination made by the Commissioner of Patents in person. A long established rule of patent law is that to the public belongs everything in every art that is not in fact the property of an inventor for the term of years provided by the statutes, and hence the showing, describing and claiming of parts of a machine is merely prima facie proof of right to a monopoly.

A patentable invention may consist solely of a combination of old and well known mechanical elements. If C. H. McCormick had in fact been first to accomplish an operative machine, by newly combining the operative parts, he would have been entitled to the reward provided for by our patent laws. I say pointedly, however, that he was not first to produce such combinations, although I have in mind the oft heard statement of recent years, that "while Hussey had all the other parts, he did not have a reel," and that "Bell did not have a divider." My reply to this is that the courts held that Bell had a divider, and Randall had reel, divider and cutting apparatus in combination with his grain-receiving platform. Furthermore, a reaping machine is a reaper whether it has a reel or not; if not so, the so-called manual delivery reaper, so extensively used in Europe, as before stated, is not a reaping machine. For reasons that will presently be made clear, the practicability of the alleged Cyrus H. McCormick machine, both as to principles involved, to mechanical construction and to proportions, must be carefully considered.

Bell's machine was the most popular of those in England, and Kerr's and Smith's machines were next to Bell's, the most practical, as stated in the cyclopedias of agriculture. All were push machines, with the tongue strapped to pad saddles. Evidently McCormick did not fully approve of those specific draft devices and so in his patent he gives his own notion of how best to carry out the broad British principle.

Let it be observed that McCormick's was a push machine, as distinguished from those adapted to be drawn by the team. It is stated that the main supporting wheel was intended to be two feet in diameter. Its periphery was armed with lugs like that of Jackson. A two foot wheel, in the light of field experience, would not be more unreasonably large for a lawn mower than small for a heavy reaping machine. The drawing shows that the push tongue B about the usual height of a draft tongue; but whatever its height, the push would be applied to the machine at a considerable distance above ground. If a line be drawn from the point of draft to that of resistance which, of course, would be the point of contact of the wheel with the ground, efforts to advance the McCormick machine of 1834 would also tend to tip it over forward. Notwithstanding this high placement of the tongue, or more properly point of actual draft at the rear end of the push tongue, no provision whatever is made for the machine maintaining itself in its proper operative position. On the contrary, the proper position of the machine was to be maintained by the team itself; not merely by sustaining the weight upon their shoulders, but by means of a bar secured to the push tongue and strapped across "pad saddles" upon their backs. This "principle" was borrowed from Smith, 1811, or at least anticipated by Smith. Unless excessive preponderance of weight should, in fact, exist behind the supporting wheels in such a machine, it would be necessary, when doing heavy work, to hold the tongue down rather than merely sustain it. To merely hang the tongue from the bar across the "pad saddles," would, be impractical. In the use of that class of machines known as Headers, having, as they do, a heavily loaded push tongue, supported on wheels, I have seen the driver thrown from his position by a sudden upward movement of the push tongue, due to momentary excessive draft. The resistance being at the ground, with the point of actual draft and the shoulders of the horses, being much higher, the tipping tendency is great. There is shown in dotted lines what is supposed to represent a pair of thills, and we find these words: "One horse may work the machine from this side by substituting shafts for the tongue." The patent laws naturally require an inventor to show and describe what he considers the best means for carrying out his invention, and each inventor is prompted by his own interests to comply therewith. It is customary to suggest other modes, as this patentee did, but in the suggestion of thills in a harvesting machine we find nothing new and patentable, in view of the fact that Gladstone used thills for draft twenty-eight years before. The judgment of this patentee seemed to direct him to follow Bell's type of machine in this regard, with the exception of the use of that inventor's supplemental wheels under the platform, for sustaining the reaper in its proper horizontal position.

We find the reel supported at its outer end by means that are neither fully described nor clearly shown. The two bars K may have been pivoted at their lower ends and by means of holes near their upper ends adapted to be shifted in their positions; and the stubble-side reel post also seems to have been pivoted at its base; such an arrangement would admit of the reel being moved forwardly or rearwardly, as well as up and down, as in Bell's reaper, if bolt holes enough were provided for the purpose. Bar L extends some distance forward of the cutting apparatus (about 6 ft. according to the description) and considerable distance forward of the axis of the reel. On this bar and the two parts K K, is shown stretched a "strip of cloth."

It will be observed that the divider is not well adapted to rid itself of any accumulation, by the aid of the reel, for its forward portion is so far in advance of the reel as to be entirely out of reach, whatever the position of adjustment of the latter, and there can be little or none of the absolutely necessary co-operation of those elements. Such a divider would necessarily be inferior to Randall's, as the foremost bar K would form an intolerable obstruction. It would act like a snag in the river's current and collect and retain all trash having any tendency whatever to cling to it. Practically the grain divider is higher than the top of the reel, else the bar shown in dotted lines (supported at the grain end by the divider) could not be there. Such a divider would, in fact, push the tangled grain that it might encounter forward and carry it entirely out of reach of the reel and cutting apparatus. The grain divider of a practical harvesting machine consists of a structure so shaped that it may nose its way between the standing straws and sway them apart so that, helped by the reel, their heads will be drawn asunder; but in order that masses of tangled straws shall not hang, the divider is made short and low, and its top part sloped at such an angle that all tangled masses are free to be moved rearwardly relative to the advance of the machine, and then be engaged by a reel, a rake, or other suitable device, and forcibly separated as much as possible before being cut. This is the theory and mode of operation of Randall's divider and reel.

The belief that at the time of C. H. McCormick's alleged invention he was familiar with the art as well understood in Great Britain, as well as its phraseology, is strengthened by his adoption of the English nomenclature and devices of the various types of mechanism known in England that were embodied in the McCormick machine.

The whole reel-supporting construction and the grain-dividing portion of the machine of the patent under consideration possibly show ingenuity, but small practical judgment. To guide a push machine by riding one of the horses and reining the team this way or that is as unsatisfactory a method of guidance as can be imagined. Two cranks are suggested for driving the cutting apparatus. To one is attached a long cutter of steel, serrated like the edge of a reaping hook, with the serrations running in a line toward the right of the machine. This cutting blade was so secured, in some manner not made very clear, as to permit the blade to move "in part of a circle." Perhaps this blade was hung to its support as one bar of a parallel ruler is connected to the other. The specification says, "This motion, when the stalks are presented, cuts through them."

Seemingly to offset the claims made by the numerous descendants of Robert McCormick that he invented the McCormick reaper, and to prove that his son, Cyrus, is entitled to the credit, as he had the straight sickle first made and used, a story detrimental to Hussey, the prior inventor of a practical reaper, went the rounds of the agricultural papers to the effect that while Hussey was at Cincinnati, in 1831, trying to invent a reaper, the latter could not get a perfect cutting apparatus, and that Hussey's son proposed the cutting devices now universally used. The facts are that the cutting apparatus was made in Baltimore, as these pages show, before

1832. Hussey did not go to Cincinnati until the winter of 1832-3; and he had but one child, a daughter, Martha, living at this writing in Rochester, New York.

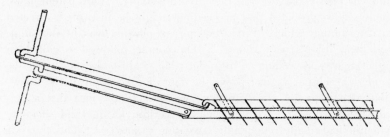

McCormick's Cutting Device.

The above sketch shows my understanding of the McCormick cutting device. Its operation was evidently intended to be much like that of a hand sickle or reaping hook, namely, not only a drawing cut, but a movement that would at the same time carry the edge forward to meet the material to be cut. The fingers, to prevent the cutting blade from moving the straws rather than to sever them, are stated to have been an inch and a half long and an inch and a half apart, and to project in a line "sloped in an opposite direction relative to the grooves in the cutters below." These teeth were supported upon a bar adapted to slide in the contrary direction to that of the movement of the straight sickle, when making its effective stroke. The patentee suggests that "This blade may be dispensed with in some cases, and the teeth made fast against the cutter and bent over its edge and under some distance, so that the cutter will then work against them and produce the same effect." This is confusing and makes it less clear what the cutting apparatus was intended to be like; the drawings show practically nothing and the description is such that it might apply to a half dozen devices.

The suggestion that the blade having the pins might be dispensed with, and stationary diagonal pins substituted, might be construed to mean that the stationary pins of Gladstone, Ogle, Manning and others could be used, but placed diagonally relative to the line of movement of the cutter. My criticisms are directed to making clear the defects which fourteen years of effort were required to correct before the McCormick machine became commercially practicable.

There came a time when a determined effort was made by McCormick to prove that he was the "first inventor." Our patent laws, then as now, provided that proceedings might be instituted, directed to determining which of two or more applicants was in fact first, and hence the "true inventor." The course followed is called an interference proceeding. In order that a just decision may be rendered each party must prove the date of conception of the invention; that is to say, the date that he conceived the idea that a certain result could be accomplished, by certain means, and the date when he had finally reduced his invention to practice. The "race of diligence" is also an important factor. In a "race of diligence" between rival inventors, "the one who first perfects an invention and embodies it in a distinct form is entitled to priority." (Reeves vs. Keystone Bridge, 1, O. G. 466.) He is not the first inventor who is first to conceive an idea, even though first to begin his experiments, for "In the race of diligence, he must be held to be the first inventor who, having started later in his experiments than the other two inventors, arrived first at the goal, and first made the completed, successful invention, and followed it up by his patent." (Taylor v. Archer, 8 Blatch. 315.)

If an inventor unreasonably delays the reduction to practice until after reduction to practice by a subsequent inventor, his patent is void. (Ransom v. Mayor of New York, 1 Fish., 252)

In 1848 Cyrus H. McCormick applied for an extension of the patent of 1834, but was required to give notice of the fact to Obed Hussey, who had patented a reaping machine during the year 1833. Perhaps this requirement was an error on the part of the Commissioner of Patents, for, if I understand the alleged McCormick invention, there was "no interference in fact"; that is to say, there was nothing whatever shown, described, or claimed in the McCormick patent which was in any sense like any of Hussey's own devices, or any such combination of devices. That there was no interference in fact became clear by the action of the Patent Office, which held that McCormick's alleged invention was anticipated, while Hussey's was not. In view of the prior art, state of the claims presented by McCormick could not have been given a construction broad enough to interfere with anything Hussey had claimed. However, McCormick's claim or claims are so extremely vague and indefinite that they might have been considered to cover almost anything.

It would be sufficient for me merely to record the result of this procedure and go on with my narrative of progress in the mechanics of husbandry, but for the fact that for a half century extravagant claims have been made contrary to court decisions and common sense to the glory of Cyrus H. McCormick, and the discredit of others in the field. Thousands of pages of false statements have been written and a score of volumes burden the shelves of thousands of libraries unwittingly aiding the perpetuation of falsehood. In the interest of truth I must dispose of this matter before continuing the story of harvesting machinery.

CHAPTER V.

Refuting Certain Claims.

Attempts have been made by others to right this wrong, but the "Lie has run so fast that Truth has not yet fully overtaken it." Already I have traced Hussey's machine from the model form into the harvest field from July, 1833, and on into the fifties; and I will add that his machine has been built continuously and is being built at the present day.

In the 1876 edition of Knight's Mechanical Dictionary is a short but comparatively fair history of the development of the art, with the exception of scant credit to Bell. Of the many machines there shown McCormick's efforts gets small space, being barely mentioned. Yet in the supplemental volume published in 1883 scant mention is made of machines other than those manufactured by McCormick. This supplemental article seems clearly to have been the work of an annual catalogue writer. Awards are mentioned, not the least important being that at the Derby Trial in England in 1881, for the work done by a machine hurriedly copied from two of his competitor's machines after the harvest of 1880. The Daisy reaper, the Advance reaper and the twine binder are also considered and McCormick given great praise when, as a matter of fact, not a single element of either was invented by him. As before stated, all that he ever claimed to have invented had perished long before the machines mentioned had been developed by others.

In his history of harvesting machinery the Hon. C. W. Marsh, a well known authority, deals with some of the *false* history in a very thorough manner. He says:

"In the face of these facts, Dr. Knight, the recognized author of Knight's Mechanical Dictionary—which appears to have been written in the interest of those who figured best, or paid the most—says: 'While there have been many valuable improvements in detail, it may be truthfully said that to dispense with Cyrus H. McCormick's invention would be to wipe every reaper out of existence. The same may be said of mowers, except the small class known as lawn mowers.' This is a sweeping assertion, and I shall meet it with one equally so. It is an absolute untruth, as any one posted knows, and as I can prove by this same Dr. Knight. In his Mechanical Dictionary, printed in 1882 (see page 1890), he traces briefly the inventions of the different features as they occurred. He gives Gladstone, 1806, credit for *front draft, side cut,* etc., as I have done; and so he comes down, mentioning devices as invented, to Hussey in 1833, who, he says, 'made the *first valuable harvester. It was patented as a mower,'* etc. And in his description he enumerates its special features, i. e., it had open-guard-fingers, scalloped sickle, front draft and side cut. It had a platform, and *'the cutter bar was on a hinged frame,'* this last feature being of more importance in the construction of mowers than everything that McCormick invented was to mowers, or reapers either. Knight says, also, '1834, McCormick of Virginia, patented his reaper which, with various improvements in 1845 and 1847, received a Council Medal at the London World's Fair in 1851;' and passes over his patents subsequent to 1834 as if not worthy of notice.

"If Hussey had the first valuable machine in 1833, and if the various features constituting a practical reaper had then been invented by him and others before him, what was left for McCormick, at most, but some distinctive devices which he incorporated into his own machine? What wonderful thing could he have had that 'to dispense with would wipe every reaper out of existence?' What, indeed, that was essential to any machine (except his own) reaper or mower, then or now?

"It is singular that we should be met everywhere with these persistent efforts on the part of the McCormick interest to build him up at the expense of other inventors, and while one hates to speak of the dead except in praise, yet, many dead as well as living inventors have been wronged by these arrogant and unwarranted assertions. I propose herein to deal justly by all, living or dead, so far as I am able. Had the rule been strictly applied which I laid down at the start, that I would notice those inventions which specially marked progress, or first showed some feature that has remained as a necessary part of a practical reaping machine to this day, I could have passed McCormick's patents, as I have many others so far, and as Dr. Knight did at first,—for lack of such special marks or features. Mr. McCormick combined with the inventions of others devices of his own, finally producing the reaper notably recognized as his, which was the first practical side delivery machine in the market, and he obtained scarcely enough from the patent office to hold this particular machine against infringement. He was a meritorious inventor, so far, and he was one of the pioneers. He was also a resolute, energetic, far sighted business man; he saw opportunity and made the best of it. He built good, reliable machines when the country most needed them. He got rich, and he earned his wealth legitimately, but one cannot say the same for his reputation as 'the inventor of reapers.'

"Mr. Hussey invented one feature at least, that has been necessary to all. He was the first manufacturer, and had he come west and had lived he would probably have stood at the head."

Be that as it may, the McCormick machine was not practical. (See statement of Cyrus H. and William S. McCormick.) But Mr. Marsh did not have in mind Ogle's machine, from the platform of which the operator, walking beside it, with the common hand rake might discharge the gavel to the ground or drop it at the rear. (He could walk and rake as well as McCormick's raker could.) Bell's reaper had an automatic side delivery. Schnebley's delivered the grain to the side automatically, also. Reapers following the Schnebley type were common in the West, but many of them in lieu of an endless conveyor were provided with a plain platform, from which the raker could move gavels, and this long before 1846, when McCormick (probably the father), first provided for carrying his raker, as Hussey had for thirteen years. I insert on page 138 a copy of an old English cut of the Hussey reaper showing side delivery of gavels. Such was the practice with all of his first reapers.

During the years 1854 and 1855 the *Scientific American* published a history of the Reaping Machine, in which, besides discussing the machine illustrated by the drawings, it says:

"June 21 a patent was issued for a reaper, which since then has made perhaps more noise in the world than all others; we refer to that of Cyrus H. McCormick, now of Chicago, Ill. This machine was constructed with a reel and some other peculiar devices."

It then gives the claim substantially as found in the patent, and nothing more.

This article next refers to the McCormick patent of January 31st, 1845, of which it gives illustrations. Unwittingly a mistake is made in line with many which have rendered McCormick mechanical history untrustworthy.

The first illustration represents the machine of the 1847 patent and not of the 1845 patent, and the second represents a cutting apparatus never patented to McCormick, but one copied from Hussey, Moore & Haskell and Geo. Rugg. This was first used by McCormick after George Rugg, of Ottawa, Ill., had placed it in McCormick machines used in that neighborhood, in 1846, in lieu of the straight sickle put out with the original machines. That the illustration is deceptive is pointed out in a letter written by Seymour & Morgan, January 12, 1855, who, in 1845, built reapers for Mr. McCormick under a contract and also worked under a license from him.

"Correction.—Messrs. Editors—The figure No. 41 and 42 in your paper of the 13th January, under the head of History of Reaping machines, you say illustrates McCormick's patent of 1845. This is a mistake, and we wish to have the matter placed right before the public. These plates represent McCormick's reaper as he made it in 1852, or possibly as early as 1851, but not before that. This is as early as he used the zigzag edged sickle. We had used it one or two years before; his patent of 1845 was for the straight edged sickle teeth, reversed every one and a half inches in order to cut both ways, and for the spear pointed fingers. (We refer you to his patent.) Moore & Haskell are entitled to the credit for the invention of the zigzag edged sickle, and also the identical straight sickle as claimed by McCormick. They made and used the straight sickle teeth, reversed in 1835 and 1836, and in 1838 or '39 the zigzag edged sickle.

Brockport, Jan. 12, 1855   Seymour & Morgan."

The editors say in correction:

"We have thoroughly examined the claims of Mr. McCormick, and find that Messrs. Seymour & Morgan are correct; his patent of 1845 embraced the straight cutter. He, however, used the cutters referred to above in the machine which he took to the World's Fair in London in 1851, and these cutters, we were led to understand, formed part of his improvements. It is our desire that every part of this History of Reapers should be reliable and correct, but owing to the great number of patents issued for improvements—some very trifling, but still diffuse and vaguely described—it is very difficult, in many cases, to separate the wheat from the chaff."

The McCormick patent of 1847 is next mentioned and a short description given, but no comments are made.

The Scientific American articles on the subject closed in 1855. They seem to have been written by someone associated with the paper and, on the whole, are very fair. Forty years later, in the fiftieth anniversary number of the Scientific American, dated July 25, 1896, a different story is told. The Quaker garb of truth is wanting. The exaggerations of modern machine advertising methods are woven with a skillful hand. In place of the story of forty years before stands this:

"In 1828 an Englishman, Rev. Patrick Bell, built a machine that did some work in the field. It was used for a few years and discarded."

What I have quoted and said on previous pages will enable the reader to judge whether it was discarded or not. It did cut grain and demonstrate all of the possibilities. Its devices were not perfect as first made, but susceptible of improvement, and it defeated McCormick in the Manny suit. The article goes on to say:

"In 1831, Cyrus H. McCormick, of Virginia, built the first practical grain harvesting machine. It contained the essential elements that have been found in every grain harvester that has proved a success from that day to this. Looking back over the work of the last sixty years in the department of reaping machines, it will be seen that thousands of ideas have been advanced. Almost every known mechanism has been tried for severing, gathering and handling the cut crop, but through all this time and all these experiments the machines that have contained the elements invented and arranged as in the first machine built by Cyrus H. McCormick have been the only ones that have been in use in the real labor of the grain harvest. The first machine had a main wheel frame, from which projected to the side a platform containing a cutter bar, having fingers through which reciprocated a knife driven by a crank; upon the outer end of the platform was a divider projecting ahead of the platform to separate the grain to be cut from that to be left standing; a reel was positioned above the platform to hold the grain against the reciprocating knife, and to throw it back upon the platform, and the machine was drawn by a team walking at the side of the grain. This machine was the first to contain these elements, which have invariably been embodied in every grain harvesting machine made from that day to this. They are the essential elements of a reaper, with which no grain harvester can be built. This machine was successfully operated on the farm of John Steele, near Steele's tavern, Virginia, in the summer of 1831.

"The first step of importance in the development of the practical reaper of 1831 was the addition of the raker's seat, which McCormick invented and applied to his machine, a device by which the raker could be carried upon the machine and as he rode through the field rake the grain from the platform to the ground, whenever sufficient grain had accumulated to form a bundle."

This article reads as one forming the substance of a pamphlet entitled "Who Invented the Reaper," the author of which for years was in the employ of the McCormick Harvesting Machine Co.

If the reader will turn to Ogle's machine, a reciprocating cutter will be found. Bell's shears I know cut fairly well, for I have known of similar ones used for years. Both these machines had reels and hence gathering devices, in the sense that the word is used above. Bell's handled the grain by delivering it to the side of the machine automatically. What, then, of the details above mentioned was left for C. H. McCormick? One thing is lacking in the picture showing Ogle's machine and that, perhaps, never entered Ogle's mind. The machine was principally designed to drop its sheaves semi-automatically and not require a man to walk the long miles made by a team of horses in cutting from sun to sun, and do the work by main strength, through the heat of harvest time. Ogle had no divider; what McCormick applied to his machine and calls by that name, would not divide, and had to be abandoned long after dividers of the present degree of operativeness and form were adopted.

Coming to self-raking reapers, after naming various ones, and barely mentioning Hussey's, the later Scientific American article says:

"They were all attached to reapers, whose principles were the same as those invented and built by McCormick in 1831 and which at the Paris exposition in 1865, in awarding him the Grand Medal, the highest honor, stated was for 'the real inventor of the system which has insured in practice the success of the new implement which is now available for agriculture.' After the expiration of Mr. McCormick's patent in 1848 manufacturing establishments started in different sections of the country, and the building of harvesting machines became a great industry."

Coming down to the self binder, and referring to the patent granted to Marquis L. Gorham, the article says:

"It was like McCormick's reaper—a machine that contained the essential elements that have been found in every grain binder since its time.*** The grain is cut and delivered upon the apron by the devices that McCormick combined and arranged more than half a century ago.*** and not only did Mr. McCormick, as the pioneer inventor, have to design a tool of this kind from the foundation, but he had to educate the people to an understanding of the possibilities of his invention, and to the advantage to be derived from it."

The article is illustrated by several cuts, one showing the alleged C. H. McCormick reaper of 1831 as drawn by a horse. Yet there is not a scrap of history extant, and I doubt if there ever has been, showing that a picture was ever made of the machine as it stood. The only early picture of unquestionable genuineness is that of the 1834 McCormick patent, which was correctly or incorrectly reproduced in 1836, and it was a push machine, with a hint that it might be drawn. There is another picture of the confessed imperfect machine, published late in 1834, but it was made, undoubtedly, more than a year after Hussey had published a picture of his machine and successfully cut grain.

Another illustration stated to represent "the McCormick reaper of 1845"; but it shows the machine of 1847, having a seat for the raker. The facts are that the 1845 patent shows a machine requiring the raker to walk every weary mile traveled by the team drawing it. The claim that McCormick's alleged reaper of 1831 was a *practical* one does not accord with the fact that fifteen years elapsed before he took the raker off from his weary legs, while Hussey's rakers had ridden for thirteen years.

CHAPTER VI

PATENT HISTORY AND HEARINGS

Of C. H. McCormick's efforts to anticipate Obed Hussey's invention many were declared unfair by the Committee of Congress considering of Mr. McCormick's efforts to get his 1834 patent extended, and unless I go into the proofs minutely, and follow them closely, my work will be likely to be waived aside as not trustworthy. Let us consider ourselves, for the time being, on the battle field of the first one of the few wars known in my chosen field of labor, and reflect upon the positions of the contending forces, the attacks and the repulses, the strategy and maneuvering, and decide for ourselves who won the laurels and who lost them. As between McCormick and Hussey, the burden of proof lay on McCormick as he came later to the Patent Office. Mr. Hussey relied upon this date of record and took no evidence, but simply made a protest when informed that his rights might be endangered, and at the second taking of the depositions he cross-examined the witnesses, as was his privilege. Mr. McCormick pleaded his own case, so we have his record and arguments. Our patent laws provided that a patent might be extended only in case the invention had not been reasonably remunerative. Thus it behooved Mr. McCormick not to paint his successes, whatever they were, in too brilliant colors; in other words, he must not overdraw the picture. I accept as true his disclosure to the Committee as to profits. Injustice to Mr. Hussey was perhaps prompted by Mr. McCormick's ignorance of what, from a patent law point of view, he claimed actually to have invented; and his ignorance of the dissimilarity of the principles embodied in the machines of the two patents in controversy. This inability to distinguish between the principles upon which mechanical devices operate may be compared with color-blindness, and Mr. McCormick seemed to have been unable to distinguish that principles embodied in one were red, as it were, and

103

that those in the other were green. In view of all that has been said and done, I accept the position of "opposing counsel" and, in such capacity will take up Mr. McCormick's case, as he presented it, and consider his arguments and alleged proofs.

During the year 1893, as well as before and since, the McCormick Harvesting Machine Co., of Chicago, Ill., carried upon its printed matter a portrait of Cyrus H. McCormick, practically as a trade mark. In the catalogue for 1893, a finely prepared pamphlet of 52 pages, are found these grotesque claims:

"Discovery of America by Columbus, 1492."
"Invention of the Reaper by McCormick, 1831."
"A benefactor to the farmer, he became a benefactor to the world. It may be said of him as of the fearless navigator of four hundred years ago—
'He was the first
That ever burst
Into that Golden Sea—'
that sea of waving grain, the music of whose billows he caused to break in fuller, grander cadences all along the pebbled shores of time." Poetic, indeed!

In a souvenir calendar, distributed at the World's Fair in 1893, is found this statement: McCormick Harvesting Machine Co. says: "62 years' dealings with the agriculturists of the world is our record," thus implying that the company and its founder began dealing with agriculturists in 1831, not dealing in plows, bellows and hemp breaks for this company never dealt in anything but harvesting machinery, and the first sales were in the early forties. On another page is found:

"Cyrus Hall McCormick invented the first successful reaper in 1831. This was the first machine having a platform, with reciprocating knife, a divider and reel, all arranged on a side-cut machine, to successfully harvest grain. These features are found in all modern grain harvesters."

"At the World's Fair in Paris in 1855 the Jury of Awards gave the Gold Medal to the McCormick Reaper and asserted that 'on the McCormick invention all other grain cutting machines are based,' and that 'not one of the imitations equals the original.'"

"The late Hon. Wm. H. Seward said in 1859, that 'owing to Mr. McCormick's invention, the line of civilization moves westward thirty miles each year.'"

"The man who has labored most in the general distribution, invention and perfection of the first practical reaper is assuredly Mr. Cyrus Hall McCormick, of Illinois. (Report of International Jury, Paris Exposition, 1867.)"

In the catalogue for 1883 are found these words: "The McCormick has the grand and proud distinction of being the first practical reaper invented in the world." In the catalogue for 1892 is the statement, "More than sixty years ago the first successful harvesting machine was a McCormick." What I have quoted is only advertising buncombe and would, of course, receive no notice whatever but for the fact that the unproved claim has gone too far, and is taken as history. When it finds its way into encyclopedias; when it fills pages of popular magazines; when it is lauded over the cups at banquets and, when, as imitation of Dobbs, who showed his machine in a London theatre in 1814, the falsehood is heralded from the stage, it should be stopped.

Particularly should advertising enthusiasm stop short of using public honors bestowed under misconceptions.

On the frieze of Machinery Hall at the World's Fair in Chicago, Illinois, appeared the names of celebrated inventors; on the most prominent side, patched over an erased name, was that of Cyrus H. McCormick. The name was well put on, but still the blotch, due to cutting out of the name first placed there, possibly Hussey's, showed until the building succumbed to the flames. Yet in the files of the United States Patent Office are the papers belonging to the application of Cyrus H. McCormick for an extension of his 1834 patent for improvement in reaping machines. There are found several affidavits which were declared informal because Mr. Obed Hussey, who stood in the position of contestant, in effect, had not then been notified. He was given notice and the ground was gone over again, he being present and cross-examining the witnesses and the previous statements were materially modified. Mr. McCormick in the statement now before me said:

"From the experiment of 1831 until (for) the harvest of 1840 I did not sell a single Reaper, except one, which I afterwards took back; although during that time I had many exhibitions of it, and rec'd favorable notices of those exhibitions; but experience proved to me that it was best for the public as well as myself that no sales were made, as defects presented themselves which would have rendered the Reaper unprofitable in other hands.

"From time to time a great many improvements were found necessary, requiring a great deal of thought and study—some at times flattered, at others discouraged; and at all times deeming it best not to attempt sales either of machines or right to manufacture, until notified that the Reaper would succeed well, and the great variety of situations in which it was necessary to operate, in relation to the condition of the grain and ground, together with the short time in each year for experimenting—and also the failures of some crops—added much to the difficulty, and delay in introducing and completing the Reaper."

Let us analyze the affidavit *first* filed by Mr. McCormick in connection with the above letter, to the Commissioner of Patents.

1st: He says that his father, Robert McCormick, built a machine and *experimented* with it in 1831, which cut well in straight wheat; (In the above statement he admits that his alleged machine of 1831 was merely an experiment.)

2nd: That he, C. H. McCormick, conceived the idea of *cutting* upon a new principle; that is, with a vibrating blade operated by a crank.

3rd: That the grain was to be supported while cutting by means of fixed pieces of wood or iron; (The patent does not so show).

4th: That a *temporary experimental* machine was immediately constructed and *partially* tried with success;

5th: That the trial was without a reel;

6th: That a reel, which he had "discovered" in the meantime, was attached, and another successful *experiment* was made;

7th: That the machine at the time of this *experiment* contained all the functional parts embraced in the patent of 1834. It had the platform; the straight sickle given a "vibrating" action by a crank; the fingers, or stationary supports to support the grain projecting forward into the grain, and a reel. (Observe that the cutting apparatus was not what he patented in 1834.)

In the correspondence with the Commissioner he further says:

That the "double and counteraction from the crank," as patented, was *abandoned on being further tested*. (If this is true, can the machine be considered a success?)

That the arrangement of the machine was such as to balance upon two wheels so that the horse might travel in front and at one side;

That Hussey *later* adopted *his* arrangement;

McCormick admits that in 1831 his efforts were *experiments,* and that not until 1840 did he sell a machine, and had to take that one back. (Clearly, then, his conceptions were not yet reduced to practice.)

He confesses that experience during the tests and exhibitions proved to him that it was best for himself and the public that no sales be made, as defects presented themselves which would have rendered the reaper unprofitable in other hands. (This true, was the machine then a practical success?)

After 1840, he says, a great many improvements were found necessary; (If, after 1840, improvements were *necessary,* was it yet a success?)

That said improvements required thought and study;

That he was sometimes flattered and sometimes discouraged; that he did not make sales or sell rights because not satisfied that the reaper would succeed well, which was as late as 1840. In view of these admissions, what becomes of all this talk about the first *successful* reaper!

McCormick was not sufficiently satisfied of its being a "useful" machine to patent the reaper, he tells us, until the year 1834, for its construction and proportions were imperfect, and its cutting apparatus was defective on account of liability to choke and get out of order. (And yet it was a *successful* reaper in 1831!)

He admits that the cutting "proved not to be sufficiently certain to be relied on in all situations" until "the improvement in the fingers and reversed angle of the teeth of the sickle" which was patented in 1845. He improved the bearers by dispensing with the underpart of the fingers to prevent grass from hanging and choking the machine.

In 1839, he says, he worked upon his reaper *again.* This must have been the second experiment for, in order to show diligence, he would certainly have said so in his statement, if he had made any other between 1831 and 1839. One farmer present at the last mentioned trial, ordered a machine but it was never delivered, for McCormick tells us he "did not then feel that it was safe to warrant its performance"; he published the exhibition in a Richmond paper, however. Two farmers, we are informed, ordered machines, but only one order was filled. This one and the exhibition reaper were sold in 1840, but failed to work well.

The serrations in these sickles were so cut that the teeth were all directed one way and they drew the blades of wheat into the fingers so as to choke the machine, but he says that he corrected these defects for 1841; later he put into one of them a sickle having the angle of the serrations reversed every inch and a half, when, he adds, the machine worked better. After this he warranted the machine in every respect. He claims that he sold seven machines in 1842, but was required to add improvements in order to cure the defects. (Inventions are not complete until the experimental stages are passed.)

Referring to Mr. Hussey he says: "I did not interfere with him because I did not find him very much in the way, calculated to *beat* him without, and suppose it might be best to do so." Let us take the charitable view and believe, if we can, that Mr. McCormick simply meant that in order to sustain himself in his assumed rights, by his dates alone, it was not necessary to consider Mr. Hussey's patent, though prior to his own. The word "beat" sounds badly, referring, as it does, to an honorable contestant. Quite different the tone of Mr. Hussey, who, in his statement of facts to the Board says:

"In view of all these facts, I feel justified in asking your Honorable Board a decision, which, while it adjudges McCormick's machine according to its merits, will not be prejudicial to my interests, seeing that Mr. McCormick makes no claims to the grand principle in my machine, which makes it valuable, and so much better than his, which principle I claim as my invention.

"I had no intention, neither had I any desire to place any obstacle in the way of the extension of McCormick's patent, but the course he has taken, before your Board and before Congress, has compelled me to act in self defense, by which I have given your Honorable Board much trouble, which I would have gladly avoided."

In his letter to the Commission the applicant for extension partly briefs his proposed proofs, and, as well, briefs his case. In so doing Mr. McCormick says: "If my claim be made out as so far appears from the evidence presented, it will be observed (as I think) that nothing will be left of Mr. Hussey's claim to which he is entitled, and all the improvements he has added since his patent have, I believe, been taken from mine." (In the above he is referring to single drive-wheel and balancing his machine thereon, as used long before by others.)

He confesses that he never received profits from first patent until after years of study (1842), and never should have realized anything from the invention but for later improvements. Then how, I ask again, was the machine a success? Continuing, he says: "If then it shall appear that I am the original inventor of all the leading and important principles of the invention, is it wrong that I should ask for reciprocal benefits for myself, who alone have brought it into being?"

Many of them are admissions by Mr. McCormick, and hence may be accepted as facts. How well are the others substantiated by witnesses?

John Steele swore that in 1831 or 1832 a machine was made. Straight sickle was used; supports were above and below *two* inches apart; machine supported on two wheels; sickle was operated by a crank; machine was drawn by a single horse; had a grain platform, machine had reel operated by a belt; and also a divider. This answer, cross-examination showed, was read from a paper prepared by Mr. McCormick, some time before, and handed witness. In further cross-examination witness admits of uncertainty as to whether supports were above and below, or merely above, or merely below the sickle. As Mr. Hussey's patent had mainly to do with the *cutting apparatus* of harvesting and mowing machines, his cross-examination was not directed to any other feature.

Another witness, Mrs. E. Steele, had "The *Impression* it was in the 1831" that the machine was operated; didn't remember whether the machine had platform or not; didn't remember whether the machine was drawn by horse or horses.

John McCown testified as to what he made, as follows, in reply to Mr. McCormick's question: "You applied to me in the year 1831—and I made one at that time, a long, straight syckle."

Leander J. McCormick stated that a machine was made in 1831 and operated in the harvest by one horse in shafts attached to gear frame; and a straight sickle was used at the front of the platform; sickle passed between fingers about *three* inches apart. There was a reel driven from the gearing by belt. There was a projection for separating the grain; does not know whether iron or steel fingers were used. Double finger was abandoned in 1842 or '43 in favor of single fingers. This witness does not say that C. H. McCormick *invented* the machine. (See "Memorial of Robert McCormick," published in 1885 by Leander J. McCormick, and "Robert McCormick, Inventor," by Robert Hall McCormick and James H. Shields, Chicago, 1910. Leander J. McCormick stated to me that he published the memorial to vindicate his father as against the claims of his brother Cyrus.)

Mary A. McCormick testified that the machine was first *operated* in 1831. She was not asked who invented the machine. (See her statement in "Robert McCormick, Inventor.")

The first question put to William S. McCormick simply asked what he knew of the machine. His answer was mainly a paraphrase of that given by witness Leander J. McCormick. He does not know whether wood or iron fingers were used. They projected forward two or three inches and turned back beneath the sickle one and one half inches; does not attempt to state exactly, but probably does not miss it a half inch. Finally says that it was less than an inch, but not less than a half inch; states that fingers were *abandoned* in 1840; does not know whether a *slide* or *wheel* was used at outer end of platform. In this he agrees with L. J. McCormick. And here McCormick rests his case. (Mr. Leander McCormick stated to me that the machine was the work of his father; that the machine was crude; had wooden cog wheels and a mere runner at the grain end of the platform.)

With the Hussey device clearly in mind, and with the McCormick construction variously described by these witnesses, I ask the reader if he can gather that McCormick had on that machine anything remotely approaching the cutting apparatus of harvesting machines of today, which, as before stated, may be considered to be an exact exemplification of Hussey's invention.

Mr. McCormick first presented his petition to the Commission with a number of affidavits, but as an extension of his patent might affect Hussey's rights, he was required, as stated, to give the latter notice, and so Mr. Hussey was placed in the position of one protesting, not merely in his own interest, but, incidentally, in the interest of the public. The law had been changed. An examination was first necessary in order to determine what, if anything, Mr. C. H. McCormick had invented. If, in fact, his claims in terms covered anything that Hussey had produced, then Hussey might be deprived of the use of his own devices. Whatever Hussey had invented would, by operation of law, become public property on December 31, 1847. Up to that time Hussey was entitled to a monopoly of whatever his patent covered, and the free use of the same forever. If now McCormick had succeeded in his efforts, and priority had been awarded to him, the public might not have become possessed of the right to avail itself of the invention until the expiration of any extension of Mr. McCormick's patent, over six years later. Mr. McCormick would then have been in position to attempt to collect royalty for several years, after the expiration of Mr. Hussey's patent. That Mr. Hussey was entitled to an extension of his patent we shall soon see, if he had conformed to the practices of the Patent Office and applied at the proper time. In short, if Mr. Hussey had not been given notice, and if the Patent Office had made no examination as to patentability, and, in consequence, Mr. McCormick's patent had been extended, then both Mr. Hussey and the public could have been wronged for more than six years, provided, of course, that Mr. McCormick could have sustained his patent in the courts. The stake played for in this proceeding, was truly an enormous one.

Mr. McCormick having been required to consider Hussey's rights, went to the shop of the latter, but Mr. Hussey declined to sign the stipulation he had drawn, with a view to having the depositions already taken considered formal, as he might thereby injure his own interests. In consequence of all this the parties met in Rockbridge in Augusta County, Virginia, where the witnesses were *formally* examined.

As Mr. McCormick's claim for the credit of having invented the reaper must stand or fall on what he actually did, and not upon what it is now claimed that he did, his proofs require minute examination. I am not called upon to question whether or not Robert McCormick built a machine in 1831, for it is not a patent granted to him which we have to consider; but rather what C. H. McCormick *did* do. Did he build a complete machine in the short time elapsing between wheat and oat harvest? The proofs do not show it. Indeed, it is perfectly safe to say that he did not, even with a sawmill, a blacksmith shop, and all the tools of a small factory at hand; such work could not have been successfully done by any two men under favorable circumstances in less than a month. I say this after more than fifty years of experience in this great field of manufacture. Did he not borrow some parts from his father's machine? Did he not, in fact, merely put a sickle into his father's machine? Evidence is extant to the effect that Robert McCormick did all the planning and all the inventing that were done. ("Memorial of Robert McCormick" and "Robert McCormick, Inventor.") Returning to the proofs, we find that the witness Steele did not positively swear *when* the machine was made, nor did Mrs. Steele. Mr. McCown simply swore that he made a long, straight sickle, in 1831. But this testimony was given sixteen years after the alleged event, the date thereof being simply a matter of memory. No documents were offered in evidence.

Neither Leander McCormick, William McCormick (brothers of C. H. McCormick), Mary McCormick (mother of C. H. McCormick), nor Mr. Hitt testified as to the definite time the machine was made. Mr. McCormick's mere statement that he built a machine,— that is, a whole machine,—between the wheat harvest and oat harvest is not definitely corroborated. Neither is there proof that he made any part of a machine, other than the sickle, between those times. In fact, it is not clear that he did not go to the blacksmith shop *for his father* and get the sickle made. We thus see that, as a matter of fact, every essential remained unproved.

Cyrus H. McCormick did not take the witness stand in his own behalf, in an effort to make out a clear case; perhaps he did not care to give Mr. Hussey an opportunity to cross-examine him. Mr. N. M. Hitt swore he saw Robert McCormick and C. H. McCormick building a reaper machine in the summer of 1831. Was, or was not, the machine the joint invention of the two men referred to by this witness? If a joint invention, the patent covering it was void, of course. John Steele does not swear that the machine tried was C. H. McCormick's invention, nor does Mrs. Steele. That C. H. McCormick invented it is merely a statement to that effect in the question put to her. Mr. McCown did not say who invented the long, straight sickle; Leander McCormick did not say that his brother invented it; Mary McCormick was silent in regard to this. William S. McCormick was asked what he knew in regard to the machine, but he did not say who invented it. The *question* merely implied that C. H. McCormick had invented it. If the examination was intended to be directed to proving that C. H. McCormick invented the machine, and when, the effort was a failure.

Coming now to the construction, only three witnesses touch upon details, and they do not quite agree. Leander McCormick testified that the sickle was straight and passed "through fingers between which fingers there was a space of about *three* inches." He does not remember whether the fingers were iron or wood. He further said "I think they projected forward." It is noticed that he did not say that they projected diagonally forward. Whether they did project diagonally or directly forward is a matter of importance, for if they did not project directly forward they were, in effect, simply copies of older ones, as far as operativeness is concerned, and not those described in the McCormick patent. William S. McCormick said that the sickle was straight edged in front of the platform, and that there were stationary fingers of wood or iron projecting forward in order to support the grain. Notice that he did not say the fingers projected diagonally forward, as in the patent.

If, as a matter of fact, the fingers did project diagonally forward, they could in no way "anticipate" Hussey's invention, even if made earlier.

In all the testimony there is no statement that the machine operated successfully, and Mr. McCormick himself admits that for several years it remained imperfect.

Vague though the description of the cutting apparatus is, a few things about it seem clear. The cutter was sickle edged, like the reaping hook, but it was straight. The points of the serrations inclined always in one direction. As nearly as we can gather the opposing fingers were hung upon radius arms, which in the patent are called "movable tongues or slips." The edge of the blade, then, would be moved forwardly when making the cutting stroke. Above this cutter a sliding plate provided with teeth was moved by a crank.

EDITOR'S NOTE:—Several pages of the Steward manuscript at this point appear to be missing.

CHAPTER VII

THE McCORMICK TESTIMONY

Let us now consider the credibility of those who are trying to perpetuate in the American mind the belief that Cyrus H. McCormick invented the reaper.

On page 7 of the McCormick catalogue for the year 1886 (one year after Leander McCormick published his "Memorial of Robert McCormick") is found a quotation:

"At length, in the year 1831, when he was but twenty-two years old, Cyrus H. McCormick constructed the first reaper that ever successfully harvested grain. It was a crude affair, from his own description of it, for he says, 'The cog wheels, made by myself, were all of wood. Every part of the machine was made by me. My father's machine was tried on a green crop, and after his failure I then designed, originated and constructed the entire machine by the time the crops were ripe and ready for cutting.'" (C. H. McCormick had been in his grave several years when this was written.)

Will any one believe that the entire machine (a successful one) was made by one man in the short time allowed between the cutting of green wheat and ripe oats in any grain growing locality. Mr. McCormick, in his sworn statement to the Commissioner of Patents, dated January 1, 1848, says, referring to his father's machine:

"By his experiment in the *harvest* of 1831 he became satisfied that it would not answer a valuable purpose, not withstanding it cut well in straight wheat."

In his "Memorial to Congress" he says his first machine was "a temporary, experimental machine, was immediately constructed, * * * and *the cutting partially* tried with success, in cutting, without a reel, a little *wheat* left standing for the trial; whereupon, the machine was improved, and the reel, which I had in the meantime *discovered;*

114

and soon afterwards (the same harvest) a very successful experiment was made with it in cutting oats in the field of Mr. John Steele."

As Leander McCormick points out, Cyrus does not say that he invented the reel. Quite likely he "discovered" it in some of the English publications showing Bell's machine. Robert McCormick, the father, was an educated man and no doubt possessed a large library of books on agricultural and similar subjects and, quite likely, was the owner of Loudon's Encyclopedia of Agriculture and other English publications. A prosperous man, he owned 1,800 acres of land, yet those acres represented "only one-half of his interests." C. H. McCormick's statement quoted posthumously in the annual catalogue for 1886, is not shown to be taken from any sworn statement, and I ask if it is reasonable on a large farm amid plenteous labor if "every part of the machine" was made by him. William S. McCormick, a nephew of Robert McCormick, in his affidavit, dated March 4, 1880, says, speaking of the first machine, "I myself and one Samuel Hite were the men who did the work for Robert McCormick while he invented and experimented with the machine." W. S. McCormick in his letter of November 7, 1878, had said: "Myself and Sam. Hite were the workmen who did the work; Cyrus McCormick helping also." In his letter of November 28, 1878, he says that he lived with and worked for Robert McCormick until the last of the year 1831.

Col. Thomas S. Paxton, in a sworn statement, dated September 10, 1878, says that he was a millwright working in the yard near Robert McCormick when the latter was working on the machine, and that the latter said that while it was his invention he intended to give Cyrus the benefit of it. Horatio Thompson, D. D., in a sworn statement of September 9, 1878, says, after mentioning the fact that he saw Robert McCormick working on the machine: "The Wheat reaper of Robert McCormick's is the same improved by C. H. and L. J. McCormick, and now manufactured in Chicago." Zachariah McChesney, in a sworn statement September 9, 1878, after mentioning the fact that he knew of Robert McCormick's having worked upon a reaper, says: "This invention of Robert McCormick's is the original of the now improved McCormick reaper manufactured in the city of Chicago by Cyrus and Leander, Robert's sons."

Leander McCormick in a sworn statement of August 1, 1885, says: "My father built a successful reaping machine in 1831." All these affidavits were prepared after the parties had become perfectly familiar with the machine at the time put on the market, as made in Chicago. (See "Memorial of Robert McCormick.")

None of the witnesses produced by C. H. McCormick, at the time of his application for an extension of the 1834 patent was before the Patent Office, swore that Cyrus McCormick was the *inventor* of the reaper alleged to have been tested in 1831. The invention, such as it was, was that of the father. There is no reason to dispute that something in that line was done, but the question arises, what was done aside from crude experiments with a crude machine, and when? The following are four cuts of this alleged "first machine."

"The original McCormick reaper of 1831," as interpreted in the McCormick catalogue for 1886. Compare this cut with others. It will be noticed that the brace from reel post to stubble side of platform is omitted as in the cut that follows.

TESTING THE FIRST REAPER NEAR STEELE'S TAVERN, VIRGINIA, U. S. A., JULY 25, 1831.

The invention of Cyrus H. McCormick — the first machine that ever cut grain successfully — and concerning which a recent standard mechanical authority says: "To dispense with Mr. McCormick's invention would be to wipe every reaping machine out of existence."

This cut is taken from the catalogue of the McCormick Harvesting Machine Company of 1886. We next have a cut taken from the McCormick Harvesting Machine Company's catalogue for 1899.

"Testing the first reaper, near Steele's Tavern, Virginia, U. S. A., July 25, 1831. The invention of Cyrus H. McCormick—the first machine that ever cut grain successfully—and concerning which a recent standard mechanical author says: 'To dispense with Mr. McCormick's invention would be to wipe every reaping machine out of existence.' "

On the fence is a large sign, in upper case letters, reading:

"In this field
July 25, 1831,
Will be tested a new *PATENT GRAIN CUTTER*
Worked by horse power,
Invented by
C. H. McCormick."

Comparing the illustration of the *machine* to the patent drawing of 1834 it departs little from the latter, except that no push tongue is secured and hence no means for strapping the same to the backs of the horses, but, on the contrary, thills are shown for a *single* horse.

In Casson's "Biography of Cyrus McCormick," published in the magazine *System,* for 1909, page 8, is the above picture of the *first* machine, beneath which is the following: "The dramatic public test of McCormick's reaper—the *first* successful harvesting machine— at Steele's Tavern, in Virginia, in 1831." (This is a half tone engraving "made from an old advertising lithograph," a copy of which is before me.) The last two pictures are not alike. Were two pictures made? Comparing them, we find that the sign upon the fence became misplaced between the time the last above shown picture was made and the other one, and the style of the fence, where the man is jumping over, is changed. The style of the fence in front of Steele's Tavern is changed from three rails to two. The horse in the lane evidently backed up some distance before the second picture was made, as he is not there found immediately under the tree in front of the house. The man in the former picture, with foot on the fence and a grain cradle at hand, is changed to a man differently dressed, but with foot on the fence and a reaping sickle

The same scene redrawn for the purposes of biography.

in hand. Either there was incongruity in the costumes of the spectators or the imagination of the artist was allowed immense scope.
The dude, with cane, seems to have had the dress of 1883. Prince
Albert, when first he had donned the coat now called after him, may
have cribbed the style from McCormick, 1831. We see the southern
colonel and the stocky Englishman, and beside him, perhaps, a college professor. The man leaning on the fence with the reaping
hook is evidently in a pensive mood. None of the white men is
giving any attention to the wonderful reaper of 1831 (?), but the
colored people all show an expression of amazement. In the original
poster from which the cut was taken was the McCormick (?) twine
binder of 1883 at one upper corner, and at the other upper corner
a portrait of C. H. McCormick, after he had become gray. Clearly
it must have been thought inappropriate to show the poster complete
(that is, with the binder of 1883, and the portrait of McCormick,
turned gray), and I think so; if the reader will turn to my reproduction of the poster he will agree with the author of "Cyrus Hall Mc-
Cormick, His Life and Work," that it *was* inappropriate.

"As first drawn the broad-brimmed, grey-coated man beside the
alleged inventor, in Prince Albert coat, had a black-snake whip (slave
whip) in hand, but through the influence of the wife of the said alleged
inventor, who was not in sympathy with Virginia ways, the lash was
touched out." (H. B. Utley)

The following is my photo engraving of one of the posters, now
hanging over my desk, from which the Casson illustration, entitled
"The Testing of the First Reaping Machine near Steele's Tavern,
Va., A. D. 1831," was made:

It will be observed that in the former engraving over Steele's
Tavern is not found a picture of the twine binder of 1883 (the date
in print in small letters beneath the machine), nor upon the right
hand upper corner do we find a portrait of C. H. McCormick. I
have drawn a dotted vertical line near each end of the picture, and
a line near the top, making the edges and top correspond with the
margins of the "System" picture. I take it that the ends and top
were removed for deceptive purposes, the reasons for so doing evidently having been to remove all evidence that the picture was made
after the Appleby binder of 1883 had been constructed, and Cyrus

THE TESTING OF THE FIRST REAPING MACHINE NEAR STEELE'S TAVERN. VA. A.D. 1831.

Photo engraving of McCormick advertising poster for the year 1883. (Photographed by the author from one of those distributed).

H. McCormick had become gray. Compare the face of the man in a Prince Albert coat near the right of the picture with that at the upper right hand corner and it will be seen that that face had become changed by many years between the time the two portraits were made. The portrait at the upper right hand corner is not one produced at a time later than the making of the original picture, and pasted in place upon an old lithograph, for the purposes of the book, but was originally there, precisely as my reproduction shows.*

No two illustrations agree as to the details of the alleged "first reaper," important as it is to the history of a great art to know the facts, and each new illustration has added confusion.

When the first picture was made the colored people were in a group by themselves to the right, and in the second picture they appear around the machine. Why were a tongue attachment and single horse taken from the machine of the first cut, and two horses attached to the machine when the second picture was made? The nigh horse in the second picture may be identified as the one in the first picture by the white spot on the rump. Presumably the exhibition was stopped while another reel support was applied; the latter overreaching from the back of the machine for supporting the outer end of the reel, as patented sixteen years later. Or, again, was it the picture shown in the line drawing on the inside cover of the McCormick catalogue for 1899, representing the alleged Steele Tavern test, where we find the divider of the 1834 patent with the great bar extending from the outer reel post to a support on the tongue omitted and thills substituted for the push tongue? Which kind of support was depended upon to sustain the reel Mr. McCormick had *"discovered?"* These queries may be considered as bringing the matter to the point of absurdity, but I am, in fact, considering these pictures seriously. Differing as they do, yet representing an alleged single step and single event, they have been injected into the history of the reaper; in so far as the details of the machine differ both cannot be correct. This confusion is mentioned because, in after years, readers of the biography of Cyrus McCormick, not aware of the fact that photography was not yet practiced in 1831, might think, except for the differences in the machines, that this second picture, in fact a late photograph of a lithograph, is a half tone made from a photograph

* The original lithograph was produced by a Milwaukee Company.

This cut is found in "Cyrus H. McCormick, His Life and Work", but the wind mill is carefully touched out.

taken at the time, and that the line drawing, in the catalogue of 1899, was sketched from the photograph. But that is not all: the second picture of the alleged 1831 machine shows the reel support of the 1847 patent. (Let it be borne in mind that the witnesses at the time of the memorable attempt to extend the 1834 patent were not at all clear as to the construction of the machine.)

The fourth picture is found on page seven of "System" for July, 1909, in the article written by Herbert N. Casson, author of "The Romance of the Reaper," as well as of "Cyrus Hall McCormick, His Life and Work."

Under the *System* picture are the words "The *first* McCormick reaper in 1831—small and crude, it yet embodied the principles on which 1909 harvesting machines are based. It could do the work of six laborers." The windmill in the scene is clearly not of the Virginia type, but, as a matter of fact, is that of Fred Runger, which long has swung its great arms on the prairie only a few miles west of the city of Chicago. Casson prepared the articles in *System,* which turned out to be mere forerunners of the later publication entitled "Cyrus Hall McCormick, His Life and Work." The chapters in *System* were published during the absence of Cyrus H. McCormick, the son of the subject, and the biography of his father, (who died early in 1884) was announced and reviews appeared before his return. For some reason, not made clear to the public, the volumes were held, with the result that "The Dramatic Public Test of McCormick's Reaper—the First Successful Harvesting Machine—at Steele's Tavern, in Virginia, in 1831" is not found in the volume that succeeded the magazine articles, but the book shows that a page was cut out, after it was bound, and the halftone opposite page 38, entitled "THE FIELD ON WHICH THE FIRST McCORMICK REAPER WAS TRIED, WALNUT GROVE FARM, VIRGINIA," deftly pasted in. Why? Perhaps because the pictures constituted a dose too great for the public to swallow? The original of the first picture was a large but cheap lithograph used by the McCormick Company for advertising purposes for the year 1884, as before stated.

It is also observed that the cut on page 7 of "System," entitled "The first McCormick Reaper in 1831—small and crude, it yet embodied the principles on which all 1909 harvesting machines are

Still another view of Fred Runger's windmill.

based," is not found in "Cyrus Hall McCormick, His Life and Work," but instead thereof is a similar field scene *without the windmill* in the background, entitled "First Practical Reaping Machine. Built and Used by Cyrus Hall McCormick on Walnut Grove Farm, Va., in 1831." Both pictures are here reproduced, the first from the "System" articles and the second from the book that resulted. Let it be observed that the two pictures are evidently from the same recent photograph, as shown by the positions of the man, the boy, the horse and the grain on the platform, which are precisely alike, to a straw; but in one the white hat of the man has become a black one, by retouching, and the windmill is no more, it having been deftly "touched out." The change in the color of the clothing of man and boy, by skillful penciling, has made the scene appear more summer-like than we experience on the lake shore, near which the windmill is located. The above picture we also find to have been neatly pasted in, the original having been bound in. From the point where the reel post at the grain end of the machine rises the scenery changes, the low trees beyond, evidently a hedge, now point directly under the windmill in the first picture, and the large tree has disappeared. Clearly the tree was cut out when the windmill of the photograph was erased. Why this change? Surely it was a blunder on the part of Mr. Casson to use the photograph having the well-known western windmill in the background. On retrospect this Illinois scene of the alleged "first reaper" seemed, no doubt, a larger pill than the public could be induced to swallow. It seems so yet. (In this connection it is proper to refer to an illustration found facing page 96 of "Cyrus Hall McCormick, His Life and Work," where, by the side of Mr. McCormick is shown a photograph of a McCormick Reaper of the 1847 type, the reaper model having a jointed tongue. This is a false representation, as no reaper of that type ever put on the market or ever shown in any authentic picture of the McCormick machine had any other than a fixed tongue,—that is, a tongue inflexibly secured to the reaper frame.) It is observed that the fly net and trimmings of the harness of the horse, in the windmill scene, seem to be very modern as compared with what was used in Virginia in the early '30s. (By the way, I have before me a half dozen varieties of the windmill harvest scene. Resorting to the language of the street, we may well say that evidently the photographer "got busy".).

In nearly all pictures of the alleged "first machine" in the field, the raker is shown as if walking backward. In a mural painting of the field scene of the alleged "first reaper," the horse is walking briskly and the raker walking backward. This attitude carries conviction, since the work of raking from the early McCormick machines was difficult and required unusual attitudes. If the raker walked close to the machine he could, at the instant of removing the gavel, so turn as to be back to back with the main body of the machine for a sufficient length of time to remove the accumulation and make a good gavel; but a long continuation of such efforts would be exceedingly fatiguing. Considering the matter from another point of view, if he drew the gavel to him while walking he would have had to step over it, which act would have been exceedingly awkward and laborious.

In Casson's "The Romance of the Reaper" is found another of the windmill field scenes; the photograph from which it was engraved was evidently made at the same time that other photographs were, but it is observed that the machines differ. In the "Romance" picture is shown the long brace extending from the rear stubbleward-corner of the platform up to the reel post, while in the *System* picture it has been removed. It was one of the braces of the machine of the 1834 patent. Why was it removed in the field and why was it not shown on the machine representing the alleged test at Steele's Tavern? I have been told that the pictures were made near Chicago, and also told that the machine was made here, and as proof that such is correct I call attention to the fact that the "Romance" picture has printed beneath it the words: "A *Model* of the First Practical Reaper." Well, which model and which machine? Is such the stuff of which history is made?

Compare again the various copies of the engravings showing the "original" reaping machine found in the McCormick publications as to their general makeup, particularly the later ones, with the lithograph entitled "The Testing of the First Reaping Machine, near Steele's Tavern, Va., A. D. 1831." In some the negro slaves have become white men and women. In one the alleged inventor claimed by Casson to have made bread cheap, if in fact it is he, has doffed his premature Prince Albert coat and turned his back. In one

the melon, green as melons are at oat-harvest time, though shown in
the lithograph of the field scene to be red and luscious, seems to be
disappearing, regardless of consequences, but the mountains are not
as transient as melons, particularly when the latter are confronted
by black lips and shining teeth, and they still render the landscape
varied. There seems to be a rivalry among the "Original" scenes.
Which will go down the ages to perpetuate fiction? I intend that
neither shall do so. In the mural decoration this pseudo-historic
scene is further changed. A wide river is seen to have cut away
the mountains and the steamboat and stagecoach have replaced the
emigrant wagon.

In the record and biography of the McCormick family, compiled
and published in 1896 by Leander J. McCormick, brother of C. H.
McCormick and long associate in the business of manufacturing
reapers, the credit of having invented the reaper is given to his
father, Robert McCormick, as before shown.

In the "Memorial of Robert McCormick," before referred to,
it is repeatedly stated that Robert McCormick was the sole inventor
of the reaper produced on the old McCormick farm in Virginia,
and the author further tells us that Robert McCormick was actively
engaged in the manufacture and improvement of his reaping machines, until his death in 1846. In describing the machine of 1831
he says: "My father built a successful reaping machine in 1831,
with which he cut some grain; this machine did good work under
favorable circumstances; it ran on one main driving or supporting
wheel; had a vibrating straight sickle, with a platform to receive the
cut grain until a sufficient amount had been cut to form a bundle,
and it was then raked off and out of the way of the horses by a man
who walked beside the machine. It had a reel to carry the grain back
to the sickle. This machine was substantially the same as afterwards
built by the family in 1844, '45, and '46.

In this connection, quotations from various affidavits found in the
"Memorial of Robert McCormick" are in place:

Mr. William S. McCormick in an affidavit dated June 5, 1880,
says, among other things:

"I was personally present when my uncle, Robert McCormick, the
father of C. H. and L. J. McCormick, first conceived the idea of his
second reaping machine, subsequently patented. This was in 1829 or

1830. I myself and one Samuel Hitt were the men who did the work
for Robert McCormick while he invented and experimented with the
machine. I know that Robt. McCormick was the sole inventor of
the reaping machine. His skillful brain invented each parcel of the
reaper in the order I now name:

"The machine was drawn by horses in front by the standing grain.
It had a master-wheel, say three feet in diameter. The sickle was
vibrating and driven by a crank which got its motion from gear-wheels
from the main axle. The sickle was supported by projecting fingers
about three inches apart. Behind this sickle there was a platform on
which the grain fell, where it was swept back by the revolving horizontal reel to the sickle and cut, and was raked by a man. The reel
was supported by posts at each end and was driven by a band from the
main axle.

"The foregoing described machine was invented solely and alone
by my uncle, Robert McCormick. This I know. There can be no doubt
about it whatever. I was present. I lived with my uncle and worked
with him on this machine. He gave his orders and they were followed
by myself and other workmen. He made his suggestions and we followed them. He directed changes and we made them. I know that the
conception and creation was wholly from his own brain. I never heard
his right as the inventor of the machine questioned by any one; nor did I
hear any one else at the time claim any of the invention. On the contrary, I know that my uncle, Robt. McCormick, claimed the invention
of the machine. He was endowed with a mind skilled and inventive,
and he had invented other matters.

"In witness of the foregoing statement, I have hereunto set my hand
this 5th day of June, 1880.

(Signed) Wm. S. McCormick.

March 4, 1880."

In a letter dated November 28, 1878, William S. McCormick
states as follows:

"Patterson, Wayne Co., Mo., Nov. 28, 1878.
"Dear Cousin: Yours of the 2d inst. just came to hand, and I am
just able to be up most all the time, but my companion is now down
while I write.

"Now, as to the machine, etc.: From the best information I can get
from my old torn books, the work was done in making the first reaping machine at your father's, in the year 1829. I made bellows at
your papa's in the year 1830, after we came back from Washington
City, where your father, Cyrus and myself had gone for the purpose
of getting a patent for the reaper. My age at that time was twenty-
five years.

"The machine was pretty much the 'Old Reliable'—the horses hitched to it in the same way. At least the 'Old Reliable' was made from it. The sickle, or cutter, was straight and cut with a crank motion, and the reel or rake turned with a band over the cutter and threw the wheat on the platform, and when there was sufficient for a bundle it was raked off by hand. This is about the best recollection of the same at this late date.

"My dear old uncle had made a small machine, or a part of one, before I went there to live with him that stood up, and a crooked cutter was to come around horizontally, but it never did any good, and I have often laughed at him about it, and he never did anything more with it after I came to live with him. He never made but the one machine while I lived there with him. I lived with him there till about the last of the year 1831. I was making bellows all the time.

"I believe I have given you about all the information I can respecting the first wheat-cutter made by your father, and if I can do anything more for you in that line it will be most cheerfully done. So, no more at present, but remain.

Your most affectionate cousin,
Wm. S. McCormick.

"P. S.—My impression was, before I left the State of Virginia, that my uncle had given it to Cyrus but I don't think I got it directly from himself.

Wm. S. McC."

In the affidavit of Col. Thomas S. Paxton, dated September 10, 1878, appears this:

"The first of my recollection is, although I think I heard frequently before, that Robert McCormick was inventing a reaper. I was working for Robert McCormick. I saw Mr. Robert McCormick frequently standing over the machine and musing and studying. On the occasion he had the machine in the yard. He was standing studying over it, drawing down, as was his habit his under lip. Finally he called me to him—the machine did not work to suit him—and asked my opinion about some change he intended making in his reaper. I was a millwright, and working in the yard near him. I gave him my advice as far as I could, and then, as he stood there studying, I remarked to the old gentleman: 'Mr. McCormick, this is not Cyrus' invention; it is yours, is it not?' He replied at once: 'Yes, but I intend to give Cyrus the benefit of it.'

"I have no doubt whatever myself that Robert McCormick was the original inventor of the machine. It was the general opinion of the community around and about Robert McCormick's that he was the inventor; and this was justified by the constant and unremitting labor and attention Robert McCormick bestowed on the machine, and his

known ingenuity and skill in work and in invention. He invented a
threshing machine, and I erected one of them that was run by water.
This reaper, invented by Robert McCormick, is the same one (improved) that is now being manufactured by Cyrus H. and Leander J.
McCormick in the city of Chicago."

In an affidavit, dated September 9, 1878, made by Horatio Thompson, D. D., I find:

"I am sure I never heard the name of the inventor of the McCormick wheat reaper questioned before the death of Robt. McCormick.
Robt. McCormick was the inventor of the original wheat reaper. This
I understood more than 40 years ago. I saw him at work on the machine
in his shops. His whole soul appeared to be absorbed in the work
of this invention. People spoke of him as being engaged in a foolish
undertaking. All persons in his community at the time of the invention, ascribed it to Robt. McCormick, and no other name in those days
was associated with the invention than that of 'Robt. McCormick.' I
heard Robt. McCormick speak, himself, of the invention of the wheat
reaper, and he told me that he had every reason to believe it would
be a success if he could get it arranged to suit him."

Zachariah McChesney in an affidavit dated September 9, 1877,
said:

"I am satisfied that Robert McCormick was the original inventor of
the McCormick Wheat Reaper. There was no doubt about this at the
time he was engaged in inventing it and at the time it was put in the
market. I never heard, during the lifetime of Robert McCormick, any
other name associated with the invention than that of Robert McCormick; although Cyrus, his son, was an efficient aid and agent for his
father after the invention and when the machine was put on the market, in making sales of the wheat reaper. I bought one of the first
reapers from Cyrus, who acted as the agent for his father."

In the Memorial is also a copy of a letter purporting to be from
Henrietta M. McCormick, dated August 1, 1885, in which she says:

"I was well acquainted with Mr. Robert McCormick's family; my
father having also been well acquainted with him. I always understood him to have been the inventor of the reaper. I never heard any
other name mentioned as having had anything to do with its invention.
"I learned for the first time, shortly before the death of Robert

McCormick, that he had given the invention to Cyrus. This I was surprised and chagrined at, as I had expected my husband to share with the family in the benefits growing out of it. I had frequent talks with Mrs. McCormick and the family, and she tried to reconcile me by saying that Cyrus had promised to 'make all the family rich if he ever made anything out of it.'

"My husband told me, while we were living with the old people at that time that he had made a valuable improvement in the machine, and that he had written Cyrus at Brockport, N. Y., and described it to him. Some twenty years afterwards I saw and read this letter with descriptions and drawings of the raker's seat, which he had written to Cyrus at Brockport, N. Y., before I was married in October, 1845. My husband found the letter among a lot of Cyrus' old papers which had been left scattered around at Walnut Grove, the old Homestead. The letter referred to was afterwards burned in the Chicago fire."

The volume, "Robert McCormick, Inventor," has made public, more clearly than ever the origin of the McCormick reaper. Every feature of that machine except, possibly, the addition of the raker's seat by Leander McCormick, who in maturer years showed much inventive talent, was the result of the inventive efforts of Robert McCormick, father of Cyrus H. McCormick. The invention was given to Cyrus, mainly at the instance of the mother, for the benefit, as she asserted, of the whole family. More than at present it was then the custom with fathers to turn over to the oldest son business affairs as he became competent to handle them, often with results not intended. In this case we are concerned merely with the taking out of the three patents by Cyrus covering the inventions of his father, in violation of and, presumably in ignorance of, the law. In order that the patent might be granted to Cyrus, it was necessary for him to swear that he was the true inventor. This wrong step having been taken, consistency required him to claim ever after that he had sworn to the truth. The facts were given in a stage whisper in 1885, by brother Leander; but as time passed these were forgotten or overlooked. Ultimately the majority of the warring reaper manufacturers became absorbed into a merger dominated by the descendants of Cyrus H. McCormick. Prompted, no doubt, by family pride, an effort was made to have enrolled in the Hall of Fame the name of Cyrus Hall McCormick as the inventor of the reaper. There, placed with that of Lincoln, Washington, Whitney, Morse, the matter then would have been settled by the great jury selected to vote on admissions, and further discussion of the merits would be treated by the public as idle talk. Casson's "Romance of the Reaper" appeared while the jury was considering the matter. It was a small pill, and the public made but little stir in opposition. Unfortunately, after a little time Casson wrote and published "Cyrus Hall McCormick, His Life and Work," which was as lacking of facts in foundation as the preceding Romance. This last straw had the same effect as that which broke the camel's back. Joseph Medill, the great editor, left a daughter of like mettle, who became the wife of Robert S. McCormick, a grandson of Robert McCormick. To her fell the larger interest in the great *Chicago Tribune*. When the portrait of Cyrus Hall McCormick was about to be unveiled in the Agricultural Hall at the University of Illinois she wrote to her paper that she hoped none of the speakers would be so simple as to claim that the subject of the portrait was the inventor of the reaper he and his brothers so long and successfully had manufactured. Casson's second book, and the fulsomeness of the speakers at the unveiling referred to, aroused all the descendants of Robert McCormick, aside from those through Cyrus, as a result an application for the enrollment of the name of Robert McCormick in the National Hall of Fame, as the true inventor of the McCormick reaper, was forwarded to Chancellor McCracken, of the University of New York, followed by the work entitled "Robert McCormick, Inventor." This publication, I am informed, reached the jury late, some time after the votes for the placement of laurels had been cast. How many votes the son had received is not known, but upon receipt of the name of Robert McCormick, the father, many votes were recalled, leaving the claimant in the minority. Has not the proposal of Robert McCormick's name fully eclipsed, for all time, that of his son? Yet if even the father's name becomes enrolled, that fact will detract, to some extent, from the weight and honor of the Hall of Fame, as the McCormick machine was later in reaching perfection than that of the prior inventor in this art, Obed Hussey, whose name may yet there find a place.

In taking his testimony when attempting to get his patent extended, McCormick brought out the fact that William S. McCormick, a brother and a witness, had no interest that would bias him. In reply to a question having that matter in view, William replied:

"I have none, as my father's will, on record in the County of Rock-bridge, would more clearly show."

If, in fact, the father had any property in the patent at the time he made his will, a copy of which is before me, such could only be because the invention was either his or because he had acquired a right by assignment, or license. The will does not mention the patent, but has much to say in regard to the reaper. The will is, as a matter of fact, corroborative of the statements made in several of the affidavits found in the "Memorial of Robert McCormick."

In the will the father gave to one daughter some furniture, a negro woman and her two children, as worth a thousand dollars, and $2,500.00 in cash, making a total of $3,500.00, and in addition thereto the proceeds of ten machines made and sold that season, with their profits or losses after deducting all expenses of building. He gave to another daughter $2,800.00 and the profits on ten machines made and sold that season. To another he gives a negro boy, a horse and outfit and $3,000.00. These gifts show that he was well to do in earthly matters. He had already deeded a plantation to his son, Leander J., and added thereto, in his will, the proceeds of one-third of all the machines made and sold that season, after de-ducting all expenses in building, delivering, etc., said machines, about which there existed a specific agreement.

The question naturally arises as to what Robert McCormick had to do with the business of building machines, and where Cyrus, who later claimed to have done all, came in. The fact that the father did have so much to do with it is corroborative of the affidavits quoted on previous pages.

The fifth article of the will bequeathed to Cyrus H. a "negro boy Sam and girl Emily," and acknowledged an indebtedness to him to the extent of $149.72 upon a settlement made on the 3rd day of February, 1846, as also in the further sum of $15.00 on each ma-chine "made and sold this season, the sale of which may or will have been actually made." We thus see that Cyrus H. was cut off with a negro boy and girl, while the others in addition to two or three slaves, were given from $2,500.00 to $3,000.00. We can only explain this on the theory that to C. H. McCormick had already been given the reaper invention, as stated by Leander and others. The various statements in the will imply also that Robert McCormick was engaged in manufacturing machines, which if true, C. H. McCormick, the owner of the invention, by assignment, was entitled to a royalty. He may have offset the gift of the plantation to Leander by the gift of the reaper invention to Cyrus H. This also accords with the statements found in the Memorial referred to.

At any rate, the son Cyrus H. was in possession of all or, at least, certain rights in the supposed monopoly. If, however, facts were sufficient to sustain the patent, another explanation as to why C. H. was cut off with so little, is possible; the father had started Cyrus in the iron business and sustained him in it for a number of years, during which time the loss was great. The share of this loss may have been charged to C. H. and deducted from the amount of his equities in the estate.

Further comments may be made of Cyrus's statements. The alleged 1831 machine was adapted to be drawn by a horse, we are informed. If it was a successful machine, why did he later, in his patent, show a machine adapted to be *pushed* by the team, and merely suggest that thills could be attached? From this point of view the machine of the patent of 1834 may be considered as evidence of an abandonment of the alleged earlier form, when practically considered, for he would not, in his patent, have shown and recommended the use of a poor form of construction if he had a better one in mind.

The next point called attention to is whether Hussey adopted McCormick's alleged arrangement of 1831, as charged. Yet in his later machine Hussey adopted the well known form used by Gladstone in 1806, that of having but a single stubble-side driving wheel, and balancing the machine thereon.

McCormick admits that his 1831 efforts were experiments and that the experiments continued long after 1834. In accordance with the patent law practices of that time and at the present day, it is perfectly clear that his *mere experiments* could not anticipate, that is, render void, a prior patent, and deprive an earlier patentee of rights.

A second McCormick reaper was not built until 1839, eight years after the alleged first one and five years after the patent which shows a machine that was *then* an admitted failure. The alleged tests in 1832 presumably were made with the 1831 machine. Although

the machine of '39 is said to have had the improved cutting apparatus
the two machines that were ordered failed to satisfy the would-be
purchasers, and were returned.

The following, quoted from Cyrus H. McCormick's letter dated
February 18, 1848, to the Commissioner of Patents, referring to
the alleged practical machine of 1831, and the patent of 1834, shows
that the machine must remain not worthy to be included among
practical reapers:

"In this connection it is but truthful to repeat, by way of calling
your attention particularly to the past, that although the *main* principles of my invention are contained in my first patent, yet from that
patent alone I never rec'd any profit at all. It was only after I had
added, after 12 years of study, labor and experiment, the further
important improvements which I had separately patented that I began
to receive the profits which since have gradually accumulated to the
amount mentioned and but for which improvements I never *should*
have realized any profits from the invention."

Here is a ridiculous position for a man to assume asking that a
patent covering an admittedly unsuccessful machine, be declared to
anticipate one covering a successful machine—which had been in
constant use for fifteen years, in hundreds of fields and right up to
the time the extension proceedings were instituted.

Although Mr. McCormick was defeated in the Patent Office, he
never acknowledged defeat. In the statement to the Congressional
Committee, he said: "If then it shall appear that I am the original
inventor of all the leading and important principles of the invention,
is it wrong that I should ask for reciprocal benefits for myself, who
alone have brought it into being?" (Evidently it did not *appear*,
at the moment, that he was the original inventor.)

In his statement he discussed improvements found to be *necessary*
in order to make his machine a success, which it is now proper to
consider, although in advance of their time, for the reason that all of
the improvements were made and patented before an extension of
the patent now under consideration was asked for. The early experiments were practically little more than attempts to sever the grain
straws by filing them in two with a knife-edge file. If one wishes
to file anything it is necessary to "bear on," and in order to file off
grain straws with this cutting apparatus it was necessary to bring

them forcibly against the cutting edges; and not only that, but to hold them there-against until, severed, they could fall away. Means for holding the straws against the straight edged sickle soon appeared necessary, and in later experiments he so shaped the fingers of his cutting apparatus as to perform that office. To accomplish it he formed them like spear-heads so as to have "an acute angle between the edge of the blade and the shoulder of the spear." This caused the grain straws to be wedged into a space by the sickle and there held until, at best, sawed off.

In order to anticipate Hussey, from a patent law point of view, he found it necessary to prove that the fingers of his alleged 1831 machine were both above and below the cutter, which his patent did not show; indeed, at the very time McCormick was attempting to so prove, he was using fingers in which he had removed the lower portion as much as possible; in short, he was getting away from his original plan as fast as he could and turning toward Hussey's cutting apparatus, which he finally adopted and later paid well for infringing the patent covering it. The spear-shaped guards soon went the way of the straight blades. Mr. McCormick seems early to have become aware that his so-called divider was only such in name, for it would not divide; consequently, he removed the forward post that supported it to a position behind the cutting blade, thus sustaining his reel more nearly as Bell and Randall had done. The change cannot be treated as an improvement on the original divider, for it was a mere abandonment of all that was new in the 1834 divider and acceptance of an older form. To his new (?) grain divider he secured a peculiar adjustable arm.

The first claim of his 1845 patent covers the peculiar angle of the "bearers," or, as previously called in Hussey's patent, guards. The second claim relates to the sickle having reversed teeth and the third to the spear shaped "bearers" so soon to be abandoned. The fourth claim refers to the adjustable "bow" or arm on the divider. This claim does not cover a divider in combination with anything else, but merely two parts of a divider constructed in a certain way and the court held that not to be new. The fifth claim has to do with bracing the reel post to the draft tongue, a most ridiculous proposition. No provision was yet made for seating the driver on the machine, and the raker was still expected to walk the weary miles of a day's travel, in the field. This seems strange since on nearly all competing machines seats and stands for driver and raker were already provided.

A raker's seat was added in 1846 and is shown in the patent of October 23, 1847, granted to Mr. McCormick. Here, too, we find Randall's divider and reel. The spear-shaped guards and straight sickle are also present, but the driving gearing is shifted to a position in advance of the traction wheel, so as to throw a preponderance of weight in advance thereof to counterpoise the weight of the raker, taken aboard after fifteen years. McCormick's 1845 and 1847 patents were extensively enlarged by re-issue and suits were brought on them for infringement; but of the re-issues, later.

Seymour and Morgan, of Brockport, N. Y., built machines for McCormick in 1845 and later took a license under his patents, not, however, that of 1847, which covered the arrangement for supporting the seat. A number of years after suit was brought against them for building on their own account, and they were defeated in the lower court, but the case was heard in the Supreme Court at its December Term in 1853, and was remanded to the lower court. These decisions are important:

"For the purposes of this suit, the machine described in the patent of 1834 (which had in fact become public property) and the improvements in the patent of 1845, and a large portion of those included in that of 1847, the defendants had a perfectly lawful right to use. This covered the whole of the improved reaping machine except what related to the seat, and its combination with the reel. It cost the defendants to make their machine, which had no seat, about $64.26. There was no proof to show the extent of the cost of the plaintiffs' seat. One was made of zinc for one dollar. The plaintiff allowed Brown in effect, in 1845, 1846, $75 each, for making machines without the elevated seat—and he proved on this trial by Blakesley that it cost him only $36, and by Dorman, $37 to make them with it. There can be no pretense that the addition of the seat, and what is covered by the last claim added much, if anything to the cost of constructing the improved machine. The plaintiff proved by Blakesley that the manufacturer's profit on the whole machine, including a $30 patent fee was $74."

The lower court held that the defendant was responsible in damages to the same extent as if he had pirated the whole machine and that the amount of profit which the patentee would have made, if he had constructed and sold each one of the machines which the defendant constructed and sold, should be the measure of damages.

In delivering the opinion of the court Justice Greer:

"It then came up by writ of error from the Circuit Court and was heard during the September term of 1856. The fourth and fifth claims of the 1845 patent were those which were alleged to have been infringed. Plaintiff obtained a verdict against Seymour & Morgan for $7750 and judgment was entered in June, 1855, for $10,348.30. Defendants appealed

"In regard to the first claim; it was shown that Hiram Moore in 1836 made a sickle with reversed teeth and this matter was proven up on the first trial. It was also proven that Bell's machine had operated as early as 1829.

"The lower court had refused to instruct the jury, as requested in regard to these matters and the Supreme Court held that it was erroneous.

"What the evidence was, of the use of Bell's machine, will be found in Loudon's Encyclopedia of Agriculture, pp 442 to 427 and from the testimony of Obed Hussey.

"We think that on this evidence (that the machine used in England was that described by Loudon), it was proper to submit to the jury the question as to its operation, and not to place it under the ban as an entire failure, which seems to be the effect of the charge, as it was given. If it operated well in 1829 and in 1853, which is clearly proved, and is assumed by the Judge, it must certainly have been capable of operating well at any intermediate time. Whether actually used or not, is wholly immaterial.

"And if the machine as a whole operated well, then the divider, reel, and reel bearer, each, operated well, and the reel was supported by practically successful contrivance, which formed no impediment in the way of the divider, or of the division and separation of the grain, and on which no straws could clog, as the entire space beneath the reel shaft is, in this machine, left unobstructed by the reel bearer, which is horizontal some feet above the platform, and completely out of the reach of the grain. There is no difference between the reel bearer in the machine of the plaintiffs in error and that in Bell's machine. Waters (McCormick's witness) on being shown the drawing of Bell's machine, in Loudon's Encyclopedia of Agriculture, says: 'As a mere manner of supporting the reel, I see no difference between the method of supporting the reel in this and the defendant's machine.'

"This prior invention of Bell's if the court had not substantially excluded it from the consideration of the jury, would have furnished a complete answer to the charge of infringement of the fifth claim of McCormick's patent of 1845."

The lower court was sustained except in the matter of costs, which were required to be stricken from the record.

McCormick vs. Talcott et al, survivors of John H. Manny.

This was appealed from the Circuit Court of the United States. The bill charged infringement of fourth and fifth claims of the McCormick patent of 1845, and second claim of the re-issued patent of 1853.

The first infringement charged is that of the divider, or the part of the reaping machine which is defined as an arrangement, or apparatus, for separating the grain to be cut from that which is to be left standing. The claim is as follows:

"4. I claim the combination of the bow L and the dividing-iron M for separating the wheat in the way described." The court said:

"The English patent of Dobbs, in 1814, had dividers of wood or metal. The outer diverging-rod rose as it extended back and diverged laterally from the point, to raise the stalks of grain inclining inwards, and to turn them off from the other parts of the machine.

"The patent of Charles Phillips of 1841 had a divider, shaped like a wedge, performing the same function, turning the grain aside on both sides of the machine, and raising it up.

"Ambler's machine had a triangular divider performing the same functions as also the machines of Hussey, Schnebly, and that of McCormick, patented in 1834, which is now public property.

"The present claim is for the combination of this bow with a dividing-iron of a certain form, and for nothing more. This dividing-iron is but a new form or substitution for that side of the triangle or wedge which in other machines performed the functions of separating the inside grain, and raising it to the cutters."

The court further said:

"The machine constructed under defendants' patents was a wooden projection, somewhat in the form of a wedge, extended beyond the cutting-sickles some 3 feet, and which, from the point in front, rises as it approaches the cutting apparatus, with a small curve (not approaching to an angle of thirty degrees) so as to raise the leaning grain.*** It more resembles the wedges in use before McCormick's patent of 1845. As an improvement on former machines, it has some peculiarities of form and construction, but it does not adopt the combination of complainants' patent."

In regard to the fifth claim of the 1845 patent the court said:

"The defendant does not support his reel by posts as was done by McCormick. He used the horizontal reel bearer connected by a frame with the hinder part of the machine. This device for supporting the reel was invented and used many years before McCormick's first patent of 1834. It had no reel-post situated as in the patent, and encountered none of the faults remedied by the change in its position.

Manny's Reaper.

This attempt to treat the earlier and better device used by defendant as an infringement of the later device to obviate a difficulty unknown, first, is an application of the doctrine of equivalents, which needs no further comment."

In regard to the second claim of the 1853 patent (re-issue) the court said:

"If this claim be construed to include all of the machines which have a reel and a raker's seat, it is void for want of novelty. Hite, Woodward, Randall and Schnebly had invented and publicly used reaping machines which had reels, and a place for the raker on the machine. But the true construction of this claim and the only one which will support its validity, is to treat it as a claim for the combination of the reel, with the seat 'arranged and located as described. And such was the construction given it by the defendant himself when the commissioner had refused to grant him a patent, claiming the mere combination of a reel and a raker's seat, because such a combination was not patentable, the functions of each device having no necessary connection with the machine.' "

It seems that not one of the claims of Mr. McCormick's patents was sustained upon its merits; although Seymour & Morgan began building Mr. McCormick's machine, they soon abandoned the cutting apparatus for Mr. Hussey's; they abandoned his (McCormick's) divider for Randall's; and his reel support for Bell's. A seat for the raker on the machine was old in many machines, as stated, before Mr. McCormick began using it; and it remains true that no device patented to Mr. McCormick was ever used by any other manufacturer for any length of time, and that he himself abandoned all that was ever patented by him, and adopted the devices of others.

John H. Manny.

Valuable as the improvements patented in 1847 were asserted by Mr. McCormick to be, the rearranged gearing was but seldom, if ever, used. The following cut of the McCormick machine of 1849, reproduced in the printed matter for the year 1871, by the Company he founded, speaks for itself.

This picture does not show the gearing placed forward of the main wheel to counterbalance the weight of the raker, standing behind it. The gearing of the 1834 patent is shown and the driver at last has been taken off the back of the wheel horse and placed upon a seat, his weight to counterpoise that of the raker.

In an interference proceeding, to which this controversy was similar, the questions of *diligence and date of reduction to practice* are important. Assuming that the general rule applied to the present case, McCormick's patent of June 21, 1834, is merely evidence of *constructive* reduction to practice. If McCormick actually built a machine in 1831 and tried it, three years' time elapsed before he asserted his rights. Hussey was diligent, on the contrary, and had his machine in the field as soon as possible, and it was successful. If, in fact, he had only experimented with his machine in 1831, then he would have accomplished a practical machine before McCormick did and would have won; if he did not begin his machine until late in 1832 or early in 1833, even then his diligence surpassed that of McCormick.

McCormick 1849.

Mr. McCormick was not only guilty of laches (delay) between 1831 and 1834, but much more so between the latter date and 1837, and probably longer, for there is no evidence to show that anything was done with the reaper by him during the years that he was engaged in the iron business. Presumptively he was guilty of laches for a total of at least eight years, and, in fact, did not awake to the commercial possibilities of a reaper until Mr. Hussey had removed his reaper factory back to Maryland, not far from Mr. McCormick's home. If McCormick actually built his machine in 1831, and did not patent it until 1834, the question again arises as to what he was doing in the meantime; and we have no *positive* evidence that he did a stroke of work on his machine. When he might have spoken he was silent, although it was important that he make his best showing before the committee to whom his application for an extension was referred. The records of that hearing follow:

DOCUMENTS

Relating to the refusal of the Board of Extension to extend C. H. McCormick's patent for the Reaping machine, and to the publication, by authority, that McCormick's, Hussey's, and Moore & Hascall's patents had expired, and BECOME PUBLIC PROPERTY; *and showing that neither Moore & Hascall, nor Hussey, filed any application for an extension of their respective patents.*

(1.)

Minutes of proceedings and decision of Board of Extension on C. H. McCormick's application, showing that evidence was EXAMINED, *not* EXCLUDED, *and case decided on its* MERITS, *not on* TECHNICALITIES.

THE UNITED STATES PATENT OFFICE.

To all persons to whom these presents shall come, greeting:

This is to certify, that the annexed is a true copy from the records of this office.

In testimony whereof, I, Charles Mason, Commissioner of Patents, [SEAL.]

have caused the seal of the Patent Office to be hereunto affixed, this twenty-sixth day of May, in the year of our Lord one thousand eight hundred and fifty-six, and of the independence of the United States the eightieth.

C. MASON.

In the matter of the application of C. H. McCormick for an extension of his patent for a Reaping machine.

The Board met, agreeable to published notice, on the third Monday (21st) in March, 1848, and adjourned to Wednesday, the 23d.

March 23d, 1848.—Board met pursuant to adjournment. Present, James Buchanan, Secretary of State; Edmund Burke, Commissioner of Patents; and R. H. Gillet, Solicitor of the Treasury; and—

Ordered, That the further hearing of this application be postponed to Wednesday, the 29th of March, and that the said McCormick be directed to furnish satisfactory testimony that the invention of his machine was prior to the invention of a similar machine by Obed Hussey; and that he be directed to give due notice to the said Hussey of the time and place of taking said testimony.

March 29th, 1848.—Board met agreeable to adjournment. Present, James Buchanan, Secretary of State; Edmund Burke, Commissioner of Patents; and R. H. Gillet, Solicitor of the Treasury; and, *having examined the evidence adduced in the case,* decide that said patent ought not to be extended.

JAMES BUCHANAN,

Secretary of State

EDMUND BURKE,

Com'r of Patents

R. H. GILLET,

Sol'r of the Treasury.

(2.)

Sworn statement of R. H. Gillet, a member of Board of Extension, showing that McCormick's testimony was CONSIDERED, *and his application decided on its* MERITS.

WASHINGTON, 3d May, 1856.

P. H. WATSON, Esq.

SIR: You have requested me to give my recollection of the proceedings before the Board of Extension, of which I was, as Solicitor of the Treasury, a member, on the petition of Cyrus H. McCormick for the extension of his patent for a Reaping machine.

I now proceed to do so, after refreshing my memory by referring to certified copies of the papers then before the board.   The hearing, under the notice, was fixed for the 21st February, 1848.   We had before us the report of Charles G. Page, examiner, stating, among other things, that McCormick's patent included matters found in one of an older date issued to Obed Hussey.   Mr. Hussey filed objections to the extension.   Mr. McCormick had filed the affidavits of several persons, which appeared to have been taken on the 17th of February, 1848.

Owing, as I presume, to the engagements of the Secretary of State, (Mr. Buchanan,) the hearing was postponed to the 23d; on which day the board met, and the affidavits filed by Mr. McCormick were examined, and, being ex parte, were deemed illegal or improper.   The board thereupon gave direction as follows: "Ordered, that the further hearing of this application be postponed to Wednesday, the 29th of March, and that the said McCormick be directed to furnish satisfactory testimony that the invention of his machine was prior to the invention of similar machine by Obed Hussey; and that he be directed to give due notice to the said Hussey of the time and place of taking said testimony."

At the hearing on the 29th of March, testimony was before us, purporting to have been taken on the 18th of March, in Virginia, on notice to Hussey, and in which it was recited that he (Hussey) attended and cross-examined the witnesses.   This testimony was not objected to by the board or Hussey, in his written argument, as improper or illegal, nor was it ruled out, but was considered and acted upon.

The board also had before it a written argument by Hussey—a remonstrance—purporting to have been signed by a large number of citizens of Monroe county, New York, and a statement prepared at the Patent Office, purporting to show the amount of McCormick's receipts on account of his patent, with an indefinite statement of expenditures made by him. On this hearing the board rejected the application. The record of the proceedings was drawn up at the Patent Office, and was subsequently signed, and contains the following:

"*March 29th*, 1848.—Board met agreeable to adjournment. Present, James Buchanan, Secretary of State; Edmund Burke, Commissioner of Patents, and R. H. Gillet, Solicitor of the Treasury; and having examined the evidence adduced in the case, decided that said patent ought not to be extended."

In this record, as drawn up and signed, there are two errors in dates, in stating that the first and second meetings were in March, instead of February, as appears by the memorandums on the certified envelope, and by other papers.

On the final hearing the question of extension was decided upon its merits, and not upon technicalities, or by throwing out testimony taken on notice pursuant to the order of the board. No motion was made by McCormick for further time, or to correct informalities. I observe, by a printed document, that one of my colleagues supposes McCormick's testimony was ruled out because it was informally taken. He has evidently confounded the testimony taken on notice with that taken ex parte, which was actually ruled out. I am the more certain of this, from having a distinct recollection of the grounds of my own action in the case, and of views expressed by one of my colleagues as the ground of his action.

Very respectfully yours,

R. H. GILLET

DISTRICT OF COLUMBIA, *ss:*

Ransom H. Gillet, of the city of Washington, being duly sworn, doth depose and say, that he truly believes that the annexed letter to P. H. Watson is, in all respects, just and true.

R. H. GILLET.

Sworn before me this fifth day of May, 1856.

WM. R. WOODWARD, *J. P.*

(3.)

Sworn statement of Examiner, Charles G. Page, showing that McCormick is NOT ORIGINAL AND FIRST INVENTOR *of machine patented in* 1834.

WASHINGTON, *May* 12*th*, 1856.

SIR: At your request I will proceed to state the extent of my official participation in the refusal to extend Cyrus H. McCormick's patent of 21st June, 1834, for alleged improvements in Reaping and Mowing machines. At the time of McCormick's application for extension, I was chief examiner of patents, and had been for six years in charge of the subject of Reaping and Mowing machines. It was the practice of the Patent Office at that time to refer applications for extension to the examiner for his investigation, and report upon the novelty of the invention at the time of the grant of the patent. The question of remuneration, and others touching the extension, were not referred to the examiner; but all papers belonging to the case were examined clerically by him prior to the action of the board. Upon examination of the novelty of McCormick's invention, I found that he had been fully anticipated in prior patents granted to others, and reported to the Commissioner of Patents, as follows:

"PATENT OFFICE, *Jan. 22,* 1848.

"SIR: In compliance with your requisition, I have examined the patent of Cyrus H. McCormick, dated 21st June, 1834, and found that the principal features embraced in said patent, viz: the cutting-knife and mode of operating it, the fingers to guide the grain and the revolving rack for gathering the grain, were not new at the time of granting said letters patent. The knife, fingers and general arrangement and operation of the cutting apparatus were found in the Reaping machine of O. Hussey, patented Dec. 31st, 1833.

"The revolving rack presents novelty chiefly in form, as its operation is similar to the revolving frame of James Ten Eyck, patented 2d November, 1825.

"Respectfully submitted.

"CHAS. G. PAGE, *Examiner.*

"Hon. EDMUND BURKE, *Com'r of Patents.*"

The opinion held by the Patent Office at that time was, that the subjects of McCormick's claims differed in no substantial particulars from previous inventions, and that if he had applied for a patent for his reaper subsequent to the act of July 4, 1836, his patent could not have been granted, except upon proof of priority of invention; and that whatever remuneration he had received was principally for inventions previously patented by others.

I have reason to believe that McCormick's case had a full and patient hearing at the Patent Office, and unusual indulgence from the Board of Extension; nor did I ever hear, during the pendency of his application, nor do I now believe, that he had not ample time and opportunity for establishing his claims.

I have no reason, whatever, for changing my opinion, expressed officially to the Commissioner when McCormick's application for an extension was pending before the board, that he was not the original and first inventor of any material and important part of the mechanism of the machine described in his patent in 1834. On the contrary, I have abundant reason for believing that opinion to be correct, and that it does McCormick no injustice, even if the patent of Hussey be left entirely out of the question, and reference is had solely to those of previous date. CHAS. G. PAGE.

To P. H. WATSON, Esq., *Washington, D. C.*
CITY AND COUNTY OF WASHINGTON, D. C., *ss:*

On this twelfth day of May, 1856, before the subscriber, a justice of the peace in and for said county, personally appeared Chas G. Page, and made solemn oath that the foregoing statement, signed by him, is true, to the best of his belief and knowledge.

JOHN S. HOLLINGSHEAD, *J. P.*

(8.)

Obed Hussey permitted his patent to expire and thereby become public property, without even filing an application for an extension.

THE UNITED STATES PATENT OFFICE.

To all persons to whom these presents shall come, greeting:

This is to certify, that on a careful search of the records of this office, no evidence can be found that Obed Hussey ever made an application for the extension of letters-patent granted to him on the 31st day of December, 1833, for a machine for cutting grain.

In testimony whereof, I, Charles Mason, Commissioner of Patents, have caused the seal of the Patent Office to be hereunto affixed, this sixth day of June, in the year of our Lord one thousand eight hundred and fifty-six, and of the independence of the United States the eightieth.

C. MASON.

(10.)

A Calculation.

C. H. McCormick filed his petition before the board, for the extension of his patent of June 21st, 1834, on the 18th day of January, 1848.

On the 29th day of March, 1848, the board decided against granting the extension.

Time between the date on which his petition was filed, and that on which the final decision against the extension was rendered, SEVENTY DAYS.

Time between the date (March 29, 1848,) on which the board decided against the extension, and that on which the patent expired, (June 21st, 1848,) EIGHTY-THREE DAYS.

It would seem that enough has been said about the McCormick-Hussey controversy, but the honors due to Hussey in foreign countries were lost to him, and in the hope of clearing an illustrious name, let us follow this controversy across the ocean.

CHAPTER VIII

ENGLISH FIELD TRIALS

In the London Exhibition in 1851, Hussey's machine, in the absence of its maker and in the hands of ignorant men, was so badly adjusted that the grain could not be gotten from the platform and the machine was pulled aside. Although the Hussey machine, when later tried in competition with the McCormick, was the victor, we hear nothing of the earlier difficulty for Hussey, modest Quaker that he was, said little about it. Through this mischance McCormick won the Exhibition award, but that the English press and public understood the real situation may be deduced from many sources, among them *Punch*. Our English cousins persist in calling small grain corn.

"Mr. Punch presents his compliments to Mr. Hussey, and hearing that his reaping machine is the best for corn-cutting, will feel obliged by one being sent immediately, as he wishes to cut his own corns. Mr. Punch would not have troubled the celebrated American Hussey, but his own wife, Judy, is such a lazy hussy, that she will not perform the operation required."

Edward Stabler published the following documents bearing on this theme in 1854 at Baltimore, Maryland:

"In presenting the following pages for consideration of the farmers of the country, the subscriber has confined himself strictly to matters selected from English papers, which will speak for itself. As a short explanation from me will be looked for, I will merely state, that at the trial in presence of the Exhibition Jury, Mr. McCormick's machine was operated by an experienced hand sent from the United States, while mine was managed by English laborers of the lower class, who were total strangers to it, and had never seen it in operation. The trial was made in unripe wheat on a rainy day. My machine was very

149

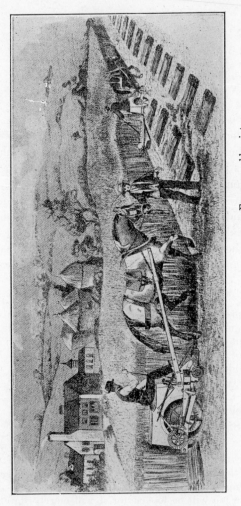

From an old print.

Hussey Reaper in England, showing Side Delivery.

improperly adjusted for the work and wrongly put together, in consequence of which the ignorant raker failed to deliver the sheaves, and it stopped as a matter of course, and was immediately laid aside, after cutting but a few feet. My machine was never tried in presence of that Jury by any other hands, or in any other condition, myself not being in England.

"It was on such a trial that the Exhibition medal was disposed of, and with what justice the reader can judge by reading the following pages. On my arrival in England I took my machine into the field that it might work its way into public favor, as it best could. After being exhibited in several places, its rising fame appeared to produce some effect, as it will appear by the following in the Windsor and Eaton Express, of Nov. 8, 1851:

"Alluding to the astonishing and unexpected performance of my Reaper, it says: 'By this unlooked for turn of events, the proprietors of McCormick's machine found that their supremacy was no longer undisputed, and that the necessity was laid upon them to look to their laurels; they therefore came boldly forward, and threw down the gauntlet!!'

"That farmers who are acquainted with my reaper may understand why it failed to perform well in the hands of strangers at the Exhibition trial where McCormick got the medal, it will be necessary for me to say, that when the machine was sent from Baltimore it was set to cut high. That when the inexperienced hands undertook to make it cut low, they pitched down the cutters by putting on the tongue, not knowing any other way to lower it. In doing so the hind part of the platform was of course raised high. In this condition the unpracticed raker failed to push the heavy wet wheat off up an inclined plane; and as a matter of course the machine choaked, and for the same reason that a mill will choak when the corn goes in faster than the meal comes out. A skillful hand would have lowered the cut at the axle of the machine, and brought the platform horizontal or lowest at the rear, as it should be in cutting wet grain.

"The following pages will show the result, the authenticity of which, if doubted, will be proved by the production of the originals in my possession.

OBED HUSSEY.

Baltimore, Md., Jan. 1, 1852."

From the *Hull* (England) *Advertiser,* Sept. 5, 1851.

"At the annual meeting on Mr. Mechi's Farm at Tiptree Heath, a few weeks ago, a brief report of which appeared in the Hull Advertiser at the time, several reaping machines were tested, the result then being that one manufactured and invented by Mr. McCormick, of America, was the only one which was considered to have done its

work properly. Amongst those tried was one invented and manufactured by Mr. O. Hussey, Baltimore, Md. (U. S.) which in the opinion of gentlemen then present, did not fully accomplish the object in
view. It should, however, be mentioned, that while Mr. McCormick's
machine had on that trial the advantage of the superintendence of persons intimately acquainted with its mechanism, and who had been accustomed to the working of the machine for some years, Mr. Hussey's
invention was (in the absence of the inventor) in the hands of persons entirely unacquainted with the proper mode of working it. Since
then Mr. Hussey himself has come over to England, in order to super-
intend his machine, and the result has been that it is now brought out
to receive a thorough trial of its merits.

"The trial of Wednesday, however, was the best. It took place
in a field belonging to Mr. Coskill, Grovehill Lane, Beverly. There was
assembled during the day a great number of farmers and gentlemen
interested in agriculture, who witnessed the trial with great interest.

"The wheat in this case was very much 'laid'; indeed in many places
it was almost flat on the ground. It therefore afforded one of the best
opportunities for judging of the capabilities of the machine under dis-
advantageous circumstances that could possibly occur.

"On the whole, the conclusion come to was, that the reaping was
done as well by machine as by hand. No one doubted for a moment
that it would cut corn well where it was standing; but some farmers
thought it would not equal the scythe where the corn laid. The result,
however, showed the contrary, and every person acknowledged that it
had succeeded admirably. After cutting a large quantity of wheat,
the machine was taken into another field, and after a slight alteration,
set to work to cut clover. We understand that on the day before previous to coming to Hull, it had been tried on clover and cut it extremely
well.

"As the machine cut along it was followed closely by groups of
farmers striving hard to find flaws in its performance. But they could
not. On the contrary, in those places where the corn was most 'laid,'
and where, consequently, the greatest difficulty must occur in the
cutting, the manner in which the reaper did its work elicited their
loudest approbation;—'Why,' said one burly old gentleman by our side,
'a man with a scythe could never cut it like that.' 'It is wonderful,'
said another."

———

"From the *Morning Advertiser,* Sept. 12, 1851.

"On Monday last, the public trial of Hussey's patent Reaping Machine took place with the permission of his Grace, the Duke of Marlbor-
ough, on his Grace's estate of Blenheim, near Woodstock, Oxfordshire, and also, on the adjoining one of Mr. Southern, one of the most

considerable landed proprietors of the country. A large assemblage of the Agriculturists of the highest class attracted by the celebrity which this ingenious and efficient contrivance has acquired for itself in a course of successful experiments performed last week in Yorkshire, were present to witness the trial, mostly from Oxfordshire and the adjoining countries, but many from a considerable distance, and all of them concurred in the most ready acknowledgments of its advantages.

"The reaping commenced at eleven o'clock in the barley field, the machine being drawn by two fine chestnut horses, lent by his Grace for the purpose of the experiment, in which he took the deepest interest, following the reaper in a car, and watching with evident satisfaction, the ease and rapidity with which the blades cut down the golden produce of the field. The crop was by no means one calculated to favor the experiment. On the contrary, some of it was down and much laid. It was cut down, however, with great regularity and speed, and the general evenness of the stubble was the subject of general remark. As the machine passed on, hewing its way at a smart pace through the dense mass of stalks, the crowd of eager observers rushed after it, and many were the cheers with which it was welcomed. Occasionally, to satisfy the ideas of the more fastidious, the level of the cutters was changed, so as to leave a greater or less length of stubble, and it was evident to all that in this respect the machine was susceptible of the nicest adjustment. Sometimes, at the end of a turn it was rested to give the farmers an opportunity of inspecting it, which they seemed never tired of doing, and then it was turned round at right angles to cut in the cross direction. In the experiments upon barley, it showed itself capable of reaping the enormous space of 15 acres, which we believe is from eight to nine times the power of the most vigorous and skillful reaper. Afterwards the machine was taken into a large field of clover, which it cut to within two inches of the ground, and with still greater rapidity.

"His Grace repeatedly expressed his admiration of the powers of the apparatus, and congratulated some of the agricultural gentlemen present with him on the prospects of greater economy and security in harvesting which it afforded them.—These opinions were generally entertained upon the ground, and yesterday at Bishop's Stratford, in Hartfordshire, the farmers of that part of the country witnessed a similar experiment, attended with results precisely similar, and which gave them the same satisfaction."

"Following upon these various successes, an advertisement from the proprietors of McCormick's machine, appeared in the public papers, as follows:

McCORMICK'S AMERICAN REAPER.

$\frac{1}{50}$ of the full size.

From on old English print.

"MR. M'CORMICK'S AMERICAN REAPER.

"Public Challenge to Makers and Venders of Reaping Machines— We, the undersigned, agents for Mr. McCormick, having observed sundry advertisements and circulars complaining of the decision of the Jurors of the Great Exhibition of 1851 in favor of Mr. McCormick's Reaper, and of the reports given in the public journals of the trials which led to such decision, do hereby give notice to Messrs. Wm. Dray & Co., Messrs. Garrett & Son, Mr. O. Hussey, and all other makers and venders of Reaping Machines whatsoever, that M'COR-MICK'S REAPER will be tried at the Cleveland Society's Show at Marton, Middlesboro, near Stockton-on-Tees, on the 25th inst., and publicly CHALLENGE them or any of them, to meet us there, with their machines, for the purpose of a comparative trial of the respective merits of each, to be determined by the Chairman and Council of the Cleveland Society, or by such Judge or Judges as the said Society may appoint.

BURGESS & KEY, 103 Newgate-street, London."

The challenge was immediately accepted, viz:—

MR. HUSSEY'S AMERICAN REAPER.

" 'In answer to an advertisement which appeared in the Times of the 18th, from Messrs. Burgess & Key, giving us a PUBLIC CHALLENGE, to a TRIAL of the AMERICAN REAPING MACHINES, we hereby announce that we shall willingly ACCEPT the SAME, and on the 25th inst., we shall be prepared at the Cleveland Society's Show, Marton, Middlesborough, near Stockton-on-Tees, to prove to the Agricultural World, the superiority of HUSSEY'S REAPER for general farming purposes. We stipulate, however, that the Machines shall be tested, not only on a particular patch of good upstanding grain, where they might, perhaps, prove equal, but on an average variety of conditions, as to short and laid corn, &c., such as the farmer will usually meet with. Its capabilities for cutting green crops, such as clover, &c., shall also be proved. It must be evident to the Farming Public that the Reaping Machine which will cut a crop of the greatest variety and difference of condition must possess the greatest merit. WM. DRAY & CO., Agricultural Warehouse, Swan-Lane, London Bridge.'

"Accordingly the matter was arranged, and the following gentlemen were called upon to act as jurors:

"Henry Stephen Thompson, Esq., of Moat Hall, Foreman; Mr. Wm. Lister of Dunsa Bank; Mr. Jno. Booth of Killerby; Mr. John Parrington of Brancepeth; Mr. Wm. Wetherell, of Kirkbridge, Darlington; Mr. Rob't Hymers, of Marton; Mr. Christopher Cobson, Linthorpe;

Henry Stone del.ᵗ

HUSSEY'S AMERICAN REAPER.

1/56 of the full size.

J.W. Lowry fᶜ.

From an old English print.

Mr. Rob't Fawcitt, of Ormsby; Mr. Joseph Parrington, of Cross Beck; Mr. John Outhwaite, of Bainesse; Mr. Geo. Reade, Hutton Lowcross; Mr. Thomas Phillips, of Helmsley, and Mr. Thomas Outhwaite, of Bainesse.

"The following were the conditions to be submitted by the representatives of the respective machines:

"'The machines to be tried on wheat and barley in such order, and for such lengths of time, as the jurymen may direct. The jury to have full power to use any means they deem advisable, in order to put the machines to the severest trial. The jury in deciding on the merits of the two machines to take into their consideration:

"1st. Which of the two cuts corn in the best manner.
"2d.   "   "   causes the least waste.
"3d.   "   "   does the most work in a given time.
"4th.   "   "   leaves the corn in the best order for gathering and binding.
"5th.   "   "   is the best adapted for the ridge and furrow.
"6th.   "   "   is the least liable to get out of order.
"7th.   "   "   at first cost is least price.
"8th.   "   "   requires the least amount of horse labor.
"9th.   "   "   which requires the least amount of manual labor.'

"As no report was made of the trial on the first day, the following may be relied upon:

"From the *Gateshead Observer*—September 27th, 1851.

"It was curious to see on the soil of a Cleveland farm, two implements of agriculture lying side by side in rivalry, respectively marked —'McCormick, inventor, Chicago, Illinois,'—'Hussey, inventor, Baltimore, Maryland'—America competing with America, on English soil.

"Mr. Hussey led off. An attempt was made to keep back the eager crowd; but their curiosity was irrepressible—they flocked in upon the machine so that the experiment could not be properly performed, nor could the jury duly discharge their duties.—P. C. Thompson did his very best—he was all but everywhere at once but what avails a police force, one strong, against a concourse of Yorkshire yeomanry and clowns? It was requisite that he should have recruits; and a body of self-elected 'specials' came to his aid, who succeeded in procuring approach to a clear course. Mr. Hussey then took his seat anew, and his machine cut down a breadth of wheat from end to end of the field. It seemed to us to do its work neatly and well. The wheat was cleverly delivered from the teeth of the reaper, and handed over to the binders by the rake."

"(To William Dray and Company.)

"Stockton-on-Tees, September 27th, 1851.

"Sir,—Having been in communication with you relative to the trial of your Reaper against McCormick's, and feeling deeply interested in the introduction of the new Implement into this district, particularly one of so much importance as a Reaping machine, I think it is not probably out of place in me if I give you the result of my observations during the two trials which have taken place. From the fact that M'Cormick's Machine obtained the prize at the Great Exhibition (though I do not pin my faith upon awards made by Agricultural and other societies,) the letter of Mr. Pusey's, in the Royal Agricultural Society's Journal, the various newspaper reports, &c., &c.,; it was natural for me to be predisposed in favor of M'Cormick's Machine; indeed Mr. M. had a prestige in his favor, which of course operated against the 'Little Hussey.' Previous to starting, at Marton, on Thursday, the gentlemen representing M'Cormick's machine expressed themselves desirous of testing the machines early in the morning when the dew was on, believing that their machine would cut the grain under such circumstances, and that yours would not. Well, on Thursday we had a deluge rain, the surface of the land was very soft, and the corn very wet. Everybody there was astonished to see your machine brought up the field at a trot, cutting its way to the admiration of all present; it not only cut to the leaning corn, but it cut cross over the corn leaning to the left of the postillion, (I presume I must call him,) McCormick's machine then attempted to start (he made two or three attempts) but the attendant confessed it was impossible to do so. That there might be no mistake about it, your representatives proposed that their machines should go up again; the jury said 'No! we are satisfied that your machine can cut it under the present circumstances,' and so ended Thursday's trial."

———

"From the *Gateshead Observer,* October 4.

"We left the members and friends of this society on Friday, the 26th ult., on the Show-ground at Middlesbrough, immersed in rain. The scene now shifts to the Townhall—where, in a handsome and spacious apartment, we find them assembled in the evening, to dinner, to the number of 150, with the Earl of Zetland in the Chair, and in the vice-chair Mr. John Vaughan, of the firm of Bolckow & Vaughan, iron-masters and manufacturers. His lordship was supported by the Rev. W. F. Wharton, of Birmingham, and Messrs. J. T. Wharton, Henry Pease, G. D. Trotter, Isaac Wilson, George Coates, J. W. Pease, George Reade, John Pierson, &c.; and the vice-chair by Messrs. C. Dryden,

W. Fallows, R. Chilton, &c. In the body of the hall were the leading inhabitants of the town and neighborhood; also, Mr. Burgess and Mr. Samuelson (who had come to the meeting with Mr. McCormick's reaping machine), Mr. Hussey, the inventor of the reaper which bears his name, and Mr. Pierce and Mr. Steevens (on the part of Messrs. Dray & Co., Agents for Mr. Hussey.)

"On the removal of the cloth, the noble Chairman—(behind whose seat was inscribed on the wall in conspicuous characters, 'Success to the Cleveland Agricultural Society—Eighteenth Anniversary'—gave the customary loyal toasts, and took occasion to observe, that had it not been for the Exhibition of Industry, projected by Prince Albert, the 'Reaping Machine,' from which he anticipated great benefits to agriculture, would not have been introduced into this country. (Applause.)

"The Earl of Zetland again referred to the reaping machine. Such an aid to agriculture, his lordship observed, was needed in Cleveland and elsewhere.

"Mr. J. T. Wharton, of Skelton Castle, said he had never witnessed so much enthusiasm in an agricultural district as was displayed in connection with the reaping machine. Had the day been fine the number of spectators present yesterday (Thursday) would have been at least fourfold what it was. Bad as the weather was, not only was there a large muster of members of the society, but 803 persons, many of them from a considerable distance paid sixpence each for admission to the ground.—The trial of the rival machines was, unfortunately, so short, and conducted under such adverse circumstances, that it was impossible to pronounce any opinion as to their relative merits; but what he saw of Hussey's was as satisfactory as he could expect. (Applause.)

"Mr. George Reade, of Hutton Lowcross, said, had it not been for the boisterous weather, the receipts of the society at Ormesby and Middlesbrough would have been marvelous. As it was, there was a large assemblage to witness the trial of the American reaping machines and they were regarded with an anxious desire that they might succeed. Indeed, let any ingenious mechanic—he cared not whether he was English, Scotch, Irish, American, or German—come before a jury of the farmers of Cleveland with an implement or machine for the improvement of Agriculture, and it would be judged with candor, impartiality and uprightness, and the inventor should go home satisfied that he had experienced fair play. (Applause.)

"Mr. Isaac Wilson proposed the health of 'The Strangers.' To those gentlemen the members were greatly indebted for their attendance. Had the weather permitted, they would all have experienced much pleasure from an inspection of the celebrated reaping machines in action, and the ingenious draining plough of Mr. Fowler, which did him very much credit.   (The toast was drank with musical honors.)

"Mr. Pierce, the representative of Dray & Co., being called upon to respond, rose and said, bad as the weather had been, he had been delighted with his visit to Middlesbrough. The kindness of the inhabitants soon made him no stranger. He was not four and twenty hours in the place before he fraternized with the whole parish. (Laughter.) He rejoiced that Mr. Hussey's reaping machine was now in the hands of a jury of Cleveland farmers. It would have a fair, honest, impartial trial; and what more could an Englishman desire. (Applause.) He thanked the company for the honor which they had conferred upon their visitors from a distance, and wished continued success to their flourishing society. (Applause.)

"Mr. Hussey was next called upon, and said that he had for many years been building machines in America. If he had had the least idea of the interest which England would take in the reaping of crops by machinery, it would have been a difficult thing to keep him on the other side of the Atlantic; and he knew not, now, after the reception which he had met with, how he should ever get home again. (Applause and laughter.)

"Mr. Steevens, Dray & Co.'s engineer, was also called upon to rise, and stated that his employers had purchased Mr. Hussey's machine because they saw it to be the best, and they would meet every competitor in the three kingdoms, fearless of the result. (Cheers.)

"(It should be stated that Messrs. Fowler, Burgess, Samuelson,* &c., had by this time left the hall, and therefor çould not be called upon.)

"Mr. Parrington, having read the award, announced that a second trial of McCormick's and Hussey's reaping machines would be made, if the weather were favorable, on the following morning (Saturday), at 9 o'clock, at Mr. Fawcitt's farm.—The jury, appointed by the committee, would give no opinion on the trial of the previous day (Thursday). That would go for nothing. They would devote the whole of next day, if necessary, to a full, fair, and satisfactory trial of the two machines. (Applause.)

"On Saturday morning the weather was so far favorable that there was no rain. The trial, therefore, took place. There was a numerous gathering of land-owners, farmers, laborers, &c., but not so crowded a muster as to obstruct the experiment.

"The foreman of the jury, Mr. Thompson, being unavoidably absent, his place was supplied by the Rev. W. F. Wharton, of Birmingham. Messrs. Lister, Outhwaite, (J. and T. P.) Booth, Wetherell, Phillips, and Dobson, were also absent. Their places were filled by Mr. William Morley, Dishforth; Mr. Thomas Parrington, Marton; Mr. J. T. Wharton, Shelton Castle; Mr. Wm. Hill, Staunton; Mr. Joseph Coulton,

* McCormick's Agents.

Sexhow; Mr. Joseph Harrison, White House; Mr. John Mason Hopper, Marton.

"The trial commenced in a level enclosure, adjoining the road from Stockton and Middlesbrough to Ormesby Hall, (the residence of Sir Wm. Pennyman, Bart.) The wheat was laid. We have seen a crop in worse condition, but not often. The straw was damp and soft. The soil was loamy and light, and the field free from wet; it was to Mr. Fawcitt's credit that he was able to place such a field at the service of the society under the circumstances; still, the earth was in a state to clog the wheels of the reapers. Altogether, the test was a severe one for the competitors. Mr. Samuelson, Mr. Burgess, and Mr. D. C. Mackenzie, (the son of an emigrant from Iverness) were in charge of Mr. McCormick's machine. The other was in the hands of the inventor himself, Mr. Hussey, and of Mr. Pierce and Mr. Steevens (who represented the agents, Messrs. Dray & Co.).

"The Rev. Mr. Wharton, (the jury, competitors, &c. having gathered round him on the field, on Saturday morning,) announced that after the lapse of an hour, when the corn would be in such a condition that Mr. Fawcitt, as he had just said, would, under ordinary circumstances, reap it himself, the trial would commence.

"The question was, now, which of the two machines should begin. A 'toss' gave the chance to Mr. Pierce and he requested Mr. Burgess to lead off.

"M'Cormick's machine then got into action, taking the crop in the most favorable manner—that is, leaning toward the knife. Passing along the field, (which was from two to three hundred yards in length,) it cut down a breadth of little more than four feet. The corn being laid, the flier, of course, did not come into practical operation; nor was it necessary that it should do so—the elements having already done its work. The corn was well cut—the stubble a little too high.

"Another breadth or two having been cut, Hussey's machine followed, and cut some breadths, somewhat wider than M'Cormick's, and closer to the ground.

"Mackenzie, when we pointed out the shorter stubble of his rival, admitted the fact, but said there would be no difficulty—not the slightest—in bringing Mr. M'Cormick's knife nearer to the ground. In America, however, where the straw is comparatively of little or no value, the stubble is no object, and there are some advantages in cutting high.

"A backer of M'Cormick's machine (and many bets have been laid on the two machines) urged that Hussey's would spoil clover when going among wheat. The reply was, that Hussey's knife could be raised or depressed at pleasure.

"The next test was cutting the crop across ridge and furrow, so that the corn was lying neither to nor from the knife, but sidewise. Both the machines cut the corn under these circumstances—Hussey's the cleaner of the two.

"The jury then required the experiment to be made along the field, with the corn lying from the knife.

"Mr. Hussey consented, and the machine succeeded in cutting the corn—leaving a tolerable stubble, but not so short and regular as before.
. "M'Cormick's machine was then tried and failed. As it scoured over the corn, making sad havock, there were loud cries of 'Stop! Stop! you're wasting it!'

"Barley was next cut, with much the same result. In this case, Mr. Hussey adjusted his platform for discharging the corn at the side.

"The binders being summoned before the jury and asked which of the two machines they preferred, so far as their particular department was concerned—decided, 4 for M'Cormick's, 6 for Hussey's.

"Clover was now to be tried, but at this stage of the proceedings we left the field. Clover-cutting, we should state, formed no part of the competition. The agreement merely refers to wheat and barley. M'Cormick's machine is not intended for clover-cutting, but some of the land owners and farmers were anxious to see clover cut by Hussey's machine. Mr. Thompson, we understand, had requested his proxy to have the experiment made. We were told on the ground that the machine had already been tried on clover at Newport, near Middlesbrough, and 'cut it well:—If the weather had been dry, it would have cut it beautifully.'

"It was pleasant to mark the anxiety and watchfulness of the gentlemen in charge of the two machines. Mr. M'Cormick suffered no loss from his absence he was so admirably represented; and in Messrs. Pierce and Steevens, Dray & Co. had invaluable agents—on the Thursday in particular, when a storm, which ravaged land and sea, could not deter them or Mr. Hussey, from practically attesting the reaper's prowess in the field. The trial, throughout, was conducted with a fidelity to self which would not throw a point away, and a courtesy to rivals which should ever mark honorable competition."

"(From a Correspondent.)

"Stockton, Monday, September 29.—A report reached me, after I left the farm, that Hussey's machine cut the barley very much better than M'Cormick's. It came to me, however, through parties who might fairly be suspected of a bias, and therefore I kept my judgment in suspense until I could obtain information on which I could more implicitly rely. This I have now got. I have been to the farm again to-day, and made inquiries of persons who saw the completion of the trial. M'Cormick's machine did not cut the barley so well as Hussey's. It cut it much too high; and as the crop was very much laid, the heads only, in many cases were cut off. We had Hussey's machine in operation to-day, both on barley and wheat, and made better work than on Saturday. Mr. Fawcitt worked it with the greatest ease. I think he would soon beat the inventor himself. Even I, townsman as I am, made fair work; and in an hour or two's practice, I would engage to cut a crop in a manner not to be found fault with. You may safely say that any ordinary workman about a farm would be able to manage the machine; and when I say this of Hussey's, it is also true of M'Cormick's. The one may be a better machine than the other, but the merits of either of them may be brought into practical action by a laborer of average intelligence and skill. It is the opinion of farmers and others with whom I have conversed, that the saving per acre, by the use of Hussey's machine, would be about 5s.

"At the close of the contest on Saturday, the knives of the two machines were placed in the hands of Mr. Robinson, engineer to Mr. Bellerby, of York, that he might report thereon, and on the machinery generally, to the Jury.

"Wednesday, October 1.—The Marquis of Londonderry, and several other gentlemen, have visited Mr. Fawcitt's farm, to see the machine at work.

"The laurels so recently placed upon the brow of Mr. M'Cormick, have been plucked off—not wholly, but in great part—by his fellow countryman, Mr. Hussey.

"We would enlarge upon this theme, but our report has left us little room. We would only say, that while the farmers of Cleveland, and of the Island generally, are turning their attention to agricultural improvement—by reaping machines, draining ploughs, and steam ploughs—we would say to them, in the words of Mr. Hussey to the Cleveland horse-jockey, when his machine was ready for its work—'Now, then, go ahead!' "

"REPORT OF THE JURY.

"The Jury regret exceedingly the most unfavorable state of the weather on the days of trial, (a perfect hurricane raging during the whole of the first day,) and their consequent inability to make so full and satisfactory a trial as they could have wished.

"The Machines were tested on a crop of Wheat, computed at 25 bushels per acre, very short in the Straw, and if possible, more laid than the Wheat.

"The Jury, taking the different points submitted to their consideration, in the order as mentioned:—

"1.—Their unanimous opinion, that Mr. Hussey's Machine, as exhibited by Messrs. Wm. Dray & Co., cut the corn in the best manner, especially across ridge and furrow, and when the machine was working in the direction of the corn laid.

"2.—By a majority of eleven to one, that Mr. Hussey's machine caused the least waste.

"3.—Taking the breadth of the two machines into consideration, that of Mr. Hussey did most work.

"4.—That Mr. Hussey's Machine leaves the cut corn in the best order for gathering and binding. This question was submitted to the laborers employed on the occasion, and decided by them, as above, by a majority of 6 to 4.

"5.—Their unanimous opinion that Mr. Hussey's machine is best adapted for ridge and furrow.

"6.—This question was referred by the Jury to Mr. Robinson, foreman to Messrs. Bellerby, of York, a practical Mechanic of acknowledged ability, whose report is appended below.

"7.—That Mr. Hussey's Machine at first cost is less price.

"8, 9.—The Jury decline to express a decided opinion on these points in consequence of the state of the weather.

"The trials took place on the farm of Robert Fawcitt, of Ormsby, near Marlbro'-on-Tees, who in the most liberal and disinterested spirit allowed his crops to be trodden down and damaged to a very great extent, especially on the 25th, when in spite of the storm an immense crowd assembled to witness the trials.

"The Jury cannot conclude their Report, without expressing the great pleasure they have derived from seeing two Machines brought into competition, that were able to do such very good work, and also at witnessing the friendly, straight-forward, and honorable way in which the Exhibitors of the respective Machines met on this occasion.

"Signed on behalf of the Jury,

"W. F. Wharton, Foreman."

————

"Mr. Robinson's Report on Question 6.

"Having carefully examined both machines, and given the subject due consideration, I am of opinion that M'Cormick's Reaping Machine, as at present made, is most liable to get out of order.

("Signed,) THOMAS ROBINSON.

"York, 30th September, 1851."

————

(From the London *Mercantile Journal*)

"The Great Exhibition and Transatlantic Superiority over European

Ingenuity—American Reaping Machines.—The close of the Crystal Palace has given rise to many panegyrics, and we would not for one moment detract from its merits; it has been deservedly the admiration of the world, and visited by thousands of its inhabitants. Brought into life by the most eminent men, and supported by royalty; the means taken were such as no private individual could have accomplished; every exertion was used to obtain the choicest relics that the earth could produce; almost every country vied in exhibiting the arts and treasures of its products and manufactures, and were with one exception, considered eminently successful. The United States of America, however, was thought to be deficient, and in one or two cases some rather strong and even coarse remarks were indulged in. But what are the results? France can boast of the richness of its silks and artificial manufactures, and England of its machinery; but we find that our own newspapers are filled with admiration at the inventions of Brother Jonathan. We shall only slightly touch upon the sensation produced by the splendid performance of the American Yacht, and the dexterity displayed in the lock-picking, which was previously deemed impracticable. But it may be said that these are trifling matters in a national point of view; still, facts have been elicited by these apparent trifling incidents, for we find that the superior build of the little American yacht involves a principle—it being now admitted that in nautical matters the Americans are equal, if not superior, to other nations in their construction of their merchant vessels, and also in the equipment of their ships of war. On the land they are equally successful; their reaping machines have astonished our agriculturists. We extract from the Gateshead Observer, and other local papers, the surprising performances of Hussey's and M'Cormick's machines. Our readers are aware that there are two rival parties competing their powers on British ground, and without entering into the question as to which of the two performed their work in the best manner, we copy the result of the trial. The *Durham Advertiser* states that the performance took place at Middlesbro, and says:

"'Few subjects have created a greater sensation in the agricultural world than the recent introduction into the country of the reaping machines of Mr. M'Cormick, and the subsequent appearance of a rival, of no inferior description, in a similar implement from Mr. Hussey. The interesting trial of the two in competition, intended to have taken place on Thursday last, was postponed, in consequence of the torrents of rain, until Saturday, when, under the superintendence of a very efficient jury empanelled to decide the respective merits of the two implements, the contest came off. The compact form of Hussey's implement was in its favor, though from the notoriety of M'Cormick's at Mr. Mechi's farm, the general preference was at first on his side. M'Cormick's machine was first tried against the inclination of the corn, and completed its portion in very good style, leaving the sheaves in a handy manner at the side of the furrow. Hussey's completed a similar breadth but deposited the sheaves behind, and consequently several binders were required to follow the machine to clear the course for cutting the next breadth, an imperfection, which, however, it was understood could be easily remedied, and the back delivery replaced by a side one. This breadth was closer cut than the one executed by M'Cormick's reaper. The two were then tried across the ridge, where Hussey's implement carried the palm, M'Cormick's leaving a very considerable portion of the straw standing behind it; and the last trial upon the wheat, in the direction of the lean of the wheat, Hussey's machine did its work very fairly, while M'Cormick's was obliged to be stopped in its course, after having taken the heads of the wheat, but left the whole of the straw standing. At this time two opinions did not exist among the company present—Hussey's being the favorite. The trial was then carried to some barley, where Hussey's again succeeded in obtaining public favor. The more compact form of Hussey's implement, as well as the superiority of the clipping action over the cutting action of M'Cormick's, entitle it to a greater share of public favor, and as the advantages of a side delivery can be easily applied to it, it will doubtless, become the more general in use amongst the farmers. We cannot, however, but think that some mechanical process might be substituted for raking the sheaf from the receiving board, and this with a few other mechanical improvements, would, we think, make Hussey's reaping machine a perfect, useful, and economical agricultural implement. The latter may be also advantageously applied to the cutting of clover crops, which is quite out of the question with the former. Another Correspondent on this subject says:—'The jury did not on Saturday announce their decision, nor have they yet made a report. Nineteen farmers out of twenty who witnessed the trial were in favor of Hussey's machine.'

"The *Gateshead Observer,* remarks:—'The great Cleveland contest between the two American reaping machines, respectively invented by Mr. M'Cormick, of Chicago, and Mr. Hussey, of Baltimore, originally appointed for Thursday, the 25th ult., frustrated, for a time by the deluge and hurricane of that disastrous day, came off on Saturday, the 27th. The trial was one of great severity, the crops of Wheat and Barley were laid, and the straw damp and soft. The laurels so recently placed upon the brow of Mr. M'Cormick have been plucked off—not wholly, but in great part—by his fellow countryman, Mr. Hussey. Both the machines proved their ability to do good work, but Mr. Hussey's attested its superiority; and the English farmer has now seen, thanks to Prince Albert and the Exhibition of Works of Industry, that his corn and grasses, hitherto slowly and laboriously reaped with the sickle and the scythe, may now be planed off the land, in five feet breadth, as rapidly as a horse can trot.'

" 'A trial has taken place before the Cleveland Agricultural Society of the respective merits of M'Cormick's and Hussey's American Reaping Machines, and the report of the jury of practical men, appointed by the consent of both parties to decide the question of merit is favorable to the latter Implement. This Decision throws considerable doubt upon the justice of the award of a great medal at the Exhibition to M'Cormick's.'—London Times, Oct. 7:

"Following upon its success at Cleveland, the proprietors were invited to exhibit the Machine at the Barnard Castle Agricultural Society, Lord Harry Vane, president.

"Barnard Castle, Oct. 8, 1851.

"The undersigned President, Vice Presidents, and members of the Barnard Castle Agricultural Society and others who have witnessed the working of the American Reaping Machine, invented by Mr. Hussey, do CERTIFY THEIR UNQUALIFIED APPROVAL OF ITS OPERATIONS AND ENTIRE SUCCESS.

LORD HARRY VANE, President.

W. F. WHARTON, Vice President.

John Mitchell, V. P., Forcett Hall, Yorkshire, Esq.

J. S. Edgar, M. D., Barnard Castle, Esq.

John Dickinson Holmes, Barnard Castle, Solicitor.

George P. Harrison, Forcett, Yorkshire, Esq., Farmer.

Edward Scaith, Keverston, near Darlington, Esq., Farmer, and Assistant Draining Commissioner.

Thomas Robinson, Hutton Hall, near Richmond, Yorkshire, Esq., Farmer.

Richard Kay, Forcett Valley, near Darlington, Esq., Farmer.

William Harrison, Greta Bridge, Yorkshire, Esq., Farmer.

Thomas Carter, Scales, near Richmond, Esq., Farmer.

Jno. Whitfield, London, Esq.

Rev. Thomas Boys Croome, Scotland.

William Watson, Junr., Barnard Castle, Solicitor.

J. R. Monkhouse, Barnard Castle, Manufacturer.

Samuel Nelson, of Scaife House, near Staindrop, Durham, Esq., Farmer.

William Thompson, Lanehead, near Ovington, Yorkshire, Esq., Farmer.

John Ethwaite, Bainesse, near Catterick, Yorkshire, Farmer.

WILLIAM WATSON, Secretary of the Barnard Agricultural Association."

———

"From the *Darlington and Stockton,* (England) *Times,* Oct. 11.

"BARNARD CASTLE AGRICULTURAL SOCIETY.

"Mr. Hussey's Reaping Machine.

"Great interest was excited in Barnard Castle and its neighborhood on Tuesday last, by the announcement that Mr. Hussey's reaping machine would be exhibited at the forthcoming meeting of the Barnardcastle Agricultural Society; and ·that a trial of its powers would be made previous to the meeting. Accordingly, on Tuesday last, the machine was brought into operation in a field of barley, belonging to Mr. George White, of Stainton, near Barnardcastle, which it cut admirably well.   The Rev. W. F. Wharton, and other gentlemen in the vicinity, besides a vast number of farmers, were present.   The judges on the occasion were H. S. Thompson, Esq., of Moat Hall, (one of the Agricultural Jury of the Great Exhibition), W. Lister, Esq., of Dunsa Bank; and T. Robinson, Esq., of Hutton.   Luncheon was provided for a large party in an out-building near the scene of the experiments, and it is a fact worthy of notice, that after dinner Mr. Thompson proposed the health of Mr. Hussey (who was present) with great fervour, and spoke of the disadvantages under which Mr. Hussey's Machine had labored when tried against M'Cormick's for the Great Exhibition Medal; Mr. Hussey not being in the country at that time, and no one being present who understood the adjusting or working of the implement.   Mr. Thompson said he was now so thoroughly satisfied of its great merits, that he would do his best to get a medal awarded to it. After luncheon, the machine was taken to the grounds of Mr. Adamson, and tried upon a field of oats, which were so laid as to form a very severe test to the machine, but it nevertheless was successful there also.   The party retired greatly pleased with it, and some of the most wary agriculturists ordered machines upon the ground.—On, Wednesday morning, a large assemblage of agriculturists met on the farm of Mr. F. Atkinson, Westwood, Startforth, to see the machine cut a field of wheat, and there again the experiment yielded all that even its inventor could desire.   We understand that a large number of orders were given for machines by the farmers present, which is perhaps the very best test of their views in the matter.   The general impression seemed to be that it would prove of incalculable value to the agricultural interest.

"At about 3 o'clock in the afternoon, a large party sat down to a sumptuous dinner at the King's Head Inn.   Lord Harry Vane, presided, and the Rev. W. F. Wharton occupied the vice-chair.   After dinner the usual loyal toasts having been proposed, the vice chair proposed the health of Mr. Hussey; that gentleman, he said, had contributed to their gratification and interest in bringing his invention there for trial; the result of that trial had exceeded everything they could have previously imagined or hoped; and therefore he begged they would excuse him for proposing his health so early, as Mr. Hussey and his agent's representative Mr. Pierce, had to leave by the first train from Darlington, which they had then but sufficient time to reach.   He proposed the healths of Mr. Hussey and of the enterprising firm, Messrs. Dray & Co., who had undertaken to bring that machine into the British market. The toast was drank with honors. Mr. Hussey briefly returned thanks.

"After some further proceedings, the Vice-Chairman proposed the health of the President, Lord Harry Vane responded.

"The healths of the Vice-Presidents were proposed. Mr. Mitchell briefly responded. Mr. Wharton in acknowledging the toast, took the opportunity of again bringing before the meeting the merits of the invention which had been the object of that day's attraction. It had been most unfortunate that when the trial took place for the prize of the great exhibition, Mr. Hussey had not arrived in this country—nobody knew how it was managed, whilst M'Cormick's was properly attended to. Mr. Hussey's machine did no work, and Mr. M'Cormick took the medal. No sooner did Mr. Hussey arrive than he prayed for a further trial, but the Jury could not grant it. All difficulty was removed by Mr. M'Cormick throwing down the gauntlet. The trial came off in Cleveland—the result was clear and satisfactory in favor of Mr. Hussey's machine as decidedly superior. Mr. Thompson, of Moat Hall, one of the Great Exhibition Jury, was also one of the Judges in Cleveland, and was so satisfied on the subject that he left, determined to urge for a medal for Mr. Hussey. It must be a source of pleasure to all, to find that justice was thus about to be done to a worthy, modest and unassuming man."

"From the *Darlington and Stockton Times,*
October 11th, 1851.
"THE REAPING MACHINES AT BARNARDCASTLE.

"To the Editor of the Darlington and Stockton Times.

"Sir:—I beg to trouble you with a few particulars of Mr. Hussey's American Reaping Machine, which I yesterday saw working in a field near Barnardcastle. I am not a farmer, and of course cannot be thoroughly au fait at describing an agricultural implement, nor am I sufficiently versed in mechanics to explain to you the construction of the machine in all its details, but of the result I can speak, and that with confidence.

"Drawn by two horses, a man seated on the near side horse as driver, this wonderful implement was drawn with perfect ease, at more than the rate of three miles an hour, round and round a field, partly in wheat and partly in barley, cutting a breadth of corn in its progress with a regularity and evenness that was surprising. No straggling stalks of corn were left—none of the slovenly irregular work too often seen where manual labor is employed, was to be discovered; on the contrary, the field after shearing, looked nearly as smooth and even as a kitchen floor or turnpike road. The farmer has now no longer occasion to be behind the reapers, dinning in their ears, 'shear low,'—'now do shear low'; for this machine, with a very simple adjustment, will cut the corn as low as he can possibly require. A seat on the machine is provided for a man, who with a large rake, and with motion resembling the pushing of a punt, removes the corn from the machine as it is cut, and leaves it for the binders to put together in sheafs.

"The assistance of two men and two horses are thus all that is required to draw and guide this wonderful sickle—and so manned, it will cut with the ease and regularity I have described, from perhaps ten to twelve acres in the working day. Nor as far as I could see, or learn from the observation of others, does there appear to be any drawback against its general adoption. Its price (£21) is not exorbitant—its construction is not so complex as to cause a fear of frequent repairs being required; men of the common run of agricultural laborers are quite competent to go with it, and the work of drawing it is not distressing to the horses. Neither does the nature of the ground appear to be much an object, for it travelled as well over ridge and furrow as it did upon a level.

"Nothing could be more unanimous, than the approval of which the machine met with from all who saw its work, and I was informed that nine machines were ordered on the ground. Among the purchasers was the Duke of Cleveland, who with Lord Harry Vane, was present, and examined its working and construction minutely. The curiosity excited by the machine was great, and an immense number of people visited the ground during the two days.—Noblemen and gentlemen, farmers and farm laborers, tradesmen and mechanics, men and women, flocked to see the implement, which from the other side of the Atlantic has come to effect so important a revolution in the labor of the harvest field, and all were agreed that Brother Jonathan, though still a young man, had some clever notions in his head, and that John Bull, in the case of the reaping machine, would not be above taking advantage of his intelligence. I am, &c.   A. B."

"(From the *London Daily News*.)
"HUSSEY'S REAPING MACHINE—TRIAL BEFORE PRINCE ALBERT.

"The celebrated battle of the Ganges hardly excited more interest in the railway world than the battle of the Reaping machines has lately created in the agricultural world; nor is the result perhaps very much less important in the latter case than in the former.

"Of the recent inventions for diminishing the cost of production, the most remarkable are undoubtedly the Reaping machines of Messrs. Hussey and M'Cormick. Perhaps it would be more accurate to call them importations than inventions, since both have been in use for a considerable time in America; and amongst the benefits arising from the Exhibition, it is certainly not the least that it has introduced to the agriculturist of Great Britain implements of the highest practical utility, which might otherwise have remained forever exclusively in the hands of their brethren across the Atlantic. It will be remembered that a trial of the two rival machines took place last summer, at Mr. Mechi's model farm in Essex, having been directed by the royal commissioners, with the view of determining the comparative merits of the two instruments, whose patentees were competitors for the forthcoming medal prizes. At that time Mr. Hussey, the American inventor of the machine called after his name, had not arrived in the country. The weather too, was very unpropitious for the trial, notwithstanding which a very large number of gentlemen were present. The machines were tried upon a field of wheat, and the result was such as to convince all present, of the superiority, in every point of view, of M'Cormick's machine—a conviction which was subsequently confirmed, by the fact of the Exhibition medal being awarded exclusively to the patentee of that machine. The tables, however, were soon to be turned. Mr. Hussey arrived in England; a challenge having been given by the agents of Mr. M'Cormick, it was accepted by Mr. Hussey, and his English agent, Mr. Dray; and, after a fair contest before the Cleveland Society, at Middlesbro', near Stockton-on-Tees, on the 25th and 27th of Sept., a jury of twelve agriculturists pronounced a verdict in favor of the unmedalled machine. They decided that of the two machines, Hussey's had the preponderance of advantages—that it cut corn in the best manner, caused the least waste, did the most work in a given time, left the cut corn in the best order for gathering and binding, was the best adapted for ridge and furrow, was the least liable to get out of repair, and was the least price at first cost. On the two other points submitted to them, namely, which machine required the least amount of horse labor, and which the least amount of manual labor, the jury declined to express a decided opinion, in consequence of the state of the weather.

"There have been many other trials of Hussey's machine in different parts of the country, and the result has been so far uniformly satisfactory.—Amongst these we have now to mention a very interesting one which took place by appointment last Saturday, at Windsor, in the presence of his Royal Highness, Prince Albert, originating in a correspondence between General Wemyss, on behalf of the Prince, and Messrs. Dray & Co. of Swan-lane, the agents for Mr. Hussey. The spot selected for the trial was behind the statue of George III., at the end of the Long Walk, fern—of which there is an abundance in that locality—being the article on which the machine had to operate. The Prince having from an early hour in the morning been engaged in shooting in the vicinity of the statue, at half-past twelve resigned his gun, and proceeded on horse-back, in company with General Wemyss, and Col. Seymour, to the spot appointed for the trial of the machine.

Dismounting from his horse, his Royal Highness saluted briefly and gracefully the assembled company, and especially Mr. Hussey and Mr. Dray. He then asked a few general questions respecting the history of the machine, and observed, that as the ground selected was very uneven (it was in fact remarkably so), the trial would be a good one. After a brief delay, the gear being declared in order, on went the machine, drawn by two strong horses, and heedless of ruts and hillocks in its course, which was very rapid, bringing down everything it encountered cleanly and completely, including two or three slices of turf at least a foot long, and more than an inch thick.

"The performances of the machine were not confined to one single course. A considerable amount of work was performed in the most satisfactory manner, Mr. Hussey himself sitting on the box at the side, and throwing aside what was cut down in the manner best adapted for gathering and binding. Indeed the work was not confined to the fern; a rabbit who was not accustomed to this species of interference was started and cruelly lacerated before he had time to escape.

"At the close of the trial, his Royal Highness gave a practical proof of his favorable opinion by ordering two of the machines for himself, one for Windsor and the other for Osborne. He then, after expressing his gratification, rode back to the game-keepers and resumed his gun. After he had left, the machine operated well upon some rushes.

"It may not be out of place to state here that Mr. Dray's explanation of the failure of the Hussey machine at Tiptree Hall (Mr. Mechi's farm), is that it was entirely owing to its not being properly managed. On that occasion, he says, the person in charge of it was simply a porter at the Exhibition, who, not understanding the matter, neglected to clear away the wheat as it was cut down, in consequence of which the action of the machine was unavoidably and fatally impeded. We witnessed the result at Mr. Mechi's and certainly there was no such fault on Saturday. The progress of the machine was notwithstanding the unevenness of the ground, rapid and satisfactory; and it was stated as a fact that on a level ground the horses used in drawing may trot, not only without weakening or impeding the action of the knives, but even with advantages, as by that means the cutting requires increased precision and force."

————

"The following is Prince Albert's certificate:

"Windsor Castle, Nov. 13, 1851.

"Sir:—In answer to your letter addressed to Gen. Wemyss, I have received the commands of His Royal Highness Prince Albert, to say that so far as he could judge of Mr. Hussey's Reaping Machine, from its performance in the high fern at Windsor Park, his Royal Highness is disposed to form a very favorable opinion of it, and has ordered one *

* The Prince ordered two Machines, one for Windsor and one for Isle of Wight.

in consequence for the use of his own farm. His Royal Highness can however give no opinion as to the relative merits of this machine in comparison with those of others which he has not seen at work.

"I have the honor to be sir, your ob't serv't,

"GREY."

———————

"(From Maidstone & South Eastern Gazette, Oct. 21, '51.)

"WEST KENT AGRICULTURAL SOCIETY'S PLOUGHING MATCH.

"Hussey's American Reaper.

"A distinguishing feature at this society's meeting on Thursday, the 16th inst., was an exhibition of the capabilities of the above machine. The season of the year of course prevented a display of its powers on anything in the shape of grain, indeed great difficulty was found in procuring even a green crop on which to operate. Undaunted by this fact, the inventor was determined to show to the anxious hundreds assembled the extent of the advantages to be derived from the use of his reaper. At two o'clock the machine was set to work upon a field of clover, short and light (as may be supposed), where its performance was effectual as it possibly could be, exciting a considerable amount of surprise as well as gratification. It was then taken to a piece of marsh land, where clumps of stout rushes in many places were growing in thick masses, presenting the appearance of stunted grain. The machine passed over this marsh, cutting the rushes with the same facility as if it had been corn, leaving the stubble about 4 inches long and very regular, giving also a good representation of the manner in which the sheaves of wheat, &c., are usually delivered. Both these operations, but especially the latter, were considered severe contests of the capabilities of the machine. Taking all the circumstances into consideration, the performance was far beyond all reasonable expectations. It was a question whether the excellent work of the fifty-eight competing ploughs, or the extraordinary novelty of Hussey's machine in operation, added most to the gratification of the large assemblage of the leading agriculturists of Kent."

———————

("From the Kentish Gazette, Nov. 11, 1851.)

"In addition to the interest naturally felt by all who live on and by the soil in its proper cultivation, there was an unusual degree of attraction in the fact that a reaping machine by Mr. Hussey, (the celebrated American Machinist) would be tested upon seven acres of mustard adjoining the ploughing field. The reaping was commenced about twelve o'clock, and continued for a considerable period. The crop of mustard was wet, and by no means calculated to favor the experiment. It was, however, after the machine was properly arranged, cut down with great regularity; and at a speed equal to four miles an hour it traversed the circuit of the field, hewing its way through the mustard, quickly followed by a crowd of eager observers, whose wondering gaze exhibited at once their astonishment and admiration of its working. Occasionally the level of the cutters were altered, so as to leave a greater or less length of stubble, which evinced the accurate adjustment to which the machine could be brought. Some portion of it was taken to pieces, and the whole of the arrangements shown, which the farmers present displayed an eager anxiety to investigate, and many were the questions proposed, and satisfactorily answered by the talented inventor.

"We should mention that the undulation of the land does not impede its operations in the least—as it was well observed by a gentleman present, that where a cart could travel there this machine could also go, and complete its design. No previous acquaintance with its principle is necessary to be able to guide its operation, as shown by Mr. Neame, Jr., who mounted the platform and discharged the functions appertaining to the party who removes the corn from the machine after it is cut, with the greatest ease and precision. Indeed the most unqualified approval was given by the gentlemen present, to the applicability of the reaping machine to the purposes for which it is designed. We have thus entered into minute particulars, because this is the first opportunity we have had of witnessing the results of such an experiment, attended as it was with every degree of satisfaction. Lord Sondes gave an order for one of the machines, and we understand that three or four orders were given in the course of the day.

"At the dinner which followed, the chairman gave a toast to 'Sir John Tylden and the visitors.'

"Sir John Tylden, as a member as well as a visitor, replied to the toast, and in a jocular strain anmadverted on the suffering of the farmers of Faversham, who were determined, like a celebrated regiment in the service, to 'die hard.' He alluded to the reaping machine of Mr. Hussey, which he characterized in contro-distinction to that of Mr. M'Cormick's and all others, as the universal reaping machine, of which he spoke in highly approving terms, and passed a warm eulogium on its talented inventor, and the country he represented, which in the space of 80 years had risen from a wilderness to her now exalted position, and proud of her Anglo-Saxon blood."

The remonstrance to the extension of McCormick's 1834 patent referred to earlier machines than that of McCormick's and also to

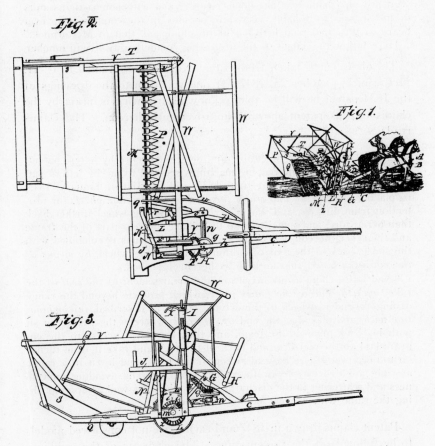

Still no seat for the driver.

the trial before the Cleveland Agricultural Society in England in 1851. They close in the following words:

"Mr. Hussey is a modest man, as well as a man of genius, and consequently the public ear has not been deafened with bombastic assaults of his success. Probably very few persons in the country have ever heard of this final trial between his machine and that of McCormick."

Here follow the names of the protesting committee, twelve in number.

The above cut is taken from patent No. 5335 as granted to C. H. McCormick, October 23, 1847. If one will turn to the drawings of the 1834 patent he will be able to know clearly what is meant by the claims of this patent showing improvements thereon. The claims read:

"What I claim as my invention, and desire to secure by letters patent, as improvements on the reaping machines secured to me by letters patent, bearing date the 21st of June, 1834, and the 31st of January, 1845, is, placing the *gearing and crank forward of the driving wheel,* for protection from dirt, &c, and thus carrying the driving wheel further back than heretofore, and sufficiently so to balance the rear part of the frame and the raker thereon, when this position of the parts is combined with the sickle, back of the axis of motion of the driving wheel, *by means of the vibrating lever,* substantially as herein described.

"And I also claim as my invention, the arrangement of *the seat* of the raker *over the end of the finger piece,* which projects beyond the range of fingers, and just back of the driving wheel, as described, *in combination with,* and placed at the end of, *the reel,* whereby the raker can sit with his back towards the team, and thus have free access to the cut grain laid on the platform and back of the reel, and rake it from thence on to the ground by a natural sweep of his body, and lay it in a range at right angles with the swath, as described, thereby avoiding unevenness and scattering in the discharge of the wheat, as well as accomplishing the same with a great saving of labor."

Patent claims drawn in 1847 and earlier are not considered models to be followed at the present time. The elements of the combinations sought to be covered may be read in the words I have italicised.

As in the 1834 patent, the cutting apparatus is aligned just in rear of the main wheel, and it will also be seen that nearly all of the weight of the machine is in rear of the main supporting wheel and the grainward-side wheel; so constructed, the machine was inclined to tip backward. As previously explained, the preponderating weight at the rear originally was supported upon the horses' backs. The

1834 patent hints, however, that thills may be used and the machine drawn. But with thills thus applied the preponderating weight at rear would be so great that the raker could not be so situated because thus placed more weight still would be at rear of the supporting wheels. Turning to Figures 2 and 3 of the patent of 1847, it will be seen that instead of a counter shaft geared to the main supporting wheel extending rearwardly and upwardly the same shaft in the later patent is extended *forwardly* and upwardly and that the bevel gear upon its forward and upward end meshes with a pinion upon a vertical shaft which has formed as one part with it a crank; upon the same shaft is also a balance wheel.

Thus the change from the machine of 1834 is such, in effect, as to swing the gearing over forward in order that its weight may be in front of the supporting wheel. This, however, was merely a mechanical change adapted to aid in producing better poise of the machine, but if ever used it was abandoned in 1848, as before shown. In order to transmit the motion from the crank shaft thus newly placed relative to the cutting apparatus the vibrating lever of Bell's machine of 1828 was adopted. The complicated cutting blade of the 1834 patent was thrown aside and that of the 1845 patent, which could be directly operated by a single pitman substituted. This substitution and adoption of the Bell means for moving the cutting apparatus enabled Mr. McCormick to put the gearing forward of the main supporting wheel, and permitting the machine to carry a raker's stand so placed that the weight of the gearing would counterpoise the weight of the raker. It seems strange that Mr. McCormick, who claims to have had a successful machine in 1831, permitted his raker to walk behind the machine and the driver to ride the wheel horse before the machine so many years, when, by a slight exercise of the inventive faculty, two seats could have been placed upon the machine, one at the front and one at the rear of the main supporting wheel, the driver upon one counterpoising the weight of the man whose duty it was to deliver the gavels to the ground sitting upon the other.

What better evidence of lack of inventive faculty and resourcefulness can be found?

Not satisfied with the 1845 patent granted, it was reissued in several divisions. Not satisfied with the 1847 patent, as granted, it was finally reissued in ten divisions. In this first reissue the claim reads:

"The arrangement, substantially as described, of a cutting apparatus and a reel with respect to a driving wheel and a grain wheel or its equivalent, and a raker's seat or its equivalent, so that the major part of the weight of the cutting apparatus and reel shall be in advance of the axis of oscillation of the machine on the said wheels, while the raker's seat or stand shall be located behind that axis, and the machine with the raker thereon merely balanced on its axis of oscillation, substantially as described."

This claim is but a paraphrase of the original two claims when considered together, and it is one clearly covering the invention, but later divisions of the reissue show an effort to broaden the scope of the invention. Reissue No. 824 was granted in 1859, twelve years after the date of the original patent, and where the patentee seemed to have awakened to the belief that he had invented more than he originally supposed he had. Division "I" of the patent under consideration brings in the frame structure of the machine. Division "H" covers still other features not dreamed of by the inventor twelve years before, namely, a dividing board having a surface inclined toward the cutter and platform, an outer dividing-line and an inner dividing-line, arranged to spread the standing grain apart in advance of the cutting apparatus. Grain dividers were old, as has been shown; the courts held that Bell's machine had a divider combined with a reel and cutting apparatus, and during the years from '47 until '59 the public supposed it had the right, as in fact it had, to use a divider of any wedge shaped form. Even if Mr. McCormick was first to make a divider of that form, by his delay of twelve years he had practically donated it to the public, but we have read a great deal in advertising columns and false history of the past about the divider and reel of McCormick's 1834 patent. In view of these facts, I say that between 1834 and 1859, when some of the reissues were granted, and certainly between 1847, in which patent the divider is better shown, and 1859, public rights had intervened.

In the early days of reaping machines, inventors sought, very properly, to make more secure their rights by correcting errors in their patents, if errors actually existed; but soon the Patent Office became lax in its duties and patentees were permitted not merely to correct clerical errors, but errors in judgment, and also to enlarge the scope of their patents. Reference has also been made in advertising columns and false history to the fact that Hussey reissued his 1847 patent, which, in fact, he did, but, as we shall later see, he did not draw claims broader, in effect, than those of the original patent. Not true, however, with Mr. McCormick. In reissuing a patent, let me here explain, the drawings of the new applications must follow the original drawings accurately, but it is privileged that the specification may more clearly explain the drawings and the claims state more clearly what the inventor for the first time accomplished. The allowance of the claims by the Patent Office is properly considered to be an admission that, as far as known to it, the inventor is entitled to a monopoly of the devices covered by the claim or claims allowed.

The machine of McCormick's 1847 patent was provided with a tongue, as all direct draft machines were. Not satisfied with Reissue 816, he followed it with 817, the essential difference between the former and the latter being that a tongue was then made an element of the claims. Clearly there was no invention in adding a tongue to the combination covered by Reissue 816, as tongues were old in vehicles and were practically half a century old in reapers. Still another division of the original patent is Reissue 818, which included a "seat or stand" for the support of the raker "laterally and in front." In plain English, the seat or stand was a bar astride which the raker might place himself, having a crossbar in front of him against which he might lean in order to steady himself. He rode backward and, though this crossbar in one sense was in front of him, in the sense of the movement of the machine is was at the rear. When this reissue was granted Hussey had had a raker's stand on his machine for more than twenty years. There was still another division of the original case; Reissue 819, which is practically a paraphrase of 816. It contains the same elements and is little more than a statement of the functions of the alleged combination, which form of claim for a number of years has been rejected by our Patent Office.

The McCormick reissues, the claims of others of which follow, well serve as samples of the abuse of our patent laws:

"Reissue No. 817.

"WHAT I CLAIM, under this patent, as my invention, is the combination of a tongue, or its equivalent, to draw the machine by; a driving-wheel and gearing arranged at the side of the frame; a short platform; a reel to gather the grain to the platform, and a stand or seat, for the raker, fixed upon the machine so as to enable the raker conveniently to discharge the grain and lay it in gavels upon the ground, at the side of the swath and out of the return path of the horses; substantially as described."

"Reissue No. 818.

"WHAT I CLAIM, under this patent, as my invention, is a seat, or stand, on the reaping machine, for the support of the raker laterally and in front; substantially as described."

"Reissue No. 819.

"WHAT I CLAIM, under this patent, as my invention, is the combination of the reel, the divider and the raker's seat or stand, co-operating together in such manner that the grain, deposited upon the platform by the reel and divider, may readily be grasped and discharged from the machine by the raker at his seat; substantially as described."

"Reissue No. 820.

"WHAT I CLAIM, under this patent, as my invention, is the combination, in a reaping machine, of the following elements, namely; the draught and the gearing arranged at the side of the machine; two compressors, one arranged at each end of the cutter; the short reel to sweep over the space between the compressors, and the short platform; substantially as described."

"Reissue No. 821.

"WHAT I CLAIM, under this patent, as my invention, is the combination of the grain-guarded platform to receive and retain the cut grain, with the divider and the reel; the whole arranged substantially in the manner and for the purposes described."

"Reissue No. 822.

"WHAT I CLAIM, under this patent, as my invention, is the combination of the reel support, at the rear part of the outer side of the platform, with the low, flat frame and the divider, arranged substantially as described."

"Reissue No. 823.

Under this patent, I claim, as my invention,

"FIRST, a dividing-board having a surface inclining towards the cutter and platform, and an outer dividing-line and an inner dividing-line, arranged and acting substantially as described.

"SECOND, I CLAIM, the combination of the inclined dividing-board with a guide-bar; substantially as described.

"THIRD, I CLAIM, the combination of a reel with the inclined dividing board; substantially as described.

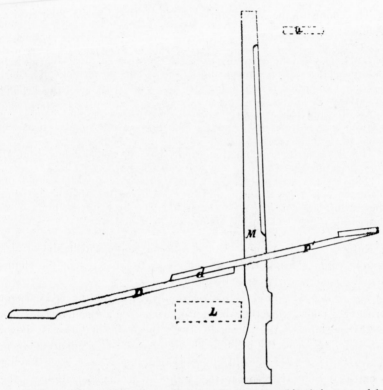

This drawing shows the parts of the machine that, combined, is covered by
Reissue 824 of McCormick's Patent of 1847.

"FOURTH, I ALSO CLAIM, the combination of a reel with the
dividing-board and guide-bar; substantially as described."
                              "Reissue No. 824.
    "WHAT I CLAIM, under this patent, as my invention, is a reaping
machine frame consisting mainly of two principal beams (D D1, and
M) crossing each other and arranged, relatively to the supporting
wheels, so as to give firm support to a platform not extending behind
the gearing, and without interfering with the cutter, on one side, or
the gavelling space on the other; substantially as described."
                              "Reissue No. 825.
    "WHAT I CLAIM, under this patent, as my invention, is the arrange-
ment of the frame, the finger-beam, the platform and the driving-wheel
and gearing, relatively to each other, so as to secure an unobstructed
gavelling space, G, at the side of the platform, behind the finger-beam;
substantially as herein described."

The claims of the McCormick patent of 1845, No. 3, 895, read as follows:

"I claim, 1st the curved (or angle downward, for the purpose described) bearers, for supporting the blade, in the manner described.

"2nd. I claim the reversed angle of the teeth of the blade, in manner described.

"3d. I claim the arrangement and construction of the fingers (or teeth for supporting the grain), so as to form the angular spaces in front of the blade, as and for the purpose described.

"4th. I claim the combination of the bow L, and dividing iron M, for separating the wheat, in the way described.

"5th. I claim setting the lower end of the reel post R, behind the blade, curving it at R and leaning it forward at top, thereby favoring the cutting and enabling me to brace it at top by the front brace S, as described, which I claim in combination with the post."

Reference to the patent granted to Read, under which McCormick bought rights, March 12, 1842, will show to what extent the claims above quoted were necessarily limited.

The reader will observe that on the drawings of the 1834 patent in the cut taken from the Mechanics' Magazine and, in fact, as late as the machine of the patent of 1845, the horizontal bar is shown as extending across the machine above the reel. It is apparent, then, that as late as 1845 he still clung to that brace bar. Such having been the tenacity, it seems to this author, that all illustrations of the alleged machine of 1834, in field tests, etc., may have been produced as late as the year 1845.

In the preceding chapter it was noticed that an attempt had been made by Mr. McCormick to show that in his alleged 1831 machine grain was supported both above and below the cutting blade so as to prevent it from partaking of the motion of the blade. Be the fact as it may, it will be seen, by a careful study of Fig. 3 of the 1845 patent, that the cutting edge of the blade B has no finger below it, or, in other words, there is nothing below the actual cutting edge; in short, there is nothing approaching the slotted finger of Hussey, and there is no nearer approach to the cutting device of the modern machine than the claimed construction of 1831. The cutting blade in this instance rests upon a bar A which is supported upon the framework of the machine. The "bearers" drop immediately behind the cutting apparatus for the ostensible purpose of allowing accumu-

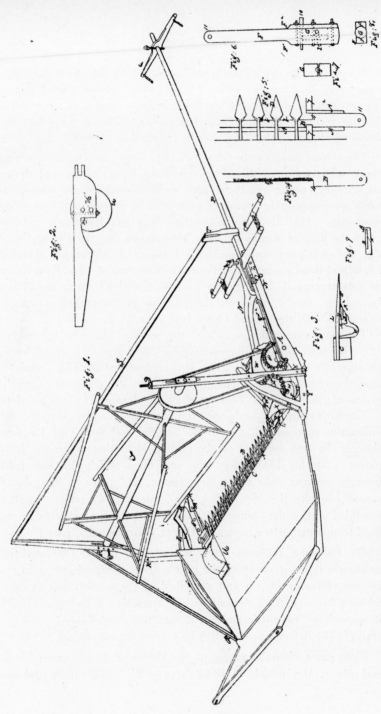

McCormick Reaping Machine, patented August 31, 1845.

lations of shreds to ultimately work out, rather than to remain in a close space between the cutting blades and the arrow shaped fingers above. On the divider is a curved iron L so shaped as to be swept by the reel and thus be cleared, its purpose being to deflect the standing straws so that they may be engaged by the reel.

The second claim of the patent of 1845 seems directed to covering the reversed angle of the serrations of the blade. Read had shown the Hussey cutting apparatus with serrated sections, and the serrations were oppositely arranged, as in modern reapers and harvesting machines. Mr. McCormick's patent was granted many months after the date of Read's patent. This shows that the Patent Office did not recognize any similarity between McCormick's serrated blade and Read's serrated sections, or there would have been either an interference declared or, at least McCormick's claim would not have been allowed, as at the date we are considering a system of examination in the Patent Office had long been established.

The third claim has to do with the peculiar shape of the fingers D. They are, as far as general outline and purpose are considered, substantially the same as Read's. It is evident that as in McCormick's case the cutting blade should be read into the claim as formerly practiced; that is to say, considered as one element of a combination.

The fifth claim has to do with the parts designed to overcome the difficulties encountered, due to placing the reel post (for the first time in the art) forward of the cutting apparatus, as in the 1834 patent. As this 1845 patent was one upon which suit was later brought we may pass it for the present, and refer to it again in connection with the McCormick 1847 patent. The patent was not extended. (For the opinion of the Commissioner of Patents in regard to this matter see copies of Patent Office records, past.)

The Palmer & Williams patent was granted July 1, 1851, and the automatic rake for sweeping the gavels from the quadrant grain receiving platform, shown and described in the patent, was at once adopted by several of the builders of reapers. It had one defect: it was wholly automatic and hence was not controllable by the operator. The defect was remedied by several later inventors

Eight years after the advent of the Palmer & Williams machines, and others, McCormick, in 1859, dropped his conservatism and applied an automatic rake having precisely the defects above mentioned, invented by McClintock Young. .

The largest stockholders in the International Harvester Company, are the descendants of Cyrus H. McCormick, Sr., and hence, very naturally, things drift thitherward.   In a recent publication, put out by that Company, is shown the alleged "First Reaper" and the Mc-Cormick self raking reaper of 1859, and beneath the words "First Self Raking Reaper."   This question naturally arises: Who winks at these false statements?

CHAPTER IX.

SELF-RAKING REAPERS—PRELIMINARY STAGES.

In the year 1848 a patent was granted to F. S. Pease, in which a raking device is shown and described that it was thought could be operated by the driver. These machines never came into use and would not be considered here only for the fact that it is a suggestion that may be considered as another mental stepping stone in the direction of self-raking reapers. The Hussey cutting apparatus is shown, but it is operated by cams formed upon the rim of the main supporting wheel. As far as the method of operating the cutting apparatus is concerned, it can only be considered an improvement on Manning's machine. Although similar cams have been depended upon in many machines that have been tried, they have not been successful because of the fact that sufficient rapidity of action could not be obtained by so simple means; probably the most practical result ever reached was by George Curtis early in the fifties.

In 1841 a patent was granted to D. A. Church for a harvester and thresher following Moore and Haskell, 1836. It merits mention here only for the reason that it was one of the first of a class of machines which later came into extensive use in the semi-arid regions of the West.

May 12, 1842, a patent was granted to J. Read. In this machine the raker delivered the gavel to the ground by mechanical means; rake teeth were so located beneath the receiving platform that they thrust upward while passing in one direction, and carried the grain therewith, but fell beneath the platform when returning to position to await a new accumulation. One feature in the Read machine deserves more than passing notice. The cutting blade is of the Hussey kind; its edges are serrated; guards are shown that are arrow-

186

shaped; they widen rapidly from the point rearward to a little distance before the angle of the cutting blades and from that point
are reduced in width rapidly, forming an angular space in front of
the cutting blade. To reduce the tendency of the grain straws to
move forward and thus escape the cutting edge, the sides of the
guards are notched. In this we have for the first time, as found in
the records of the U. S. Patent Office, what has been termed in
comparatively modern machines the equivalent of serrated guard
plates. The guard fingers are slotted as in Hussey's patent of 1833.
Read accomplished very little from a business point of view, nevertheless, his serrated guards, and the serrated sections which Hussey
early used—but did not patent—are valuable suggestions.

The next patent of importance is dated September 30, 1845. It
was granted to F. Woodward, of Freehold, N. J. The date of actual
invention is not known, but machines of the type were very early on
the prairies of Illinois, made at several localities. About the year
1843, Marcus Steward, of Little Rock Township, Kendall County,
Illinois, became possessed of a machine very similar to the Woodward, made at a country shop, nearby. The resemblance between this
machine and that shown in the Woodward patent, and Schnebly's
patent, is so great that I believe Woodward or Schnebly introduced
machines in a simple form some time before patents were granted.
The machine was supported upon four wheels, the rear axle being
so pivoted that the wheels could be turned in either direction in order
to steer the machine, precisely as a vessel is steered by its rudder. The
machine was pushed as was Bell's, but immediately back of the
grain receiving platform a stand was provided for the raker, and
with a suitable wooden fork the latter swept the grain off the platform, out of the way of the team in making the next round. This
machine, as first made, cut ten feet in width, but it was rebuilt later
and adapted to cut an eight foot swath. The greater width rendered
the raking off too laborious. Mr. McCormick began introducing his
machine in that county about 1845, and while traveling over the
country visited the Steward Farm to see this machine operate. Mr.
Steward was at once threatened with an infringement suit, but made
the reply that he probably understood the patent laws of the country
as well as Mr. McCormick did, and the machine continued for more
than twenty years to cut grain. That McCormick thought that his 1834

patent covered a push reaping machine is shown by the fact that he threatened to bring suit for infringement, the Steward machine also being of the push type.

To what extent the building and operating of this reaping machine influenced the six Steward boys cannot be determined, but this fact remains: the two eldest for twelve years were deeply engaged in manufacturing Marsh Harvesters, and one of them, the author, has spent a half century in the great art. This machine and its rebuilding by John F. Hollister assisted, in a measure, to develop the Marsh Harvester, on the same farm, eighteen years later.

A patent was granted to A. J. Cook, November 20, 1846, which shows an attempt to produce a self-raking reaper. The drawing of the patent was evidently made from a model which, like many, was ill proportioned. The cutting apparatus of Hussey is shown and over the receiving platform a shaft is placed parallel with the cutting apparatus, and an automatic rake suitably supported at each end of the shaft, was adapted to rotate, moving forward over the grain and in its rearward movement sweeping the latter from the platform, directly behind the machine. It cannot be said to have been a successful self-raking reaper, but it no doubt gave added impetus to the efforts of other inventors.

August 17, 1847, a patent was granted to Obed Hussey for an improvement on his cutting apparatus of 1833. In its early form it was found that shreds of grass could occasionally accumulate above the cutting sections and cause more or less annoyance. The cutting being mainly effected against the lower portion of the guards, and the actual cut thus being some distance from the upper part shreds would be carried under the latter and gradually forced backward so as to require removal. This difficulty he obviated by cutting the rearmost part of the upper portion of the guard away so as to leave a clear space for shreds to work out. As made in 1831 or 32, it met no successful competitor, and from the day of this last improvement the cutting apparatus of harvesting and mowing machines has not been modified. In order to prevent the cutting edge of the blades from shearing into the guard and thus rounding it off, the sections of the early cutters were slightly beveled beneath. A statement in this patent has led to misconstructions in regard to the precise form of the cutting apparatus of the earlier patent. In his specification he

refers to the new cutting apparatus as being an improvement upon
his old, and in the application says:

"In my original invention the blades are ground with a bevel on both
sides of the edge. The purpose of this is that by means of the shoulder
of the bevel the sharp edge is prevented from coming in immediate contact with the iron in passing the guard."

It is no doubt true that when the sentence quoted was written, Mr.
Hussey had in mind some form in which he had constructed his
cutting apparatus in the early day, and not the exact construction of
the patent of 1833; for in that there is no suggestion whatever of
beveling the under side of the edges of the blades. The last part
of the quotation shows the extent to which they were beveled,
namely: "The sharp edge is prevented from coming in immediate
contact with the iron in passing the guard." This simply means that
the under side was slightly beveled so that the edge could not cut
into the iron guard. In this day when the guards are made of hard-
ened steel, the blades of mowing machine knives are not so made,
but the blades in grain cutting machines are often slightly beveled.
It was desirable, he thought, to bevel the blades upon their under
sides only for a portion of the length of the cutting edge, and little
at that. This 1847 patent was reissued in several divisions. In his
first division, 449, he claims the specific construction of his cutting
apparatus. In his second division, 450, he covers what formed the
subject matter of the second claim of his original patent. In his
third division, 451, he claims the open top guards specifically. The
claim is merely another form of expressing the idea embodied in
claim 1 of the original patent. A study of previous pages will show
the figure that Mr. Hussey's cutting apparatus cut in the art. It
has not been modified up to the present time except in one detail
that deserves more than passing notice.

Mr. Hussey's reapers, as we have seen, were introduced into
Illinois in 1834. Late in the '30s they became well known. Before
1844 little factories throughout the country had begun the manufacture of reaping machines, some of the Hussey type and some of
the Woodward type, having either shears or the cutting apparatus
of Hussey. Mr. Rugg built a reaper in 1844 and the next year, in
connection with Otis Rockwood, began manufacture in a small way

at Ottawa, Illinois. In his machine Mr. Rugg embodied the improvement (previously tested by Hussey) that has proved of great importance. Jonathan Read had suggested that the blades of a cutting device, like that previously patented to Hussey, be serrated. He crudely showed that arrangement in his patent, but it is not known that his suggested improvement ever cut any material figure. It remained for George Rugg to demonstrate that when cutting *grain* the operation was more perfectly performed if the edges of the Hussey blades were serrated. This he demonstrated in his own machine, and by applying such sickles to Hussey's machines of different forms, then in use, and to McCormick machines after they had otherwise become successful.

I have before me the affidavits of responsible parties that enable me to fix the date and the importance of Mr. Rugg's invention, and he has told me his own story. He filed an application for a patent in 1848, in which the invention is very clearly described. The invention is concisely explained in a letter written by Mr. Rugg, published in the Implement Age of June 15, 1897.

"The invention consists in the use of a sickle with an edge on which the teeth are cut curved, that the teeth may be so put as to point in a direction parallel, or nearly so, with a line in which the sickle is designated to move, as will be seen by the accompanying drawing, where C, Fig. 1, represents the sickle with the front edge curved, which is made to vibrate in the direction of its length a distance equal to that between the grain holders B, which are fastened to the front edge of the platform A and project forward over the sickle, then doubling under the sickle nearly to the platform. Fig. 2 represents the sickle by itself inverted which consists of a thin plate of steel with one edge crooked, as seen in the figure, and sickle teeth cut on it, and a bar of iron (D) riveted to its back to stiffen it. The general frame and gearing or propelling apparatus may be constructed like any of the various harvesting machines now in use, whose cutters vibrate," etc.

In 1845 Mr. Rugg applied his cutting apparatus to a McCormick machine purchased by one Shaver (father of Jackson R. Shaver, from whom my information is obtained) of LaSalle County, Illinois. Mr. Shaver also had Hussey's machine in use. Into this Hussey machine was placed one of Mr. Rugg's serrated cutting blades; I learn also that the McCormick machines, a number of which were later in the neighborhood, were changed by Mr. Rugg. In 1846.

Reaper of the Woodward-Schnebley type rebuilt by Hollister and Steward for the harvest of 1843.

Seat of McCormick's 1847 patent.

Mr. Rugg applied a serrated knife to a Hussey machine owned by Mr. Otis Rockwood. (I get my information in this last regard from David Strawn, who was one of the most extensive farmers in the world, a man of eminence, and he informs me that the Rugg "sickle" was applied to McCormick's machines "all over the country," as they came in.) Jesse Green of La Salle County, Illinois, purchased a Hussey reaper in 1844. To this was also applied Mr. Rugg's "crooked sickle." In 1846 Mr. Marcus Steward and his brother-in-law, John F. Hollister, substituted for the shears previously used, the cutting apparatus as improved by Rugg, as before stated. Several Hussey machines were in the neighborhood and McCormick's machine was soon introduced.

In Kendall County, Illinois, resided John Bullard, a Virginian acquaintance of Mr. Cyrus H. McCormick. To him in 1845 a McCormick machine was sold, which was operated by Mr. Bullard's son-in-law, George Gale, who found it seriously defective. Although Mr. Gale had had experience with that machine he could not recommend its cutting apparatus, but, being a good mechanic, was engaged by Mr. Hollister and Mr. Steward to aid in reconstructing the shear-like cutting apparatus of the ten foot machine of which I have spoken. He had before helped in applying the shears to the rebuilt machine and knew of their defects, and later helped apply those Mr. Rugg was then applying to various other machines. The sections were cut from old hand saws, gathered by traveling many miles horseback over the thinly settled country, and, after being substituted for the shears previously used.

For this harvest of 1847 one hundred McCormick reaping machines were manufactured by Gray & Warner, presumably of Chicago, forty of which were made for D. I. Townsend, of Kendall County, Illinois. Mr. Townsend had contracted for two hundred reapers if orders could be obtained for them, but the orders were far short of his estimate. Later Mr. Townsend manufactured a few at his country shop, near Oswego, Ill.

In 1850 Mr. McCormick tested the Hussey-Rugg cutting apparatus, and to that device, more than to anything else, can be credited his success, such as it was, in England, during the great Exhibition one year later. Injustice was done by Woodcroft, to both Hussey and Rugg, by accrediting McCormick with the invention thereof.

in his "Specifications of English Patents." While Mr. Rugg's application for a patent was pending in the United States Patent Office something occurred, perhaps a remonstrance, which required the taking of testimony in behalf of McCormick. The contestants brought out the fact that Rugg's cutting apparatus was fully adopted by McCormick in 1851.

Editor's Note: The theme of Self-Raking Reapers is taken up again in more detail in Chapter XI. Mr. Steward evidently thought this foreword on the subject necessary to an understanding of his review of the 1847 patent from the standpoint of a patent expert, which immediately follows.

CHAPTER X.

Expert Review of the 1847 Patent.

Of the many manufacturers of reapers John H. Manny, a western inventor, and his associates stood at the head to numbers of machines made and sold, and their efficiency. In the suit brought by McCormick against his Company Manny made a successful defense, and he was also one of the contestants at the time McCormick attempted to have his 1847 patent extended, of which attempt this chapter treats.

The petition for extension applied mainly to reissue No. 816, only one of the ten in number to which the patent of 1847 had been expanded. I first consider the claim of the patent from an expert and judicial point of view, in order to determine the new element, if any, that lent patentability; the claim purports to cover an *"arrangement"* of cutting apparatus and reel *"with respect to"* a driving wheel and grain wheel (or their equivalents) and a raker's seat (or its equivalent) for a certain specified purpose. Thus reduced to its simplest terms this whole matter seems to be too simple, in fact, to rise to the dignity of invention. All of the elements are old in the art. All but the raker's seat or stand are found in his 1834 and 1845 patents and all in Hussey's and Randall's machines. The claim of this reissue very properly presupposes a raker's seat or stand as well as all other elements mentioned, as being in existence. It does not even hint that the patentee was first to locate the seat or stand at the rear part of the machine, nor does it hint that he claimed to be first to make use of a "grain wheel" for supporting the grain end of the cutting apparatus. At this time what was left for him to do? Simply to "arrange" something so that he could apply the seat or stand and not have a preponderance of weight (that of the raker in his place) behind the axis of oscillation; that is, behind a line drawn from

194

the axle of one supporting wheel to that of the other. Now, what *did* he do? He moved the grain wheel backward; that is, he swung the grain end of the line of oscillation backward. (His rearrangement of gearing has to do with one of the reissues and is not to be considered in this. Each patent must stand on its own terms.) The claim in reissue No. 819, however, purports to be for a *combination* of elements, and not, as R. 816, merely an *arrangement*. It seems to accord, in terms, with the position taken by the attorneys for McCormick in the Manny infringement suit. The new element, in *this* claim, appears to be the seat or stand, but we find merely the elements combined "in such a manner" that the desired end can be accomplished "substantially as described." Clearly this claim also could be held only as a group of mechanical elements associated in "such a manner" (that is, so arranged) not as to accomplish a result, but to *permit* some specific thing to be done; that is, to permit the raker to ride at his work. After all, the grouping of the elements being old, broadly considered, again we may say that no other construction than that of *arrangement* can be given to this claim.

Is there here sufficiency of invention to sustain a patent? The seat or stand had been used by Hussey for twelve years, and by Randall for eleven years.

In the McCormick 1847 extension case, William S. McCormick, applicant's brother, swore as follows: "As a farmer, I used the reapers without a seat, before a good one was invented, and am perfectly certain it was so nearly worthless, that a machine without one could not be sold at any price that would pay, in competition with one having a raker's seat; this is my experience from my intimate connection with the business for many years." (Quoted from Commissioner Holt's decision January 28, 1859.)

We cannot see why the claim was allowed by the Commissioner of Patents unless the words "substantially as described" were intended to have the meaning in this claim as in all others where the phrase is found. The raker stood on the end of the finger beams, or he could sit astride of a narrow plank that projected rearwardly from its supports and rest his feet on the end of the finger beam. What else but this specific arrangement differentiated from the prior art? If this *alleged* combination is not to be construed as a specific arrangement, that is, the associated parts arranged in *"such a manner,"* the claim should never have been allowed. Construed as a *combination* it must fall, as there is no co-operation of the elements grouped. As a matter of fact the elements, in the sense of patent law, are merely *aggregated,* the seat being but an inert part. It is not the seat that co-operates with the reel and divider, making them efficient by the gaveling and removal of the accumulation of grain, in order that they may continue to operate; that is done by the man, whether sitting on the seat or walking behind the machine.

Aggregations are but the result of judgment, and hence not patentable; but combinations, that is groups of mechanical elements in which one or more gives the others added functions, greater efficiency or new functions, may be the result of the action of the inventive faculty, and hence patentable; that is the law. What McCormick invented, if anything, was made clear in the original patent, namely: the rearrangement of the gearing of his earlier machines, so as to place enough weight in front of the main wheel to counterbalance the weight of the raker, when supported behind, as set forth in R. 817. This fact was ignored by the attorneys who prepared the other reissue applications, and it seems clear that the other reissues would not have been allowed had not the words "constructions" and "arrangements" been considered limiting terms. The courts have construed these words as limitations, precisely as the Patent Office no doubt intended. The claims are weak and probably would not have stood the tests, had the courts found them infringed, and, in turn, considered them on their merits.

The seat was applied to the machine at Cincinnati, where the father and Leander were aiding Brown and Magness in building the 100 machines contracted for. ("Memorial of Robert McCormick," by Leander J. McCormick.)

It is not clear who invented the seat and who located it. The author of the Memorial told the writer that he suggested the addition of the seat or stand, and Mrs. Leander McCormick at the same time mentioned the fact that her husband wrote her to that effect, while he was at Cincinnati. In the case made out by the contestants against the extension of the reissued patents it was shown that the seat was applied at the suggestion of some workman, one of whom Leander was, or other person, and not by Cyrus McCormick. Brown, in answer to Q. 9, says: that the seat was applied by "consent" of himself and Mr. McCormick, but, referring to the latter, added that "His remarks generally showed that he hadn't much confidence in having a seat." In answer to Q. 16, witness said: "The suggestion to put a seat on I understood at the time, came from some of the workmen." In answer to X. Q. 4 he says: "I do not recollect what his first remarks were upon that subject. I do not recollect that he did not at first approve of the idea of a seat." X. Q. 17 brought out the fact that the witness had testified in the McCormick vs. Seymour & Morgan case and had said that he recollected that when the subject of a seat was talked of between him and McCormick, of asking the latter whether it had been tried, "that his answer was that he had tried it sufficiently to know that it would be useful." The words that he had tried it *sufficiently* to know that it *would be useful,* harmonize with the efforts of Hite, who, in 1842, had brought a machine made by the McCormick family in Virginia and had attached a small truck with seat thereon behind the machine, on which the raker might ride, and so used it. (Statement of Isaac Irvine Hite in "Overlooked Reaper History", p. 16.)

From the testimony of Magness we gather that he contracted with A. C. Brown to build, wholly or in part, McCormick's machines, a sample of which was furnished, having no provision thereon for a raker's seat or stand. "It was put on at my shop, but I can't tell who was the projector of it, but whether it was McCormick, his father, myself, or one of my hands, I can't tell." "I recollect of his objecting to a seat, but whether it was the position or the construction I don't now recollect." I quote further from this witness for contestants: "Q. 13. Look at Exhibit A, hereto attached, and state how far the diagrams represent the seat for the raker, as to construction and position, which you first put upon the McCormick machine?" A. "The position of this is about the same, but the construction is nothing like it. There was no cross piece on the seat that I put upon the McCormick machine; it was a plain board—had not the crosspiece to it. There is a drawing of two there." Asked about the seat shown in the other drawing, he replies: "I have seen one—one I built myself. It was the first one I ever saw it on. It was in the same position on the machine as that of McCormick's, and in the construction it wasn't so long or wide as McCormick's, and had a crosspiece." The raker sat "a-straddle of the seat behind the crosspiece. He could sit or stand—the crosspiece merely kept him from falling." "I don't know as anybody suggested it to me, but the nature of the seat would suggest it to anybody; for sitting a-straddle of a board riding backwards, he would be apt to fall off."

(It was also brought out in cross examination that the witness had testified in the McCormick vs. Seymour & Morgan case that a sample machine was furnished for him, Magness, to work from; that he did not then recollect whether the sample machine furnished by McCormick had a seat on it or not; that there was a seat belonging to it; and whether it was actually attached to it at the time, he did not remember.) In the answer from which the facts are taken the witness, in effect, replies that he does not remember that the machine, in certain details, was constructed thus and so. The cross examination failed to bring out any contradiction as to the sample machine brought to Cincinnati having no seat; and, clearly, throughout the record there is found no corroboration of McCormick's claim that he invented the seat. After having built and sold over a hundred reapers, and having been in various contests with Hussey, on every one of whose machines a raker had ridden, very naturally he thought a raker's seat would be "useful." (See statement of W. S. McCormick, page 176.) McCormick's trouble was that his earlier reapers were already so heavy behind the axis of support that to place a raker in position relative to the grain receiving platform, as Hussey and Randall had placed workmen, would have disturbed the poise of the machine. Evidently he had come to see the folly of strapping the draft-tongue to the horses' backs, as shown in his 1834 patent; with that machine he might have used a raker's stand. We learn that the machines of 1849, and for many years after, had the gearing in substantially the old position, and a seat for the driver, where Randall had placed it, in front of the supporting wheels, as shown.

In short, having taken the driver from the saddle, and placed him in position on the machine, in front, and thus counterpoised the weight of the raker, he retained his old system of gearing.

The applications for extension of the reissues were contested by Manny and others (as in the case of the 1834 patent, by Hussey), for the plain reason that the patent might be used unfairly against them; as, in fact, the earlier McCormick reissues of the original 1847 patent had been used against Manny, one of Hussey's licensees, which necessitated great expense in defending. McCormick's application for extensions was accompanied by a sworn statement, as required, but by no means a clear one. Now, what a man purposes to prove is one thing, but what later he actually proves is often quite another matter. Such was true in this case. He did not appear as a witness in his own behalf, and thus substantiate his formal statement; hence, as in the former case, the contestants were given no opportunity to question him as to his *alleged* facts. Why did he hold aloof? In so far as his mere statement was not corroborated it fell flat, as it was not proof; but we cannot dispute that it was a confession of the weak effect upon the public, of his alleged valuable inventions. A few points may be quoted: His inventions, claimed to have been made during the previous fourteen years, "were brought to such a state of maturity in the year 1845 as gave *promise* to the *complete success** which has since been realized." Realized, that is, by the addition of a raker's seat, and that only, thus bringing his machine nearly up to the other half dozen, or more, machines with which he had to compete. Referring to his improvements, as patented, in 1847, he says: "He retained counsel to draw his specifications," and that his counsel suggested that he go to the Patent Office to aid in procuring his patent. His capital being inadequate, he could not manufacture in sufficient quantities to introduce into general use. (The machine itself, it seems, did not appeal to the public.) "No responsible parties would make an adequate number of machines to supply the market, and pay this applicant a reasonable license fee thereon; none would make any considerable number of machines, unless payment therefore, independent of the possession and control of the machines and of the proceeds of their sale, could furnish to them, either in the form of contract for the purchase of machines when completed by responsible farmers, or personal or other security." This last quoted paragraph is a little confused, but the intended meaning seems clear. The former "security he could not give, and contracts for machines were difficult to obtain, as it involved a personal visit to the farmer, and such an explanation of the practical advantages of using the machine embracing the aforesaid patented improvements as would induce him to sign a contract for the purchase of a machine

* And yet his descendants claim that the alleged machine of 1831 was a complete success.

on the delivery to him before the harvest." This does not say that
farmers could not be induced to buy *reapers,* but that reapers with
his "improvements" did not find ready sale. The statement that he
could not give security may be true, and if true it sheds a light by
means of which we may plainly see that the inventions were not so
promising as to induce his father to aid him or others to back him
to any great extent; the father was at Cincinnati during the building
of the machines there, as well as to have constructed, or helped construct, the machines made in Virginia from 1840 to 1845. Where
Cyrus got the capital necessary to build the machines for the harvest
of 1846 he does not say, but we recall that his father, who died in
1846, left considerable property, and it seems likely he advanced
the amount required. That he was an interested party is shown by
the fact that he willed much more to his other children than to
Cyrus, and that to some of them he devised "royalties" due him on
a certain number of reapers. No licenses seem as yet to have been
granted to outsiders. As Leander McCormick and others say, in
the "Memorial of Robert McCormick," the father was the true inventor of the first machine, and, I add, possibly of the second, also.
Hence it may well be that under some agreement, verbal or otherwise, he was to receive a royalty in consideration therefor; or, if
such were not the case, he may have been entitled to a certain amount
per machine for money advanced.

No details are given of 1847 but of 1848 Mr. McCormick says:
"He succeeded at length, in associating capitalists with himself,
jointly, with whom he established a manufactory of his improved
reaping machine, at Chicago" * * "on the borders of the great prairies
of the West," where Hussey, Esterly, those who followed Schnebley,
and others had been for many years.

The applicant for the extension says, "it was not until the year
1850, after the original associates of this applicant had withdrawn,
that the factory was successfully established on a permanent basis."
Leander, his brother, had helped in the building of the machines in
1845-1846, and both he and William S., another brother, became
associated with Cyrus in 1850. The latter "had a special talent for
finance and general organization and management of a business of
the kind," while Leander "had equal talent for organizing and carrying on the mechanical department of the business; and these brothers

have had the chief management of the establishment ever since, and have conducted it with such integrity and efficiency as to leave this applicant at liberty to bestow the greater portion of his time upon the improvement of the machine and its introduction into general use, and to the management of his patents." Although devoting much time to his patents he failed to sell them, or to grant exclusive territorial rights, and so concluded to enlarge his business of making and selling under his monopoly, such as it was; but as will hereinafter be explained, "other manufacturers at once seized upon *his* inventions and manufactured and sold them in competition with him, in every market in spite of every effort he could make to restrain them, with a single unimportant exception." In view of the fact that, in 1847, so many had long been building reapers, in little and large factories about the country (three little shops were located within ten miles of the author's home in Illinois), and that the applicant claimed, as his descendants now claim, "that he was the inventor of the reaper," how does the following confession strike the reader? "Prior to the application to the reaping machine of the improvements of 1847 the machine had not been found capable of general use for the purpose of harvesting grain, and consequently grain was then as generally harvested by hand with the scythe, as it is now by horse power with the reaping machine." This alleged inventor of the reaping machine goes on to say that, "from the year 1831 until the addition of the said improvements to his machine, he had been endeavoring to introduce into regions peculiarly adapted to the use of reaping machines * * * the best and most perfect reaping machine that had been made; but he found that the machine, for want of said improvements, soon fell into disuse."

He patented the improvements, and in his statement further says that infringers "proceeded to manufacture it (his reaper) without his authority, and against his will, and competed with him in its sale all over the country." Let it be recollected that he had employed an attorney to draw his application for his 1847 patent, and that counsel recommended that he bring suit for infringement; still, that he failed in his attempt "to restrain them by injunction." McCormick brought suit in 1850 against Seymour & Morgan, and tells us that "the validity of the patent was, however, affirmed by the Supreme Court." (See McCormick vs. Seymour & Morgan, 16

Howard.) But, he continues, it was learned, during the proceeding that "the specification of the original patent was so defective that it would not cover and protect applicant's invention unless amended pursuant to the act of Congress." In 1853, "under the advice and with the aid of eminent counsel," the patent was reissued, "and the validity of the reissued patent was sustained by Judge Nelson, in a proceeding in equity, against Seymour & Morgan."

"By advice of counsel" suits were instituted against John H. Manny and others, but in the suits "the defendants availed themselves of the defects still found to exist in the claim of applicant's patent, notwithstanding the amendments." Although he had employed "eminent counsel," in obtaining his reissue, he surrendered this reissue and, in December, 1858, was granted another reissue. "At length," McCormick goes on to say, "on the 20th of September, 1859, under the advice of counsel * * * the patent was again surrendered, and separate patents, with amended specifications and claims were taken out for the several inventions comprehended in and intended to be secured by his original patent of 1847." The reissue, in *ten* divisions, of the 1858 reissue of the reissue of 1853 of the original patent of 1847, shows to what extent McCormick succeeded with the Patent Office, only to fail in the courts.

Again I quote: "In order to keep pace with competition in the manufacture of reaping machines, and to derive any benefit from his invention, he was compelled to be unremitting in his efforts to improve his machine." That is precisely what his competitors had been doing for many years, and patenting their improvements, as the records of the Patent Office amply show.

"He has, at the expense of much thought, time, and money, added many other important improvements to it since 1847, which have contributed to the profits of his manufacture." "Among such improvements by others as he has had to pay for, are the inventions of his brothers, of Obed Hussey, of Jonathan Read, of Henry Green, of Solymon Bell and of Joseph Nesen." (It will be remembered that he acquired rights from Hussey only at the end of a suit for infringement.) It is but fair to suppose that the patents he bought, and those under which he took licenses were valid and covered many of the improvements he found it necessary to adopt in order to make his machine as good as others. (In later years, however, he and his successors bought patents to use in attacking competitors, and so used them for what they might earn or for purposes they might serve in suppressing competition; for instance, patents granted to Gorham, Locke, LeValley, Spaulding, Sevard, Greenhut, &c.)   He tells us that as all the improvements he bought "enter into and form a part of the value of the machine as it has been made, sold, and used, it is evident that the value of the inventions specified in the patents now asked to be extended cannot be measured by the amount of receipts and profits derived from the manufacture, license and sale of the entire machine."

With the patents of 1834 and 1845 before us let us now take up other of the reissues and examine them in the light of patent law.

R. 816 we have already taken up.

R. 817: It is not plain what the gist of the claim is. Suffice it to say that it is limited to the specific placement of the gearing, which, if McCormick ever used, he at once abandoned.

R. 818 covers merely the specific form of seat or stand. The part on which he might stand, the end of the finger bar, was already on the machine, hence it is only the seat portion that was added.

Seats for all imaginable purposes had been made, from single legged milking stools to the thrones of kings. The reader can judge whether any great effort of the brain was required to conceive and perfect this one.

R. 819 covers practically nothing; its assumed elements of a mechanical combination form, in fact, but an aggregation, as already shown.

R. 820 is limited to the specific placement of the gearing.

R. 821 covers but an *"arrangement"* of parts. The difference between the arrangement in the machine of this patent and like parts in the 1845 machine is not clear, unless it is the placement of the outer reel support more rearward than that of 1845, and still more rearward than that of 1834, mere matters of degree. (He finally got it fully out of the way as Bell and Randall had.)

R. 822. It is not clear that there was patentable differences between the devices of this claim and the similar parts found on Randall's machine, which was not patented.

R. 823. The inclined dividing board and the guide here appear to be the new elements, but nevertheless we find all in the 1845 patent and in Randall's machine.

R. 824. This patent covers a frame "consisting of two principal beams crossing each other and arranged relatively to the supporting wheels," &c.

R. 825. The new element is found in the claim; it covers but an alleged new *arrangement* of old parts. The claim is also limited to the placement of the gearing.

Unfortunately for the inventor, the value of his inventions must be recognized by the public or established by the courts. The courts held that competing manufacturers did not take from McCormick what they required, but went to the prior art, or invented what they needed. The McCormick statement says that while he had built only 32,700 reapers up to the time of his application for extension, his competitors had put out 150,000. Of the various competing machines Manny's seemed to the present writer to take the lead, and the court held that it did not infringe McCormick's patents. It is true, as McCormick states, that the courts did not declare his patent invalid. A patent on a milk stool may be valid, but the stool may be of so little value as to not be accepted by the public, and hence the patent not be infringed. Such was the fate of McCormick's patents. The principal claim, in which the raker's stand or seat formed an element, was the bone of contention in the Manny case, and Justice Grier, in his decision said: "The true construction of the claim, and the only one which will support its validity, is to treat it as a claim for the combination of the reel with a seat *arranged* and *located* as described; without this construction the claim is neither patentable or original." This merely refers to an old combination of parts rearranged.

McCormick's raker's stand was at the end of the platform, following the generic idea embodied in Hussey's and Randall's machines, while Manny's was at the rear of the platform, as was that of the reaper of the type followed by Woodward and embodied in the reaper rebuilt by Steward and Hollister in 1843, which, as stated, McCormick had seen in operation on the Steward farm. If it was his judgment alone, held by the court to be erroneous, that prompted the bringing of suit, the alleged infringing devices being so very different from his, then we need not wonder at his assertions that all reapers follow the principles found in his reaper. If he merely followed the advice of counsel, a glance at the facts will show that he was easily misled, or that the *true merits* of the case were considered by him of little moment.

S. S. Fisher was counsel for contestants and presented his view of the matter to the Commissioner of Patents very clearly, and the latter, in his decision, is shown to have fully concurred. I quote from Mr. Fisher's argument:

"The claims of these ten reissues are set out in full in the statement filed by the applicant, and need not be repeated here. They are all for combinations, and in one or more of them are found all of the following elements, viz.:

> Cutting apparatus.
> Reel.
> Driving wheel.
> Grain wheel.
> Raker's seat or stand.
> Tongue.
> Gearing at the side of the machine.
> Short Platform.
> Divider.
> Compressors.
> Grain-guarded platform.
> Reel-support.
> Low flat frame.
> Cross-beams for frame.
> Finger-beam, and
> Guide-bar.

"Of these elements, which are all that go to make up the thirteen combinations patented in these ten reissues, the driving wheel, grain wheel, tongue, frame supported by beams, finger beam, and cutting apparatus, are common to all reaping machines, old and new, and were found in Cummin's, Salmon's, Ogle's, and Phillips' English machines from 1807 to 1841, and in Woodward's, Randall's, Hite's, Schnebley's, Hussey's, Read's, and McCormick's American patents from 1833 to 1844.

"The reel is found in Bell's machine, 1826; Schnebley's, 1842; Read's, 1842; Randall's, 1837; Church's, 1841; Duncan's, 1840; McCormick's, of 1834 and 1845, and others.

"The raker's seat or stand is found in Read's machine of 1842; Hussey's, 1833; Randall's, 1837; Schnebley's, 1833; Hite's, 1844; Woodward's, 1843; Foster's, 1846, and others.

"Side-draught—Found in Gladstone's, Scott's English machines; Randall's, Schnebley's, Hussey's, Read's, Cook's of 1846, and many other American machines, in which both draught and gearing are at the side, and the same side of the machine.

"Short Platform—By which is understood a platform no longer than the cutter. Found in Henneman's rejected application of 1842; Heman Field's rejected application, filed April 1, 1847; Foster's machine of 1846; Cook's, 1846; Schnebley's and others.

"Divider—Found in Moore & Hascall's machine, 1836; Read's, Hussey's, McCormick's, of 1845; Randall's, Schnebley's, Henneman's rejected application of 1842, and others.

"Compressors—Found in Foster's machine of 1846; Cook's, of 1846; McCormick's, of 1845; Lamb's of 1840; Read's, of 1842; Ketchum's, of 1846, and others.

"Grain-guarded platform—Found in Randall's machine of 1837; A. J. Cook's, of 1846; Henneman's rejected application of 1842; Heman Field's rejected application, filed April 1st, 1847, and many others.

"Low, flat frame—Found in Hussey's machine of 1833; Randall's, of 1837; McCormick's, of 1845, and others.

"Side-delivery—Found in Foster's machine of 1846; Field's, April 1, 1847; Randall's, Schnebley's, and others.

"Reel support—Found in Schnebley's machine, Moore & Hascall's, Read's Church's, Phillips' (English) 1841; McCormick's, of 1834 and 1845; Randall's, and others.

"Thus it will be seen that every single element of McCormick's present reissues is found again and again in other machines, in successful operation before his discovery. And, by looking over the foregoing list, it will be seen that many of them were found in mutual combination upon the same machine.

"Let us now examine the manner in which they are grouped in the claims of McCormick's ten reissues.

"The cutting apparatus and finger beam are found in the claims of reissues No. 816 and 825.

"The reel is found in the claims of reissues No. 816, 817, 819, 820, 821, and 823.

"The driving-wheel is found in the claims of reissues No. 816, 817, 824, and 825.

"The grain-wheel is found in the claims of reissues No. 816 and 824.

"The raker's seat is found in the claims of reissues No. 816, 817, 818, and 819.

"The Tongue is found in the claims of reissues No. 817 and 820.

"The side-gearing is found in the claims of reissues No. 817, 820, 824, and 825.

"The short grain-guarded platform is found in the claims of reissues No. 817, 820, 821, 824, and 825.

"The divider is found in the claims of reissues No. 819, 821, and 823.

"The compressors are found in the claim of reissue No. 820.

"The reel supports are found in the claim of reissue No. 822.

"The low flat frame is found in the claims of reissues No. 822 and 825.

"The cross beams are found in the claims of reissue No. 824 and

"The guide bar is found in the claims of reissue No. 823,

"In the order of the reissues, this grouping is arranged as follows:

"Reissue 816.

"Combination of cutting apparatus, reel, driving wheel, grain wheel, and raker's seat or stand.

"The same elements are combined, though not arranged in the same manner in relation to each other, in the machines of Read, Randall, Hite, Schnebley, Foster, and others.

"Reissue 817.

"Combination of tongue, driving wheel, and side gearing, short platform, reel and raker's seat or stand.

"All of these elements, though not arranged in the same manner, are found in Schnebley's machine, and most of them in the others above referred to.

"Reissue 818.

"A seat or stand for the support of the raker laterally and in front.

"The raker was supported laterally and in front by the seat on Hite's machine, though the support was not afforded in the same manner as by McCormick's; the Hite seat more closely resembling, as to the manner of its support, the supports for the raker on the iron harvester, Seymour and Morgan, and Hite's machines.

"Reissue 819.

"Combination of reel, divider, raker's seat or stand, and platform.

"These are precisely the same elements as are combined upon the Randall and Schnebley machines, where they are arranged in a manner very nearly resembling that adopted by McCormick. The same combination was found on Hussey's machine after he put a reel upon it.

"Reissue 820.

"Combination of side draught and gearing, two compressors, short reel, and short platform.

"The same elements are found combined on the Schnebley and Field machines.

"Reissue 821.

"Combination of grain-guarded platform, divider, and reel.

"This combination is found in Randall's machine, where it is difficult to distinguish it from McCormick's, also in Cook's and Field's machines.

"Reissue 822.

"Combination of reel support in rear of platform, with low flat frame and divider.

"The same elements are found in combination on Phillips' English, and Randall's American machines.

"Reissue 823.

"1. Combination of inclined dividing board, cutter, and platform.
"2. Combination of inclined dividing board with guide bar.
"3. Combination of reel with inclined dividing board.
"4. Combination of reel, dividing board, and guide bar.

"Reissue 824.

"Frame of two cross-beams.

"This patent may be new, for aught we know and as McCormick has himself abandoned it, (see testimony of Henry B. Renwick, direct question,) it may perhaps be conceded by both sides, that the invention herein set forth was not used before the date of the patent, nor since.

"Reissue 825.

"Combination of frame, finger-beam, platform, driving wheel, and gearing.

"These elements are all old, and may be found in combination in many of the machines named above, especially in those of Foster, 1846, and of Field, April 1, 1847."

* * * * * * *

"From the foregoing considerations it would appear that McCormick's merit as an inventor, under his patents of 1847, consists in his having had the wit, when he found a good thing upon the machines of others, to put it upon his own reaper, and then claim it in combination with its surroundings. He took the children of others, put them into his own nursery, bestowed upon them the family name of 'McCormick,' and claimed the couples, quartettes, and groups thus formed as his own offspring."

Mr. Griffin, one of McCormick's witnesses, on January 25th, 1861, stated that there were about three hundred and fifty manufacturers of reapers, in the United States, yet McCormick was not able, with his great array of legal talent, to convince the courts that any one of his inventions had been pirated, except possibly by Seymour & Morgan, who had built machines for him, under a contract, and later in their own interest, using some of his devices, which were, however, soon abandoned.

Mr. Fisher continues:

"He tells us (State, page 28) that 'it has been ascertained, by agents sent expressly to make inquiries on the subject, and by personal observation by the patentee himself, that more than nine-tenths of all the reaping machines that have been made and sold during the lifetime of this patent have embraced either all or most of the improvements described and specified in said patents.' Agents sent expressly to ascertain this astounding fact, and who, he says, did ascertain it, and yet not one of them called to the stand to testify!"

Mr. Fisher closes as follows:

"The enunciation of the doctrine that if the patent be infringed, if the exclusive possession be interrupted 'but for a single year,' the public are bound to pay for it by an extension, would render extensions universal; for how many patents are there which have not been at some time infringed? If the principle is worth anything, it is capable of universal application, and hereafter the applicant will only need to invite or connive, or wink at, infringements to render his right to an extension indisputable. Well might this patentee ask for some rule by which his patent could be extended, be his profits 'small or great'; for nothing is clearer, than that with a machine whose day has gone by, which is being rapidly superseded, he has collected from a generous public and now holds in his coffers over two millions of dollars. He has enjoyed his day of triumph and of profit. Let him stand aside, and remove the shadow of his gigantic monopoly from the path of other men, who, with less capital but more skill, have invented and would use improvements more adapted to the march of mind and matter, and better suited to the present wants of those who till the soil."

Looking over patent history, it is clear that extensions were sometimes obtained by unfair means. Judging from the Commissioner's decisions, the grounds upon which applications were founded were not always made clear, leaving the courses followed by applicants not above suspicion. Although not strictly in its chronological order, I quote from Commissioner Holt's decision, dated January 28, 1859, in the matter of the application of Mr. McCormick for an extension of his 1845 patent, reissued August 3, 1858. After citing the machines used by the Gauls, as referred to by Pliny, during the first century of the Christian Era and later by Palladius, he states that "It was not until towards the close of the last century, that the inventive genius of the world seems to have been again directed to this agricultural implement." Referring to the report of the Examiner, the Commissioner continues:

"It is manifest, from the very lucid and elaborate report of the Examiner in this case, that at and before the date of the applicant's invention in 1845, the reaping machine already comprised, in varying combinations, all of those fundamental elements which at present enter into its composition. To enumerate, it contained the frame to support the working parts; two wheels for carrying the frame and operating machinery; a platform to receive and carry the grain until raked off by a raker seated on the machine or walking at its side; shafts to draw the machine, arranged at the side of the frame and cutter; the vibrating straight cutter; driving the gearing by the wheels that carry the machine; the spear-head guard-fingers; a crank and pitman for communicating the reciprocating motion to the cutter; reel-posts or supports; the arrangement of the outer reel-post behind the cutter and bent forward; the reel; means for adjusting the height of the reel in its supports; an arrangement for regulating the height of the cutter; the lateral arrangement of the platform to and behind the driving-wheel, for enabling the raker to remove the grain at the side; the arrangement of the outer wheel for supporting and balancing the machine; the combination of a vibrating serrated cutter with guard-fingers; the blade case; the divider, and the raker's seat. The Examiner, from whose report this enumeration has been extracted, designates the several patented inventions in which these component parts of the reaper appear; and this review of the then actual condition of the machine is essential to a correct appreciation of the character and extent of applicant's invention of 1845, not under consideration. The operation of the several parts thus named had proved more or less satisfactory, according to the combinations in which they were found. It seems to have been the purpose of the applicant to improve the efficiency of the functions performed by the divider and reel in separating the grain to be cut from that left standing. This appears not to have been perfectly accomplished before, especially when the grain was lodged or tangled; and if we are to judge from the suggestions of counsel, the special aim of the applicant was to remedy this defect. If so, it is very clear from the testimony that he has failed. There are several witnesses, practical farmers, who used the machine as constructed under the patent of 1845, and who declare that in lodged or tangled grain it was wholly inefficient, unless the grain chanced to lean towards it; that the reel was constantly stopping; and that the machine would not cut the grain, but would run over it. This divider, within the limits of its own narrow track of twelve inches, certainly lifted and parted the fallen grain, and thus secured the uninterrupted progress of the machine; but the same result had been effected—possibly under peculiar circumstances, not quite so well—by other and well-known dividers, among which may be specially named that of the applicant, as appearing in his patent of 1834. For the broad pathway of the cutter, having a width of five or six feet, no provision was made by the invention of 1845 for lodged or tangled grain, beyond the pre-existing imperfect instrumentality of the reel.

"The applicant's invention of 1845, as set forth in his reissued patent of 1858, consists of two points:

"1st. The curvature of the bearers supporting the cutter apparatus, which, it is insisted, will facilitate the discharge of any clogging matter that may enter. It is presumed that this improvement upon the straight bearer formerly in use has a measure of utility; but as it has not attracted the special attention of the witnesses or counsel, it will be dismissed without further comment.

"2d. 'The employment of the projecting ends of the reel-ribs to effect the separation of the grain to be cut from that to be left standing, in combination with a dividing apparatus, which effects a division of the grain by forming an open space between the outer and inner grain for the ends of the ribs of the reel to act in, in which open space there is no reel-post or other obstruction to prevent the free passage of the grain as it is brought back by the ends of the reel-ribs to the platform of the machine, and by which means a separation of the inside grain to be cut from the outside grain to be left standing is made complete by the action and power of the reel.' The 'dividing apparatus' referred to consists of a device substantially the same with that previously in use, with this exception that a crooked iron rod is employed to secure the same divergence on the inner side, which had been previously effected by the inclined edge of the well known wedge-shaped divider. It probably secured but little, if any, greater divergence than the old device, nor could this have been done without resulting in throwing so much grain between the first pair of fingers of the cutter as to choke it at that point. This feature of the divider was, however, new in form, and presented a further marked trait of novelty in its adjustability as to height, by means of a slot and screw-bolt. The invention of 1845 consists, then, in the curvature of the bearers and the combination of this precise form of divider just described, with the projecting ends of the reel-ribs, for the purpose of separating the grain. The patentability of this improvement having been recognized by this office and the Supreme Court, it will be treated in this discussion as a settled question."

Here we find the inventions covered by the 1845 patent well considered and limited to specific devices, which devices have never been used by the public and but little by McCormick himself. Mr. McCormick accompanies his petition by a statement, which seems not to have been clear, and the Commissioner remarks accordingly:

"The statute, in requiring the patentee to make a true and faithful exhibit of his receipts and expenditures, clearly intended that his account should assume such a form as would enable the public to investigate it and contest its accuracy, if inclined to do so; such a form too as would place it in the power of the Commissioner to pronounce upon its intrinsic legality, and apply the testimony offered for and against it. Some relaxation of the rigor with which certainty is exacted in all accounts that propose to become the basis of judicial action, has been recognized as proper in behalf of inventors because of their peculiar character. The utmost relaxation, however, of the rule could not sanction a statement so utterly vague as that under consideration. The transactions covered and concealed by its ample folds are without any ear-mark or designation whatever, which could render it possible for the Commissioner or the public to examine them. It may be safely added, that the applicant is not in a condition to claim the benefit of any such relaxation of the general principle referred to, as is insisted on in his behalf. He is an inventor, it is true; but, unlike the class to which he belongs, he is also a man of remarkable business habits, who wields millions of capital, is surrounded by his agents and clerks, and keeps the records of his vast transactions with strict commercial accuracy. Had he therefore chosen to open his ledger for our inspection, it would no doubt have exhibited an account of his 'expenses for litigation,' as complete as that presented by the merchant's books of his daily purchases and sales. With such lights at hand, the applicant's pressing upon our consideration an account so obscure and darkened as this, is wholly without excuse. This item must be disallowed because of its indefinite character, and for the further and all-sufficient reason, that there is no testimony in the case showing, or tending to show, that this amount, or any part of it, was ever expended for the purpose charged."

The Commissioner continues:

"The invention of 1845, considered in itself, and examined in presence of the reaping machine as then in successful operation, both in Europe and America, can scarcely be regarded as brilliant, or in any degree extraordinary. Waiving any notice of the curvature of the bearers—which has not been deemed worthy of special comment in any quarter—we have, as a prominent feature, the inside divider taking the form of a crooked metallic rod, and performing the same function as that previously accomplished by the inclined edge of the wedge-shaped wooden divider. The substitution of such a rod for the diverging edge of the divider previously in use, was certainly within the scope of ordinary mechanical skill. The adjustability of this rod was undoubtedly a new and useful improvement; but even with this, in certain conditions of the harvest, it was inoperative. Ansel Chappel deposes that when the grain was damp or a little green, it wound around the rod and clogged the machine; that in consequence, under applicant's orders, he detached it, and directed others using it to do the same; and that applicant said to him, the machines with this rod would do well enough in dry grain, 'but that he thought they would do better in any grain to have the iron off.' So much for the position taken that this form of divider is invaluable, if not indispensable, for the successful working of a reaping machine. The outside divergence is fully shown in applicant's patent of

1834, and is a well known device, while the divergence in a vertical direction is apparent in Dobbs' patent and in Beale's improvement on Ambler's invention as patented in 1835.

"There are at least twelve patents of an earlier date than 1845, in which the reel and divider operated in combination, and in which the former aided, with a measure of success at least, in the division of the grain. Among these may be specially enumerated the applicant's patent of 1834, and Schnebley's of 1833. While the combination of the ends of the reel-ribs with the divider, as set forth in the invention of 1845, has been recognized as presenting a patentable novelty, its improvement upon the pre-existing and distinctly developed idea, is not marked or distinctly defined.

"The open space in which the ends of the reel-ribs revolve, and which is necessary to prevent the entanglement of the grain, though found in the machine as now constructed under the patent of 1845, cannot be credited to applicant. In this patent this space was obstructed by the reel-post, which has been since removed, and the horizontal arm substituted as a supporter. This substitution seems to have been first made by the witness D. T. White, and has since been adopted by the applicant. It is a device borrowed from Bell's machine patented in 1826.

"Not to pursue further the examination of the details of this invention, the question arises, what was its value as a whole? The answer on this point is distinct and uncontroverted. The machine as constructed under it was without a seat for the raker, who had to perform his task walking at its side. The applicant's brother, an intelligent practical farmer, in his deposition says, 'as a farmer, I used the reaper without a seat, before a good one was invented, and am perfectly certain it was so nearly worthless, that a machine without one could not be sold at any price that would pay, in competition with one having a raker's seat; this is my experience from my intimate connection with the business for many years.' There is nothing in the record in any manner assailing this evidence, or tending to show that the machine of 1845 had any success. Indeed it was impossible that it could have. The stoutest man could not endure the toil of following it and raking incessantly as it progressed. However well, therefore, it may have divided and cut the grain, for want of the seat it was valueless. And yet it is precisely this machine, thus practically inoperative and worthless, that on the expiration of the patent will be surrendered to the public, and no more. It is therefore for such a machine only that the public are bound to make remuneration, and it is such only that can be examined in the estimate we are now considering. It was a conviction of the inefficiency of the machine that led the applicant to make his invention of 1847, which, by a modification of pre-existing elements, provided an advantageous location for the raker's seat. Upon this his fame as an inventor rests, and to this is his reaper indebted for the triumphs it has achieved. This seat had been previously known in at least nine patented reapers;

but it had not been well placed, and an appropriate location for it was, up to 1847, an acknowledged desideratum. What, however, may have been the value or the success of the reaper as improved in 1847, such value or success can exert no influence in determining the issue under discussion."

The second machine, alleged improvement on the first, having been a failure, must we believe that the first was a success?

"It is constantly urged as a means of exalting our estimate of the invention of 1845, that a reaper is not complete without it; and it would seem to be the aim to deduce therefrom the inference that this invention should be treated as embodying the value of the whole machine. When it is remembered that Hussey's, Bell's and other reaping machines had long been in successful operation, both in Europe and America, this assumption is a proof rather of boldness than discretion on the part of those who make it. Could it, however, be maintained that this invention is indispensable to a successful reaper, still the conclusion sought to be drawn from it would by no means follow. The same thing might be said of the cutter set forth in the patent of 1845, and which was and is public property. Take it from the reaper as made under that patent, and applicant's invention, as described, would be wholly inefficient, and so of the other well known parts of the machine. Nothing can be more illogical and fallacious than to maintain that the entire value or usefulness of a machine may be properly assigned to any one of its component parts, merely because the withdrawal of such part would leave the machine imperfect. Such a doctrine virtually asserts that each spoke in the wheel may claim to embody in itself the worth of the whole, because its absence would leave such whole incomplete.

"It is alleged, in effect, that however much the invention of 1845 may be lacking in those characteristics which excite admiration and dazzle the imagination, yet that it has conferred immeasurable benefits upon the country, for which a corresponding compensation should be made. In this regard, the preparation of the case is signally and fatally defective. Of all the experts acquainted with these machines, or mechanics engaged in their manufacture, or farmers employing them in their fields, none have been called to testify either as to the intrinsic value of this invention, or as to what share it has had in the advantages which the reaper, as an entirety, has bestowed upon the public. Upon this point, so vital to the applicant's case, the record is a perfect blank. If any judgment could be formed on the subject, it would be done gropingly and in the absence of that light which the law requires that the applicant, who holds the affirmative of the issue, shall furnish. The account assures us, in sweeping terms, that 'the public has derived an immense advantage from the fact that the use of these machines has at least doubled the wheat crop in the western prairie states, whereby a gain to the whole country of not less than $100,000,000 in the term of the patent has been produced.' No data whatever are afforded which would enable us to scrutinize the process by which this conclusion has been reached. The 100 millions are set forth as the profits of 73,200 reaping machines operating in the West, of which those of the applicant constitute but a part. Yet we are furnished with no statistics, either as to the amount of land in cultivation, or the quantity or value of the grain grown, nor, as already stated, as to what part this particular invention played in producing this extraordinary result. The entire region from which this estimate is drawn, as presented to us, is one of absolute and wild conjecture, too dimly lighted to be pressed by the feet of public justice. The testimony justifies the opinion, that the wheat crop of the West has been doubled by the reaping machines there in use; but it leaves us without any means of judging as to the amount or value of that crop, or what proportion the machines made by the applicant have borne to those introduced by others and known to be in successful operation throughout the West. This item—vague, extravagant, and unsustained as it is—deserves not a moment's consideration. The account further sets forth, that the 73,200 machines claimed to have been made either by the applicant or those infringing his patent were, after reimbursing their cost, worth $500 each to the farmers using them, which exhibits an aggregate profit of $36,600,000. Of these machines, but 23,200 were manufactured and sold by the applicant; and it is not easy to perceive on what ground he can insist upon being credited with the benefits bestowed by the remaining fifty thousand. If it be upon the assumption that they were infringements upon his patent, then the law gives him ample remedy by suit against the infringers; and should he be credited in this proceeding, as demanded, his right of action would still exist, and, if pursued, might result in giving him virtually a double compensation. The testimony, however, is not such as to warrant me in pronouncing them infringements. A large part of them were made under the Manny patents, which the Supreme Court has decided are not infringements of those of the applicant. Dismissing, then, from the account these 50,000 machines, there remain 23,200, which, at $500 each, will give $11,600,000. It will be observed, that this sum is what the entire machines, including the inventions of 1845 and 1847 and all pre-existing elements, yielded to those who used them. After the enumeration which has been given of the component parts of the reaper existing prior to 1845, which were public property, and which were adopted by the applicant, it must be sufficiently manifest that his invention constituted an exceedingly small part of the machine, and that, in consequence, an exceedingly small part of this sum of $11,600,000 should be set down to the credit of his patent of 1845. The attempt on his part to exclude from the estimate those portions of the machine which had been the gradual accumulation of the intellectual toil of the preceding sixty years, is wholly unwarrantable. Without the parts thus slowly accumulated and combined, his own invention would have been as valueless as would be a shingle to him who could find no house-top on which to nail it. The construction insisted on would compel the public to pay again, and pay extravagantly, for that which is already its own, alike by purchase and by long uninterrupted possession.

"If, however, the supposition can be indulged, that the applicant is entitled to compensation for all the benefits conferred upon the public by these 23,200 machines, is not his claim one which he could compromise or abate at pleasure, and has he not done so? It was competent for him either to sell his invention or dispose of licenses for its use, or use it himself, by manufacturing and selling the machines. The public was necessarily passive, or, at least, could act only in response to his action. It would make him no remuneration, beyond what he himself prescribed or rendered practicable. He did not sell or attempt to sell the invention, and, with a few isolated exceptions, refused to grant licenses upon any terms. To those who approached him on the subject, and desired to purchase, he declined, stating that it would be more profitable for him to manufacture the machines; and this he has continued to do to the present time. Without the pressure of necessity, or of any influence that could improperly sway his judgment or feelings, he set a price upon the machines, which, with the complete knowledge he had of their cost, he was satisfied would yield him an ample remuneration. If they proved profitable to the public beyond the remuneration thus embraced in their price, is it not a fair inference that he intended generously to bestow this profit upon those who used them? This inference certainly could not arise if the public had been unwilling to buy licenses, or had not purchased the machines which he manufactured and put upon the market. The proof is clear, that neither of these conditions existed. The public sought to obtain licenses, but could not, and the machines have been bought as rapidly as made; indeed, there have been times when the supply was not equal to the demand. The public, then, has filled to the very brim the measure of compensation which the applicant demanded. It could do no more. If it is insufficient, it is undeniably his own fault, and cannot be urged in support of this application.

"The theory that each of the 23,200 machines having yielded to the public a benefit amounting to $500, a corresponding compensation should be made to the applicant, has been rendered impossible by his own action. He deliberately fixed a price upon them, which gave him a profit of about $70 on each, which being deducted from the $500 realized from it by the public, must leave that public in his debt $430 for each machine sold. The more machines therefore sold, and the longer patent should exist, the greater would be the indebtedness, and the more glaring the inadequacy of the compensation made. Assuredly this theory, in view of applicant's own course of conduct, is utterly delusive.

"In the criticism which has been necessarily made upon the invention of 1845, there has been no design to detract from the acknowledged value and usefulness of the machine, as constructed under the patent of 1847. It has had its brilliant successes in England and France, but it has also had its marked discomfitures when competing with other machines. Though enjoying a great and perhaps a still expanding popularity, it is by no means a universal favorite. Operating but indifferently upon hilly or broken ground, it is but little used east of the Alleghanies; and for exportation, Hussey's seems to be preferred. Its proudest triumphs have been achieved upon the vast level prairies of the West, on whose border the applicant resides, and it is there that it is probably destined to find the theatre of its future and permanent usefulness.

"No disposition has been felt to disparage the claims of the applicant as an inventor. He has, it is alleged, devoted twenty-seven years of his life to perfecting his inventions and introducing them into public use. For his patience, zeal, and indomitable energy, in the midst of almost life-long difficulties, and for the genius with which he has surmounted them, he has deserved, and is receiving, the warm commendation of the world. As a public benefactor, the measure of his fame is already great, and is perhaps still enlarging, while the colossal fortune in his hands is proof conclusive of the lavish liberality with which his labors have been requited. He has been so fortunate as to link his name indissolubly with a machine which, unless outstripped in the race of progress, may endure as a proud memorial, so long as the ripening grain shall wave over the boundless plains of the West, or the songs of the reaper shall be heard in its harvest-fields. Yet, were it permitted to embrace in this estimate value of the reaping machine as entirety, I might hesitate to pronounce his reward sufficient, great as it has been. But remembering, as must be done, that in 1845 it was already in practical, successful operation, and its essential elements public property, or the property of other patentees, and that its crowning excellence as constructed by the applicant—the raker's seat of 1847—still belongs to him, and can be enjoyed by the country only upon such terms as he may dictate; and confining, therefore, as I am compelled to do, my estimate to the isolated features patented in 1845, I am constrained to say that, for this improvement the public has made to the applicant not only a reasonable, but a most abounding remuneration.

"The application must therefore be rejected."

Probably the first instance of a *popular* writer, in referring to American inventors, to say McCormick was not the inventor of the reaper is found in the *New York Sun* of April 13, 1913. Referring to Cyrus Hall McCormick, that writer said: "He is commonly supposed to have invented the reaper. That supposition is wrong." But the writer goes on to say: "And yet, after all subtraction of undue credit, he stands head and shoulders above everybody else

concerned in bidding engines and machines take drudgery from the
nerves and muscles of farmers the world over." This statement is
wrong as the first quoted is right. McCormick was a large builder,
but at times was exceeded by Walter A. Wood Mowing & Reaping
Machine Co., Manny & Co., by Whitely, Fasseler & Kelley, and
several other manufacturers in agricultural lines. His conservatism,
as the following pages will show, was so great that he was always
behind; his energy, however, permitted him to make and sell large
quantities of reaping and mowing machines.

CHAPTER XI.

THE ARRIVAL OF THE SELF-RAKING REAPER.

One of the earliest conceptions, probably prompted by the action of the scythe in mowing grass, and the cradle in reaping grain, was to deliver the cut grain straws in a continuous swath. This was indifferently accomplished by Gladstone, Smith, Bailey and others in England. In the Gladstone machine a continuously moving conveying device was placed immediately above the circular cutting discs; but Salmon in 1808, not using a cutting disc, but shears arranged in a line transverse to the line of advance of the machine, found it necessary to provide supplemental means and applied an orbitally moving rake that could sweep across the platform, rise thereabove and drop at the grain end of the cutting apparatus and again sweep across the receiving platform, thus delivering the grain straws in the form of gavels. He was evidently first to gavel the grain he cut. The illustration found in Woodcroft shows a machine of very narrow width guided by a man behind, as one controls the old-style plow.

Following Salmon, in the efforts to gavel the cut grain, came Ogle, who prostrated the cut straws of grain upon a platform immediately in rear of the cutting apparatus, his reels serving to lay the straws neatly thereon. At intervals the attendant, walking behind, by means of a lever within his reach, lowered the hinged platform and thus permitted the gavels to slide rearward and be drawn off by contact with the stubble. This method was thoroughly practical and is practiced today throughout a large part of Europe, the Manual delivery attachment, previously referred to, being in part a refinement of Ogle's dropper. From 1860 to 1880 there were, in extensive use, particularly in the United States, what were known as "Droppers,"

219

following the Ogle type. This principle was so availed of by John F. Seiberling that machines embodying it became very popular, and so remained for a time. Following Ogle came Bell with his practical *side* delivery reaper, which moved the cut straws stubbleward, and permitted them to fall to the ground in a continuous swath. The Bell machines, as before shown, were long used and well satisfied the farmers of Great Britain, as the grain was permitted to lie in the swath and dry before binding. The principle of delivering the swath continuously to the ground is still followed in many countries, particularly in cutting flax. One of Bell's machines was brought to America by Yates, of the State of New York, but this method of delivering the grain was not popular, our climate being such as to dry the cut grain rapidly, and a machine that permitted gaveling was still preferred.

Hussey's machine was first on the American market both in point of time and early popularity with buyers. They were adapted to deliver the cut grain either rearward, to be bound by men stationed in different parts of the field, or delivered sideward, when necessary, to permit the gavels to remain unbound until another day because of lack of help.

A self rake, produced by Goble & Stuart, was patented November 21, 1848. In this a reel of the Ogle type was used, but one of its arms was adapted to sweep the platform and deliver the gavel immediately to the ground in the rear. On November 21, 1848, D. Cushing was awarded a patent in which is shown a reel adapted to move the gavel sufficiently far backward to place it upon an endless conveyor. This conveyor carried it further to the rear to a supplemental platform from which it could be swept laterally to the ground. This was one of the first American attempts to deliver the gavels automatically out of the way of the team in traveling round a field.

F. S. Pease in 1848 arranged a reciprocating rake beneath the surface of the receiving platform; the teeth of the rake extended upwardly and swept the gavel stubbleward from the receiving platform. This somewhat impractical type was followed by many inventors. Its advantages over a reel rake were apparent. Soon there came a type of automatic rake, in which the accumulation of grain straws were swept backward along a so-called quadrant platform and deposited in the rear of the main portion of the machine, thus leaving a path of travel for the team and machine in cutting the next swath.

March 27, 1849, a patent was granted to Jonathan Haines for a "Harvester Dropper." This machine, provided with a push tongue, was adapted to cut the grain in advance of the team. In view of the Bell, the Esterly and the Woodward machines, Haines' machine merits no attention, aside from the fact that it soon found great favor on the western prairies. The machine was adapted to cut ten or more feet in width and deliver the swath into a wagon, provided with a huge box, drawn by the side thereof, by an extra team. The custom was to have such a number of wagons and teams that an empty wagon might ever be in position to relieve a filled wagon. The machine was extensively built and known as the Haines Illinois Harvester. The general name "Header" was later applied to all machines of its class, and they are still extensively used in the West and Northwest. The conveyors, like Esterly's consisted of a slatted endless canvas. That portion which extended laterally and upwardly from the cutting apparatus was hinged to the main frame, and could be raised or lowered at will on a rope support. This part carried the swath of cut grain upwardly into the wagons.

To Aaron Palmer and S. G. Williams must be given the credit of a great and lasting improvement. Their patent is dated February 4, 1851. The machine became very popular and was built at many small towns throughout the country. To Seymour & Morgan, of Brockport, N. Y., (who by the way, manufactured machines for McCormick on a contract in 1845) must be given the credit of developing this important invention. They followed it for many years with various machines embodying automatic raking devices founded upon the same principle, but much improved by their adaptions. For many years they put out a first class machine, "The New York Self Rake." The Palmer & Williams patent was litigated and sustained. The quadrant platform, having shown its superiority, rapidly found its way into the fields, and the use of the invention will probably continue as long as reapers, as such, are made.

Owen Dorsey was one of the pioneers in arranging a *reel* which would also serve as a rake and deliver the gavel stubbleward from the quadrant platform. In order that Dorsey's reel arms might become rakes, he provided one or more of the set with teeth and adapted all to revolve upon a vertical axis near the stubble end of the platform. By means of a cam track, surrounding the axis, these arms were permitted to dip into the standing grain, just in front of the cutting apparatus, and laying the cut straws upon the platform. The toothed member of the reel then raked the grain in gavel

Dorsey's Reaping Machine.

form to the ground. It is possible that others had made the attempt before Dorsey, but Dorsey's machine became successful at once and until as late as 1900 machines of the type were used in England. They were crude, but served a fair purpose.

Thomas S. Whitenack and others followed Dorsey. Whitenack used Dorsey's general construction, but pivoted the raking arms to the vertical shaft and adapted them to operation at will. A suitable cam and guiding wheels were secured to upreaching arms on the main frame and adapted to control the action of the rakes. By the side of the machine, with its end in reach of the driver, was placed a lever having at its rear a hinged part of the cam track. By means of this lever, the reel arms were elevated after having delivered the grain

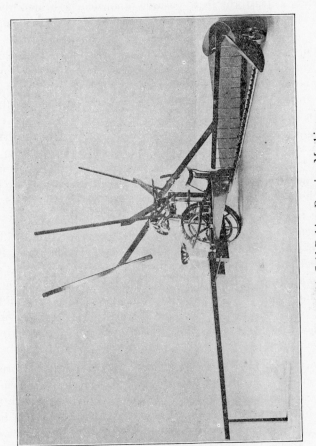

Whitenack's Self-Raking Reaping Machine.

to the platform. On the part of the cam track raised every arm became a reel. In case it was desired to rake the gavel from the platform, the movable part of the cam track was lowered, permitting any arm to work as a rake. The gavel was thus swept at will from the quadrant platform to a position immediately behind the machine. These innovations made the reel-raking reaper practical, but it was left for Samuel Johnston to put on the finishing touches. Mr. Johnston's patent, granted February 7, 1865, was a decided improvement on the Dorsey machine. The fact that the Johnston rake is now universally used is proof of the value of the improvement. In this machine each arm acted as a reel and moved through a definite orbit controlled by a cam, except when a switch was opened by the operator, when any arm became a rake. An anti-friction roller was provided for each arm which ran over the cam track with little resistance. The switch, automatically closed, could be opened at will. Later Johnston applied a regulating device by means of which the switch opened at predetermined movements of the arms.

Little time need be devoted to the reel-rake reaper, as no claims have been made for special honors and the records of the Patent Office may be depended upon as correct. As a rule, however, few of the actual finishing touches are shown in patents.

The Palmer & Williams quadrant platform rake having at once been made popular by Seymour & Morgan was adopted in different forms, William N. Whitely, later known as the "Reaper King," being one of the first to avail himself of the principle already proved to be so valuable.

Following Dorsey, efforts were made to embody in the *ordinary reel,* as used by Ogle, Bell and others, a raking device moving the grain from a quadrant platform. The only one of these which found its way into the market, however, was that produced by McClintock Young, shown in his patent of September 18, 1860. This rake, applied by Mr. Young to a McCormick reaper, operated so successfully that Mr. C. H. McCormick later took a license from Mr. Young and manufactured it until he fell into line by adopting the Dorsey rake, as improved by Johnston. McCormick reapers embodying the latter devices were made and sold in large numbers. The Young to McCormick license is before the writer. Mr. McCormick was one of the last of large manufacturers to apply to his machine self-raking mechanism. To his conservatism must be charged the fact that he was late to change and then, too, adopted a form which did not persist. This was a raking device which swept the quadrant platform at every revolution and, consequently, was uncontrollable, and soon abandoned; the Dorsey type, substantially as improved by Johnston, being adopted.

Application for the reissue of the McClintock Young patent for improvement in harvester rakes, filed by C. H. McCormick, assignee, was made May 17, 1870. Mr. Young says in his affidavit:

"I also adapted my rake to a McCormick reaper, which I purchased at second-hand for the purpose, with such success, that in July, 1861, Mr. FitzHugh and myself, as joint owners of my patent, made an arrangement with Cyrus H. McCormick, of Chicago, Illinois."

The automatic rakes were first regularly applied to the McCormick reaper for the harvest of 1862 and their use continued until after the application for the extension of the patent (Testimony of William R. Baker). The Palmer & Williams, the Seymour & Morgan, and other prominent self-raking reapers had been on the market for over ten years, and nearly all the rakes were controllable at will; and yet at that late date McCormick, forced to apply a rake to his machine, was too conservative to so modify his reaper that it could take a controllable rake. He chose to apply the ready made automatic rake of Young, which swung, uncontrollable, through its course at every revolution of the reel. The reaper has so nearly approached perfection that little improvement may be expected in that line henceforth. By controlling devices, of which there are many forms, the operator may set the machine to swath,—controlling the mechanism so that every arm will rake. Or, by the movement of a lever, the operator may adapt every other arm to rake, or, every third, or fourth, or fifth, to sweep the platform; in fact he may control the sweeping of the platform at will. If he wishes, he may prevent the action of any of the rakes until desired, say, at the corner of the field, in order that gavels may not be left in position to be trod upon by the team in traveling the next round.

The creditable efforts of those following other than the Dorsey type of self rake should be mentioned, particularly Walter A. Wood and Lewis Miller. Mr. Wood produced a machine the platform of which was provided with an endless chain moving in a continuous groove. From this chain projected upward a stem to which a rake was secured. The rake, suitably connected to the rear of the platform, was held from rotary motion, but was carried in an orbit, the rake portion sweeping the platform and delivering the gavel at the rear of the gearing frame. This movement was that of the open hand sweeping litter from a desk. No machine was more deservedly popular and stood by the farmer longer than the Wood. The traveling chain which gave movement to the rake was connected to the gearing proper by means of a clutch which, thrown into action, would permit the rake to be moved and stopped at will. By this means gavels of chosen size might be produced.

The Buckeye system of reaping and mowing machines, introduced by Aultman & Miller, became very important. These inventors as early as June 17, 1856, produced practically the doubly hinged coupling frame of mowing machine which has persisted up to the present time, and, it seems, will persist until the end of man. The cutting apparatus was adapted to float over the ground, no matter how uneven it might be. To the cutting apparatus of the Aultman & Miller machine was secured a platform to receive the grain, and at its center was a short, vertical shaft which projected above the platform, and, provided with a crank, gave movement to a rake sweeping the platform in a manner similar to that of the Walter A. Wood reaper. This shaft was suitably connected to the gearing of the main frame by means of a clutch and other necessary devices, permitting the operator to control the movement. It became very popular and persisted until the reel rake as perfected by Johnston and others took its place.

Summing up, we may say that the reaper of today follows:

Gladstone, in that the team travels at the side of the standing grain.

The cutting apparatus is that of Hussey.

To Palmer & Williams must be accredited the quadrant platform.

To Dorsey, the reel rake (broadly considered).

To Samuel Johnston, the practical form of controlling devices.

To a score of others the finishing touches which have brought the machine to its present perfect condition.

The reaper, developed by the men and in the stages mentioned, was almost exclusively used until the advent of the Marsh harvester (next to be considered), which wrought a revolution as great as that which the reaper before had accomplished.

So stands the case of the reaper proper. In view of the claims so persistently made, it is not out of place to repeat that no element nor combination of elements found therein was invented or developed by Cyrus H. McCormick.

CHAPTER XII.

THE BINDERS RIDE.

The hand rake reaper may be said to have reached the point of culmination by 1850, at which time automatic means for delivering the gavel to the ground, long suggested, had become practical.

About the same time other inventors, in their daydreams, foresaw possibilities, some of which proved of practical value. To bind grain manually while riding upon the machine, and avoid the labor of walking, as well as that of converting the gavels into sheaves, was no doubt an early thought, but the first of record is that shown and described in an application for letters patent of the United States, filed May 12, 1851, the invention of Augustus Adams and James T. Gifford, both of Elgin, Ill. The specific means whereby the desired end was sought was clearly impractical, yet the generic idea, carried out by means later devised, found embodiment in machines which wrought a revolution in harvesting methods. Through this revolution I lived and wrought, becoming familiar with its every detail.

Adams and Gifford conceived the possibility of so contriving a *reaping* machine that the men who were to bind the grain might ride thereon; their attempt, as far as I know, was the first of record. With this machine I early became familiar, as Mr. Adams was at one time a near neighbor.

I am unaware, however, to what extent Adams and Gifford carried their early ill starred experiments in this direction, but it is certain that Adams and another associate, Philo Sylla, deviated from the foundation lines of the Adams and Gifford machine to produce one shown in their patent of September 20, 1853.

Referring to the Adams and Gifford drawings, it will be observed that running gears differing little from those of an ordinary farm

228

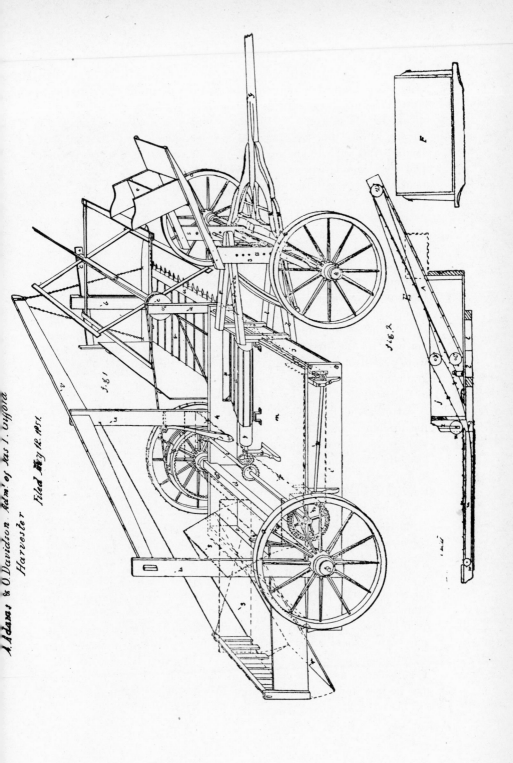

A. Adams & O. Davidson, Adm'r of Jas. J. Clifford

Harvester

Filed May 12, 1857.

Fig. 1

Fig. 2

F

wagon are adapted to support one end of the grain receiving platform. This platform extends stubbleward to the extent, presumably,
of six or seven feet. At the outer end it is supported, not by a
"grain wheel," but by a strong arm extending from the general
frame structure. In the present stage of the art it is clear enough
that the *general* structure, as revealed, is impractical, but one particular stands out. In the rear of the cutting apparatus, the latter
evidently of the Hussey kind, is an endless conveyor, upon which the
grain was intended to fall and by which it was to be moved and
elevated to such a position as to be delivered into a receptacle,
formed at the stubbleward portion of the general framework. Here
men could stand, and, it was thought, bind the grain, falling in a
continual swath at their feet. At the tail of the machine was a dumping box, into which the bundles could be placed, as completed, and
from which by a tilting movement of the bottom, they could escape to the ground in bound condition, provision having been made
not only for the driver, but for the binders to ride while doing their
work. Bell had successfully provided for the delivery of the cut
grain in the form of a continuous swath, but he passed it unbound
to the ground.

Adams and Gifford not only sought to provide for grain binding on
the machine, but, familiar with the fact that it was sometimes advantageous to merely head the grain,—that is, take the heads and
leave the straw standing,—also provided an extension to their elevator
by means of which the grain could be delivered into the box of a
wagon drawn by a team at the side of their reaping machine, thus
also doing the work of "headers."

To elevate the swath by a continuous conveyor, deliver it into a
receptacle, and dump it in gavel form to the ground, had been accomplished by Mann & Mann.

Impractical as the Mann patent proved to be, it cut a figure in
the controversy over the Marsh Harvester. The claims of the
Manns, father and son, had been voiced in the courts and the country
over, by H. F. Mann, the son, after the Marsh Harvester had won its
way. The general construction of this Mann machine is made clear
by reference to the earlier patent, No. 6540, dated January 19, 1849.
The reader is asked to consider its construction carefully in order
that he may for himself determine to what extent the actual inven-

tion of the Messrs. Mann aided the Marsh Brothers in the revolution in harvesting methods wrought by them. The Messrs. Mann provided a gearing frame supporting the usual reel and cutting apparatus, behind the latter of which was the grain receiving platform. Upon this platform moved toothed belts, carrying stubbleward the grain constantly falling upon them. All of this was old in the art. The generic idea that possessed the minds of these inventors was the production of a machine which might deliver the grain in *gavels* to the ground, to be bound by men following the reaper, as in the case of all previous reapers, as well as all reapers since made. First, they sought to have the swath of grain fall into a receptacle capable of being rotated, in order that an accumulation of the straw might be dumped, at will. The receptacle was, in fact, quadruple in form, consisting of four receptacles mounted upon a single rotary shaft (*m* of the drawing of the earlier patent). This shaft was rotated by a capstan wheel, and the four receptacles were formed by boards of thin wood, the whole being X-form in section. With the parts in the position shown in the drawing and the conveyors moving, the swath of grain could be delivered into the particular receptacle at that moment in position. Upon its becoming filled, the operator, by turning the capstan wheel, dropped the accumulation to the ground, at the same time putting a new receptacle in position. This may be considered to have been a hand-raking reaping machine, in that by manual means, only partly aided by the conveying and elevating devices, the gavel was delivered to the ground to be there bound. Mann & Mann were not first to elevate the swath of grain, but even if they were, no credit is due them, since neither the Marsh Harvester nor the modern self-binding harvester were the outgrowth thereof. The rear portion of the early Mann machine was supported on the large driving-wheel. The forward end was supported by wheels provided with a tongue and draft devices. As the working parts of the Mann machine are between the supporting wheels, the grain is not elevated over a supporting wheel. I call attention to this fact because of the claims of Mr. H. F. Mann that they enriched the art materially by the devices of the patents of '49 and '56. The Mann machines were manufactured for a few years and some of them gave fair satisfaction, but while they, to a

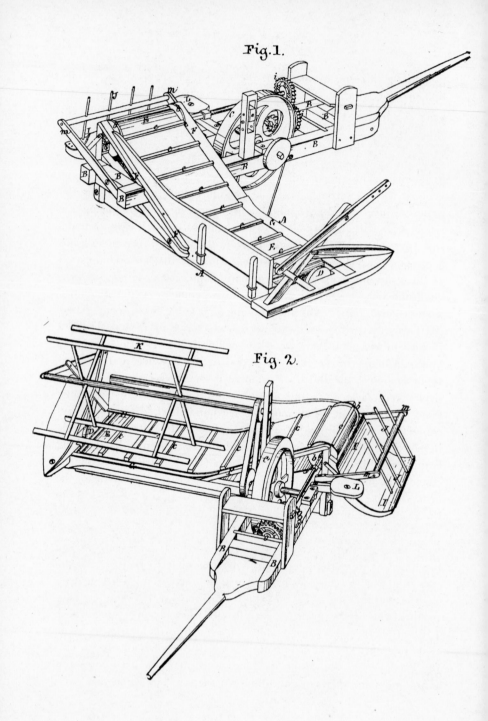

Fig. 1.

Fig. 2.

slight extent, reduced the labor of the man whose duty it was to deliver the gavels upon the ground, no material benefit resulted.

Mann & Mann improved their machine, as indicated by patent No.
1544, dated June 3, 1856, their latest effort. It was one of these machines that the Marsh Brothers bought, and with it cut their harvest
of 1857. It will be observed, by reference to the drawings, that the
1856 Mann machine is not poised on its two wheels. The axle of the
main supporting and driving wheel is such that in a large machine
it would be at least four feet forward of the axis of the small supporting wheel, under the divider at the grain end of the machine as
usual. Reference to Figure 4, of this last patent, will show that the
cut grain was elevated only sufficiently to fall into the curved receptacle (I), and that the latter was close to the ground. A seat
(L) was provided for the operator, who could there sit and dump the
unbound straw from the receptacle to the ground. As before stated,
nothing was gained, because the harvest force was not reduced.
The labor of the binders, walking from gavel to gavel, and the sting
of the stubble field, remained to be endured.

The Mann principle, that of receiving the grain in a rotary receptacle, finds embodiment in a patent to Hurlburt, No. 7928, dated
February 4, 1851. This inventor planned the framework of his machine so that the main supporting wheel might be directly under it.
By placing the weight of the machine largely upon the wheel the traction was materially increased. Hurlburt improved the early Mann
dumping device by making it automatic in its action. His effort was
the first to produce uniformity in the weight of the gavels, but not
in their girth. Upon an increase of weight due to the accumulating
gavel, the locking device freed itself, and the gavel, by its weight,
turned the receptacle and deposited itself. Plainly, the plan was impractical, as the size of gavels must necessarily have varied according
to the length of the cut straw. Hence it cannot be said that Hurlburt enriched the art in the direction of producing gavels which,
when bound, should be uniform in *size*, regardless of length of straw
or weight, as so successfully accomplished in the automatic harvesting
machines of the present day. No information is given that Hurlburt's machine was capable of being tilted,—that is, rocked upon the
axis of the main supporting wheel in order that the cutting apparatus might operate nearer to or farther from the ground, depend-

ing upon the length of the straw to be cut. However, I find his machine to have been a two-wheeled cart, with the main supporting wheel and grain wheel practically in line, as in the machine of today. Although his machine may be considered to have been but a materialized dream, yet Hurlburt brought about a slight enrichment of the art by publishing his invention in patent form, although his principle of regulating the amount of grain in a gavel is impractical. Watson & Renwick were neck and neck with Hurlburt in showing that the grain might be elevated over the master wheel; but of their patent later, when treating of semi-automatic grain binders.

At Massillon, Ohio, during the late sixties, Edwin Bayliss undertook the manufacture of *Marsh Harvesters,* under a license, and produced a fairly good machine, with the exception that it failed to work well in long and heavy grain, on account of the elevating devices acting vertically. On this machine the features were a platform on which the binders could stand, a receptacle to receive the grain from the elevating devices, and tables upon which the bundles could be bound. The grain was elevated over the main wheel as in the Marsh machine. Mr. Henry F. Mann brought suit for infringing his patent #15,044, dated June 3, 1856, (Reissue #4,281). The suit was promptly dismissed, but Mr. Mann to the day of his death insisted that Marsh Brothers, of whose machine that of Bayliss was in most respects practically a copy, had pirated his invention. The facts were, however, that what Mann sought to do the Marsh Brothers sought not to do, and each provided mechanism to accomplish the object sought.

An explanation of the cause of Bayliss' ill success of the Bayliss machine will enable one to understand why the elevating devices of the Marsh harvester and of the modern automatic binders are placed at a considerable angle, not far from 45 degrees, relative to the horizon. Marsh Brothers soon discovered that when operating their first machine, particularly in a thin growth of grain, the severed straws would begin to drop long before they became prostrated upon the conveying devices of the platform; in other words, they would slide forward slightly while being prostrated backward by the reel, and this would cause the butts of the straw to be thrust forward into the yet standing grain. This caused the straws of the swath to assume a diagonal position. In long grain the Bayliss machine could not operate because of the fact that the masses of straw, laid diagonally, would not enter the vertical elevator well. Even when it did, they could not pass upward without being bent, and the resistance to bending of a large mass of long straw interfered with the traction. The less the angle of the elevator relative to the horizon the less the straws of a massive swath will be bent.

Suit for infringement was brought by the Messrs. Mann against the manufacturers of the Bayliss form of the Marsh Harvester, with the following result:

U. S. CIRCUIT—NORTHERN DISTRICT OF OHIO.
Henry F. Mann vs. Edwin Bayliss.

"The court held:

"If this claim is to include only a piece of curved metal fastened to the side of the harvester so as to receive the fallen grain, then his Honor though it was antedated by several other devices given in evidence. It was answered, he said, that none of them had been found in combination with an elevated delivery. He thought, however, it would not be a good combination claim to take such a device from a horizontal delivery and combine it with an elevated one.

"He could not impute to the officers an intention of granting a patent for such a combination. There was no invention in taking it from one and placing it upon the other. It was the other features of the combination which secured the grant, and which accidentally could be used only with an elevated delivery. Take away these features and there was nothing like a patentable combination growing out of the union of an elevated delivery with the piece of curved metal.

"The position that defendants infringed, even though the claim was construed to include a receiver with an outer edge so as to collect the grain into gavels that it may be discharged by revolving a rake, was considered at some length. Answering the arguments of complainant's counsel, among other things, Judge Emmons said the broad level surface of the table was no mechanical equivalent for the narrow basin and turned-up outside edge of the receiver. The one collected the grain into gavels, the other did not. The one was intended to perform the particular function of arranging the grain so as to permit the action of a rake to sweep the straw in suitable parcels to the ground. The other required no such function, and could by no possibility perform it. The position was pronounced wholly untenable, that the bodies of the men in the manholes, and their arms and fingers, when in action, were the mechanical equivalents of the outer edge of the receiver and this action of the rake.

"His Honor said, while he did not assent to the argument of the learned counsel for the defendant, that the complainant was estopped

by the declaration of his pleader in the Patent Office, that this curvi-
linear receiver was old, and that, therefore, he did not claim it, still in
cases of this character such a deliberate assertion was not without its
influence. He felt some relief in denying this injunction, that he was
not compelled to go outside of complainant's own record for a plain
declaration that he was right in the construction of this claim. He
should be unwilling to have it thought the concession found in these
papers constituted a very influential element in the reasons which induced his judgment. But when the whole history of this case was
looked at, and it is remembered that this is a·reissue seeking to claim
something thought of originally only to be disclaimed, this matter may
be well mentioned as a provocation to pretty close scrutiny of the extraordinary claim now insisted upon—one which declares to every citizen
that he shall not insert between a novel device and an old one, to neither
of which complainant has any right, a thing so simple, so utterly desti-
tute of everything like invention as the oblique board or common 'chute'
down which the grain falls upon the binding-table, in the case before us.

"Judge Emmons said, in conclusion that although he could give no
reason for any doubt in this case, and the decision seemed to him
plainly right, yet compelled as he was to dispose of them upon the
moment, having no more time elsewhere than here to examine them, it
would do the court great injustice not to suppose it recognized fully the
great liability to error in such conditions. He had in this instance
given, as in all similar instances he gave, to counsel, the opportunity of
meeting and overcoming the objections of the court. It was a satisfaction to him to know that the complainant in this instance had been represented by counsel as experienced, learned, and able as they had been
zealous, and, as he might say, enthusiastic in argument.

"The usual decree dismissing the bill will be entered."

CHAPTER XIII.

The Story of the Marsh Harvester

Although I am familiar with this story almost from the beginning, having been intimately connected with the manufacture of the Marsh machine from a time before it was first successfully placed upon the market until the present, I prefer to present the Marsh Brothers' own story as far as it goes. These brothers lived in DeKalb County, Illinois, near the grove deeded by the Government to the Indian Chief, Shabbona, "the white man's friend," as a reservation. In Kendall County, adjoining DeKalb County at its southeast corner, lived my grandfather, Marcus Steward and his brother-in-law, John F. Hollister, before referred to. Very early in the '40s, a neighbor of Mr. Steward had bought a reaper substantially of the Woodward or Schnebley type (later shown in the patent granted to F. Woodward, of Freehold, N. J., and dated September 30, 1845). The writer, with a mental photograph only of this machine which successfully cut more than twenty harvests, cannot distinguish between it and the Woodward Reaper, except that in the Woodward machine, as the patent will show, were special devices intended to drop the gavels at the time a certain weight of the grain had accumulated upon the flooring of a part of the receptacle, by the work of the raker riding thereon.

The machine, I am informed, had been manufactured in Kendall County, Illinois. The original purchaser, neither a mechanic nor a farmer, could operate the machine successfully. Mr. Steward and Mr. Hollister, the latter an excellent mechanic, built a new machine, using some of the old parts, and operated it for two or three seasons, getting along fairly well with the somewhat defective cutting apparatus. Late in the '40s, however, they applied the Hussey cutting apparatus, its sections having sickled edges. In this they followed

237

the example of George Rugg, of Ottawa, Illinois, who had for two
or three years been improving Hussey's machines, owned by farmers,
by serrating the knives, and who had substituted Hussey's cutting apparatus having the serrated or sickled edges for the McCormick
straight sickles in a few McCormick machines that had reached the
vicinity.

Thus rebuilt and improved, the Steward machine became well
known, and the Marsh Brothers, learning of its continuous efficiency
and of its builders, came to the farm of Mr. Steward and took away
with them the oldest son, who had operated the early machine. The
result of the visit is mentioned by Mr. Marsh.

In the winter of '60-'61 William Wallace Marsh, the younger
brother, came to the town of Plano, which is located on both the
original Steward and Hollister farms. There, with the aid of Mr.
Hollister, made the first fully successful Marsh harvester, which I
launched in waving rye. The brothers had attempted to build machines on their farms, as stated, but, although Wallace was very ingenious, they were not yet skilled mechanics. The machine built by
Wallace Marsh and Hollister worked during the harvests of '61 to
'65 inclusive. I cannot speak farther of the first machine from personal experience as I was absent in the South on business for the
Union, but upon my return in August of 1865, I became directly
connected with the manufacture of the machines. Consequently I
can speak, from experience, of the struggles of the little company,
Steward & Marsh, both farmers, in their efforts to manufacture the
harvesting machine which ultimately revolutionized field methods.
This work, of such vast import to civilization was done with inadequate facilities, in an ill equipped sash factory.

In the winter of '63-'64 the concern began the manufacture of fifty
machines. Practically all work was done by hand. Money was
scarce; ear corn was at times cheaper than coal. Even as late as the
winter of 1865-6 I shoveled thousands of bushels of the best Yellow
Dent corn into the furnace to keep the wheels of the improvised
factory turning. Every bolt and nut for the machines, except the
most common sizes, was forged and threaded by hand. All holes
in wrought metal parts were drilled in a lathe or upon a wooden drill
press. We had no punch press of any kind. Two circular saws, a
rip and crosscut, worked out, in the rough, the wooden parts. A

single planer, and that of an early type, aided materially, but every part of the machine had to be finished by hand labor at the bench. About half of the machines were finished and sold for the harvest of 1864 and the remainder for the harvest of 1865. All worked well, but it was difficult to induce a farmer to give an order, as none believed it possible for two men to bind as much as a machine cutting a 5-foot swath could pass over in a day. The younger Mr. Marsh was particularly active. Wherever he went, and wherever the machines had a chance to reveal their powers, prejudice was overcome and public incredulity slowly faded.

Marsh Harvester, 1858.

The manufacture of self-raking reapers was then at its height, and the makers of those machines were after several years, led to believe that the Marsh harvester might become a competitor. So, with printer's ink, by the barrel, the new comer was cried down. Dealers handling reapers would sometimes challenge the agents of the Marsh harvester to a test, declaring that two men on the ground could follow their reaper and cut and bind an acre in as short a time as the Marsh harvester could cut the same amount with two men riding thereon binding the grain. Oftentimes they succeeded by adopting the plan of the Marsh Brothers in 1857, namely, that of following the reaper on foot, and, rapidly running from gavel to gavel, making the band for the next bundle in the meantime, one man taking one gavel and forming it into a completed bundle, and the other the next, and so on, alternately.

Every harvester had to be put up and started by a mechanic, who, preferably, was an expert binder. The steps of the Marsh harvester agents were dogged by the agents of other machines, who never failed to show what poor work the Marsh harvester turned out. They would go to a field where a machine had just been started, before the farmer and his help had become accustomed to binding well, and take loose, badly bound bundles to their agencies to show farmers that poor work must be expected from a Marsh harvester should they buy one. I was in the field every year until the harvester had won its laurels, and have been in the field every year, often for months at a time ever since. For the manual binding of the gavels on the Marsh harvester was substituted, first the semi-automatic binder, and then the wholly automatic twine binding attachment of today.

In handling the Marsh harvester, I found the better course to be to instruct the driver of the machine to cut very narrow and be careful not to give the binders more than they could easily do. A foot in width was often sufficient, when beginning, but that foot, by night time, was often increased to five. One day's practice was usually enough time to train the hands to the new work. So easy did the work of binding become that harvest time was considered, as compared with the old method, "a picnic," not only to the three men who could lay from twelve to fifteen acres of grain in neatly bound bundles on the ground, but to the farmer's wife it proved to be a Godsend, reducing the number of men to be cared for in the harvest from a dozen men to three or four.

Once the hands were trained, operating the Marsh Harvester was easy. In southern Illinois, during the early days of the revolution in harvest methods, an agent advertised that the Marsh harvester would be exhibited in a field of grain on a certain day on a certain farm. The crowd gathered and the question was raised as to who was to do the binding, one man bantering another to make the attempt. Presently a carriage arrived bringing a neatly dressed young lady. Stepping upon the binders' stand of the machine, she bound round after round amidst the cheers of the surprised spectators. Her father, a German, the year previously had bought a Marsh harvester and she had been appointed to do the driving. To drive day after day became irksome to her and she begged her brothers to change work with her, which they did. So much better did she like to bind than drive that she was granted her choice; to bind grain on the Marsh harvester soon became as second nature to her deft hands.

Little can be said as to the stability of the early machines, but the matter of durability was mainly left in the hands of the excellent mechanic who had built the first real successful Marsh harvester. Material for the wood framework could seldom be got well seasoned, the castings procured at various foundries were not always of the best quality, and the struggles against what oftentimes seemed to be Fate, resulted in little more than discouragement. So great was the prejudice and, consequently, so slow the growth that but 100 machines were put out in 1866. These were followed by 150 in 1867, by 250 in 1868, by 750 in 1869, and by 1,000 in 1870, after which the numbers multiplied rapidly. Dear-bought experience proved to be a good teacher, and in the middle '70s the Marsh harvester had won its way and new ones were entering the fields at the rate of between 10,000 and 15,000 per year. Manufacturers of reapers, seeing the beginning of the end, went headlong into building the machines, some almost identical in all details, and others varying but little in form and to no extent in function. One of the earliest of these to go in extensively were C. H. and L. J. McCormick, for the harvest of 1875.

Early in the history of the Marsh harvester Ralph Emerson, of Rockford, Illinois, had learned of the new machine. Being connected with a manufacturer of reapers, Mr. John H. Manny, and thoroughly familiar with the demands of the field, Emerson took stock by purchase of rights under the patents taken out by the Marsh Brothers. John D. Easter and Elijah H. Gammon also became interested, and for the harvest of 1865 Parker & Stone, of Beloit, Wisconsin, manufacturers of reapers, supplied the latter with 100 Marsh harvesters, made in fulfillment of a contract. For the season of 1867 Warder & Mitchell, of Springfield, Ohio, manufactured for the Marsh harvester interests a large number of machines, and also some for sale in the state of Ohio, under a license. Although they were made by experienced builders, strong and generally considered durable, Fate seemed to be pursuing these Beloit, Plano and Ohio machines, and the writer remembers well the many weary days he spent rushing over the country and working from one morning almost until the next morning in repairing the machines, mainly in successful effort to keep them efficient in green hands. The main difficulty found was the supporting traction wheels. Some had to be practically rebuilt in the field, and others, particularly the Springfield machines required to have their split rims joined by strong wrought lugs reaching from side to side. Had the appliances of the present day been available the machines could have been manufactured quite cheaply, and the sales price of from $225.00 to $300.00 would have netted ample remuneration. Yet the cost of selling and the vicissitudes of the machines in the harvest field reduced the net profit to a very small figure. In 1869 the Marsh Brothers withdrew from the Plano group and organized a factory at Sycamore, Illinois, which for many years turned out good machines.

William R. Lowe, a cousin of the Marsh Brothers, in the employ of the little company, invented an elevating device, shown in the patent granted to him. A license was taken under the Marsh patents, which practically dominated the Lowe machine. Manufacture was begun by Lowe & Adams at Sandwich, Illinois, and for a few years Lowe-Marsh machines, capable of excellent work, appeared in the market.

The first patent taken out by the Marsh Brothers on August 17, 1858, shows only a portion of the harvester, which, to say the least, was not prepossessing in its details of construction. The machine was supported upon two wheels and the cut grain elevated over the main supporting and traction wheel, so that the machine balanced upon the two supporting wheels. However, a bundle carrier was provided at the rear of the machine and inflexibly secured thereto. Into this large receptacle at the rear of the binder stand, bundles might be placed. The parts lettered K, 1, p and o, which constituted it, are shown clearly. Upon the bottom part, 1, at its lower edge, is shown a hook, O, adapted to engage the lower edge of the pivoted door, p. A lever, L, extended rearwardly from the binder stand, and pivoted at its middle thereon, supported the bottom part, 1. The operator, with feet upon the forward end of the lever, held all of the parts in place until such time as he wished the bundles to be discharged. He then took his foot from the lever, which permitted the bottom part, 1, to fall, and the hinge door, p, to open and the bundles to slide out rearwardly. In Figure 3 is shown a supporting wheel, Q, directly beneath the bundle carrier. This wheel was for the purpose of

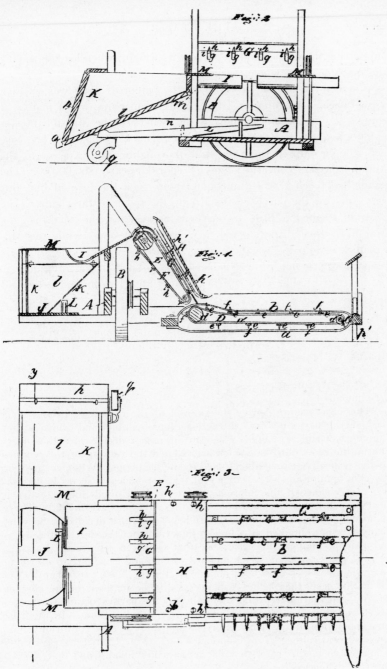

Marsh Harvester, patented August 17, 1858.

supporting the carrier and to prevent its weight, when loaded, tipping the machine, as a whole, backward.

Whether the Marsh harvester of the patent of 1858 was, in fact, a two-wheeled machine or a three-wheeled machine was a matter of controversy in the suit brought by the owners of the Marsh harvester patents against the C. H. & L. J. McCormick Company. The case was fought out energetically and thoroughly, the expense to the Marsh harvester concerns being, as reported, nearly $60,000.00. The patent had been reissued and defendants took the ground that this was done for the purpose of enlarging the scope of the claims. The position seemed a little inconsistent because of the fact that the Marsh Brothers had reissued their patent but once, while the Mc-Cormick Company were claiming to work under some of their reaper patents, one of which had been reissued in ten divisions, as before stated. The case was heard by Judge Drummond, who held as follows:

"Circuit Court of the United States,
Northern District of Illinois.

Charles W. Marsh et al,   ⎫
    -v-   ⎬
Cyrus H. McCormick et al, ⎭
Drummond, J.

"This case was argued by the counsel of the respective parties upon the general merits involved in the pleadings, exhibits and evidence; but the court considers it unnecessary to discuss or decide any other question in the case than that which arises upon the validity of the reissues of the respective patents mentioned in the pleadings. Whatever may be my own opinion upon the validity of these re-issues, it seems to me that recent decisions of the Supreme Court of the United States render it necessary for this Court to hold that these reissues are invalid. There is no doubt that the Supreme Court has heretofore decided to be valid many reissues obtained at a longer interval from the date of the original patents than in this case; but that Court in its recent decisions, several times repeated, seems inclined to hold and to adhere to its ruling that when reissues have been obtained after the lapse of so many years as in this case, that laches will necessarily be imputed in the absence of any explanation repelling the same to the parties obtaining the re-issue, and therefore that they are invalid on that account. In this case no explanation of the delay is given, and therefore in conformity with these several rulings of the Supreme Court of the United States, I think I must hold in this case, that the reissues are invalid and that the bill must be dismissed."

It will be seen that he did not hold that the patent was void for lack of invention, nor for any other of the possible score of reasons, but merely that too much time had elapsed before the application for the reissue. All this following a Supreme Court decision, then recently rendered, putting a new construction on the reissue laws. Later, in discussing the matter, he told the attorneys for the Marsh harvester interests that but for the Supreme Court decision in Miller vs. Bridgeport Brass Company he would have decided for the complainants. He held up the matter for a long time, and it was during this period that the Supreme Court decision was rendered. The reissuing of patents for the purpose of enlarging the scope had been carried to such an abominable extent that our highest tribunal very wisely put a stop to unfair methods of the kind. The courts vibrate, however, not as frequently as the pendulum of a clock, but by periods of years. The Patent Office practice and the courts had swung to the reissue side for a long time, and when once the practice gravitated backward it went to the other extreme, and for a number of years reissues were frowned upon by the Patent Office and many were declared void by the courts, because of enlargements, until, at the present time, the granting of reissues is controlled wholly by the judgment of the Patent Office, which carries out very sanely the sections of a patent law providing that reissues may be granted for the purpose of correcting errors mainly, and also for permitting the patentee to restate his case and file claims commensurate with his invention.

The following account (from all appearances a paid advertisement) of the alleged invention of the Harvester is found in an old scrap book in possession of the author of this work, clipped from the *Western Progress, of* May 5th, 1875, credited to the *Austin Register*:

"Harvesters.

"Some twenty-four years ago, in the early days of Reaping Machines, an implement was devised to cut grain and carry the binders. An experimental machine was tested near Cincinnati; over seventy acres were cut and successfully bound; the binders doing their work on the machine; but the idea was far in advance of the wants of the age. Grain farms were principally new, the land rough, the grain heavy. The era was a transition one from the use of cradles; and the single step of cutting down the grain with a machine drawn by horses, was a long one to take from the use of the cradle. The inventor of this implement was a mechanic in the then modest Reaper Works of C. H. McCormick. Years afterwards the idea was taken up by others, and in 1865 assumed a definite shape before the public in the Marsh Harvester. There was very little modification to the first machine, except in detail; even then the implement was in advance of the age, and a large proportion of the number tested that year were thrown aside. The most urgent personal efforts of Mr. Marsh failed to introduce them with any rapidity, and the writer of this saw him in 1865, at the end of an unsuccessful trial, pretty thoroughly disheartened and discouraged. A great obstacle to their introduction was the shabby manner in which they were built, and although this has been improved somewhat, they have never yet been really well built. Still they gradually grew in favor in some localities, and have now become very popular in a section of country representing about one-third of the grain-growing part of the United States. In much the larger part of the country their use is yet unknown. This is indicated by the relative number of machines built last season in round numbers something less than twenty thousand Harvesters as against over sixty thousand Reapers.

"The large manufacturers have but just seen the need of building them, and now that their attention is being given to the matter, we may expect a great deal better implement to be sold for less money. More especially is this the fact, as there is no patent on the essential features of the Harvester that any one need to respect. If Mr. Marsh's claim to priority of invention was well founded, the Edward, the Massillon, the Lowe, Adams & French, the Wood, the Werner, the Garnhart, and the Osage would not all of them been built and sold with impunity last season, and some of them for four or five years back; be assured that if there was a royalty in it Mr. Marsh would have had it long ago. The fact is, the old invention covers the whole ground, and any one has a right to build a Harvester that chooses. The consequence of this is, that the purchaser will have no patent fee or royalty to pay for, in buying a machine, while a brisk competition will drive the poorly made ones out of the market.

"Last year the Messrs. McCormick instructed the inventor of the old Cincinnati Machine to unite all the valuable features used in the leading Harvesters into one machine. Of all the men in the country, he was the most eminently fitted to do this work, and the sample machine now on exhibition at Mr. Van Valkenburgh's Implement Store, is ample evidence of the conscientious and painstaking manner in which he carried out his instructions. A man familiar with Harvesters will at once recognize the most valuable and distinctive points of the leading machines combined in symmetrical proportion, with some improvements over any and all of them. Those who have feared that from the desire the Messrs. McCormick have always shown to build strong, that their Harvester would be unduly cumbersome, will be agreeably surprised to find it compact and light, while it is finished and put together in the very highest style of mechanical excellence. The frame is solidly bolted and fitted together at the factory. This is in marked contrast with some of the others, whose frames are sent out loosely, to be shabbily hung together by the agent. The Messrs. McCormick would not allow so important a piece of work to be done out of their factory. The details of the cutting apparatus are as excellent as those of the old Reliable, while many of the minor difficulties found in other Harvesters are entirely obviated. The machine is the embodiment of the experience and experimenting of nearly thirty years, and will come to the farmers of Minnesota, not an untried machine, but a thoroughly tested and proved one, prepared to take its chances in a rough and tumble fight with all the rest, and come out ahead. Its merits are obvious and easily recognized. Farmers are recommended to examine for themselves.— Austin Register. 308t4."

The phraseology makes clear the inspiration of this article. If such a machine was made at the McCormick factory twenty-four years before, or anywhere, invented by a McCormick workman, what inspiration, if any, could it have given to Mr. McCormick, who built no harvester until 1875, twelve years after the Marsh Harvester had been prominently on the market? Why was this alleged machine and its operation not set up by the defendants, in their answer? Do they refer to the Adams & Gifford machine, with which they had nothing to do, and which Adams admitted was not successful? All that the above long article demonstrates is that hindsight is better than foresight.

In the earliest Marsh patent the conveying devices, that for moving the grain stubbleward along the receiving platform and that for elevating it to the binding receptacle, consisted of endless toothed belts, the teeth projecting upward through slots in the platforms and withdrawing from the straw at the top of the elevator. The cut grain fell upon the moving platform conveyor and was carried along in the form of a swath and elevated and delivered into the binding receptacle. The operator upon the Marsh harvester, at the approach of the first straws, seized a wisp and formed a band. At such time as the accumulation in the receptacle became sufficiently large, he thrust his hand holding the band through the swath and passed the band around the gavel, then quickly converted the latter into a bundle. In practice, when one man was doing the binding upon the machine, as in grain not heavy, the bundle could be bound in the gavel receptacle, but two binding tables were provided, and the operator, thrusting the band through the swath and passing it around the gavel, moved the latter to the table, there to complete by uniting the ends of the band. Attempts to bind gavels by placing a band of wire, twine or straw around them had been made, but for the first time in the history of harvesting machinery the operator on the Marsh harvester successfully thrust the band through the flowing swath and parted from the latter the accumulation that was to form a bundle. That was the gist of the Marsh invention, but it was only after the coming of the automatic binder, which, with its steel hands, thrusts the band material through the flowing swath, that we appreciated the immense value of the accomplishment of the Marshes. The inventors who had striven for years to place automatic binders upon reapers, depending upon a rake to sweep the receiving platform and convey the mass into the gavel receptacle, soon awoke to the fact that by the Marsh harvesters the way had been paved to probable success.

Upon the original Marsh harvester was a footboard, upon which the two men might stand and perform their task. Further inventive faculty was taxed to no great extent, when the various inventors placed upon the footboard, or its equivalent, the binding attachments with which they had struggled, unsuccessfully, for many years. Although binding upon the machine manually is now an unpracticed art, the Marsh harvester still exists. It did not cease to be, as might the play of Hamlet with Hamlet left out, as the automatic substitutes for the men now ride where they rode and it does their work. The Marsh harvester in the early days was crude. For the toothed conveyors were soon substituted endless slatted cloth conveyors. As early as 1851 Watson & Renwick had dreamed. Renwick was an examiner in the Patent Office and had examined the application of John Heath, who attempted to produce a binder, mainly manual. The joint inventor, Peter H. Watson, Assistant Secretary of War during the Rebellion, was also ingenious and thoroughly practical. Although they patented the embodiment of their ideas in model form, they never built a machine; in the model they embodied three systems of endless conveyors, one conveyor upon the receiving platform. The elevating of the swath was accomplished by two systems of conveyors, between which the grain was moved upward and deposited in the primary receptacle. I say "system of elevators" because instead of having one wide, endless slatted canvas below and a similar one above, as now, two series of belts were used instead. They "builded better than they knew," and Mr. Renwick lived to see all the grain grown in civilized countries elevated by substantially the means he had prophesied; having built no machine, however, he had *demonstrated* nothing. In time the platform conveyor of the Marsh Harvester became to be a single wide, slatted canvas, and the elevators to be precisely the same. All harvesters now embody these last mentioned devices.

In the earliest days of the reaper it had become necessary to vary the height of cut in order to conform to the requirements of grain of different heights of growth. The first successful Marsh harvester was not provided with adequate means, but the machines for '66 were adapted to be adjusted to the desired position, as to height, by lifting the machine relative to the main supporting wheel and there securing it. This had always been done by means of anything capable of use as a lever; the top rail of a fence often served the purpose. In short, the machine was pried up. In the middle ages of the reaping machine proper the short main axle was supported at its ends and secured to the frame at such position as desired. Pinions had been secured to each end of the axle and adapted to run in quadrants secured to the main frame. Means was also provided whereby the axle could be rotated and the machine thus lowered or elevated to any position desired; then the axle was secured from further rotation. This device, borrowed from the early reapers, was applied to the harvester by the Marsh interests in 1866. Improvements in details of construction followed from time to time. The machine was provided with a tilting apparatus whereby, by rocking it upon its supporting wheels, the height of cut could also be varied. This tilting of the machine carried with it the platform upon which the binders stood, which rendered their footing unstable. In order to overcome the objection the footboard of the machine was so connected to the main framework that the latter might be tilted without affecting the horizontal position of the footboard and the binding tables.

From the beginning, in this art, the more that was given the farmer the more exacting he became, and a clamor was made for means by which the reel could be placed in any desired position, whether high or low, or far forward or rearward, and, in fact, anywhere between.

The reapers of the middle ages of this art had mainly been provided with reels, and, in some instances, provision made whereby they could be raised and lowered by means within reach of the driver in

The Marsh Harvester in Operation.

his seat. Such an arrangement, although but "half a loaf," as it were, was, as applied to reapers, fairly satisfactory. But with the advent of the Marsh harvester it was learned that better means for controlling the prostration of the cut straws on the platform were desirable. It was not until 1875 that to harvesters were applied adjustable reels; this was accomplished by Gammon & Deering successors to the original Marsh companies at Plano, Ill. This reel thoroughly tested during 1875, and since applied to nearly all reaping machines, whether manufactured by the original company and its successors or not, could be handled by a single lever and placed in any desired position with the machine still in operation. During 1875 the Marsh Brothers also applied an adjustable reel not differing very materially, as to general principles, from the Steward reel adopted as above. The Sandwich Manufacturing Company, which from the start had made the Lowe & Adams machine, applied an adjustable reel to their harvesters. Patents were granted covering all these reels, and reference to the patents obtained by Marsh, by Shogren and by Steward will make clear the forms first introduced. That of Steward and that of Marsh differed but little in principle. Each was supported upon a post pivoted at its lower end to the harvester frame, and each by suitable means was held parallel to the reel shaft relative to the cutting apparatus. In examining the Steward patent the means for supporting the reel must not be lost sight of because of the prominence of the wooden bars constituting the lazy tongues, which were provided for preserving parallelism. Other and simpler means of doing this were later provided by the same inventor. It may be said that, at the present time, but two types of reel exist. The Shogren type consists of two metallic frames, the lower pivoted to the harvester frame and the upper pivoted to the first frame and reaching upward to support the reel shaft. These two frames may be compared with the elements of the human arms. If a person will take a cane in the two hands and hold it horizontally, he can, by raising his arms and flexing the elbows, place the cane in any desired position. The other principle, as carried out, consisted of a support adapted to be moved to and fro and the reel support made capable of being moved up or down upon it as desired by the driver, and that easy of accomplishment by means at hand.

The Marsh harvester has been receiving finishing touches up to the present day, and now has become a machine of steel. Since the devastation of our timber lands began to be felt and our mines to yield their abundance more liberally, lumber suitable for the manufacture of agricultural machines has constantly increased in price. About 1880 some of the far-sighted men in the trade considered that in the near future the price of lumber and the price of steel would pass each other, the price of lumber going upward while steel prices fell.

D. M. Osborne & Company, of Auburn, New York, were among the earliest to apply binding attachments to Marsh harvesters. Mr. Osborne in the East and William Deering in the West seem to have been first to foresee and prepare for the approaching shift in material. During the year 1885 each had brought about the construction of a harvester with all steel framework. For several years Mr. Deering and I had been discussing this change. Mr. Osborne had licensed

Harris & Son, of Brantford, Ontario, to manufacture a machine under patents belonging to his company, and Mr. John Harris was one of the first to profit by the models made by Mr. Osborne. These machines were constructed of steel to as full an extent as at the present time. Early in the '80s the price of wrought iron and low grade steel did pass each other, steel coming down. All manufacturers, knowing steel to be preferable to iron, had substituted steel for the few pieces of iron used in the wooden framework, namely, a dozen pieces, more or less. Among others to substitute steel for iron in making these lesser parts, was the McCormick Harvesting Machine Company. Although that company, down to the sale of its business claimed precedence in the all-steel field, its so-called first steel harvester was steel in name only. No sooner had the Osborne and Deering companies proved the practicability of the use of steel than other manufacturers fell in line, some quickly and others tardily.

Aultman, Miller & Company, of Akron, O., were the last to change.

Among the final touches to the harvester was provision of means whereby the machine may be readily reduced in width from front to rear by folding the dividers and moving the reel well back. Another of the finishing touches provided means for self-transporting over the road and from field to field. As there is no controversy as to whom credit is due on these points, they need not be dwelt upon. The records of the Patent Office show to whom credit must be given.

Although I have been an active worker in the art from the beginning of the Marsh harvester to the present time, it is well to let the brothers speak for themselves. Mr. William Wallace Marsh writes as follows:

"Sycamore, Ill., April 6, 1902.

"Mr. John Steward,
"Dear John:—

"Your kind letter is at hand and contents noted. In the first case the idea of binding on a machine by hand was mine. I bound the first bundle on the ground to test the time required to bind a bundle in comparison with the time required to cut and deliver a bundle off of a machine. I can now go to within five rods of the place where the first bundle was bound. In the evening it was discussed at the supper table, and the next day I had to go to a neighbor's to repay changed works while my brother carried on the test which was the understanding as I was reluctant to go.

" 'Tis true that C. W. had as much to do with the planning of the first machine as I had, if not more, as he and Bartlett built the patent model and the bundle carrier was put on behind, which lost us the McCormick lawsuit. When model was brought home, or I should say when informed of the bundle carrier, I thought it was all right, so I was as much to blame as he was. If we had only put it on the side, as we did afterwards, we would have hit it. He and Albert Hinds did the building of the first machine, 'our nearest neighbor,' which I saw about every evening. We thought on account of the elevator having to do the most work it should run faster than the lower canvas, and the machine was built accordingly. We started it up in Timothy and the Timothy went up heads first and clogged the machine down. I saw the trouble at once and ran to the barn and got a lot of old belting and nailed it on the elevator pulley, which was of wood, increasing the motion of the platform canvas until it ran faster than the elevator. Then we cut the eight acre piece, you might say, without stopping. After that I built the sample machines, two in Chicago, one at Plano, one at Springfield, Ohio. Above are the facts connected with the infancy of the harvester.".

Mr. Wallace Marsh showed his ingenuity in many lines, a large number of his inventions having been patented, as the records of the Patent Office show. While the younger brother came to be a practical mechanic and had more to do with the development of the machines, Charles Wesley, being better qualified therefore, gave his attention to business matters connected with the organization and carrying on of the companies founded by them. He was recognized as a man of affairs and served in several official capacities, the most important one being that of Illinois state senator. Mr. C. W. Marsh in 1897 wrote as follows:

"J. F. Steward,
"Dear Sir:—

"We, C. W. & W. W. Marsh, purchased a Mann reaper in 1856, which carried the grain on an endless apron elevating it sufficiently at outer end to permit of gavel being formed in receiver below point of delivery. I did the raking off generally and W. W. led the binders. Probably before the beginning of the harvest of 1857 we discussed the advantages of carrying binders, the saving of time in going from gavel to gavel, the saving of the stooping over gavel and gathering it out of the stubble, and the saving of stringing of the gavel through striking the stubble as delivered from the moving machine. Anyhow, it was early in the harvest of 1857 that we made the test of fast binding on the ground, the gavel being delivered with great care and the binders running from gavel to gavel and making bands between. They then bound four measured acres in about four hours. I also placed gavels close together and timed the binders. In this way I satisfied myself that the binding could be done on the machine. Then I placed some boards at each end of receiver, and bound on them, taking grain from receiver; but found that the delivery was wrong, as the tuck of the band was toward the butts instead of the heads; hence the cut of the machine had to be reversed, so we desisted from further experiments.

"After harvest we discussed the matter, and during the following winter invented the toothed rake and slotted platform style of elevator. In the spring I made a model at Little Rock, with S. W. Bartlett's assistance and applied for patent, and immediately after began on a machine in connection with our uncle Hinds, who besides farming did some tinkering as a country blacksmith and wagon repairer. We built the machine out of the Mann reaper and such castings as we could find. With it we cut our harvest in 1858, some 50 acres, and did good work, binding easily full cut after a little practice. Next winter Wallace went to Chicago and laid the foundations of a new machine, getting necessary patterns made there. We finished and put up this machine at home. It worked well and we cut and bound with it about 130 acres. This machine was not provided with picker belt to help up the butts, but the front row of teeth were forward of the sickle beam.

"In the winter of 1860 we built a little shop (which is shown in cut enclosed), and commenced on 12 machines, with a carpenter and helper as workmen, besides ourselves. The castings were made, some of them in Chicago and some in Sandwich. The boring, keyseating, etc., were done in a little machine shop at DeKalb. In 'assembling' the parts in our shop, where we did the work, we found that the machine work had been poorly done, and the machines came together badly. We patched, braced and bushed, but they were a poor lot. The grain of that year was of unusually rank and heavy growth. Our machines lacked capacity and strength and broke or pulled apart. Our customers refused to take them and we were greatly discouraged. Still we cut and bound over 100 acres with one, and a couple of other machines did considerable work. Their cost, however, was a dead loss, and a big loss for ordinary farmers to stand, especially as times had been very hard since 1857 and grain was very low in 1860. I had become acquainted with your brother Lewis meantime, and having great faith in his judgment got him to come up and see the machine. He did so toward the end of harvest. Wallace bound heavy grain alone, but the machine broke down after running 10 or 12 rods. He saw the possibilities, however, at a glance, and said the idea was right because the binding could be done; also that if the machine could run 10 rods it could be made to run 10 miles, and there was a man at Plano 'Uncle John,' who could build it so it would run. I think if your brother had not thus encouraged us we would have given it up, except to use it on our own farm, though probably later on might have tried again or enlisted some one. We tried to get the Adams' interested, also old man Gronberg, then building reapers and mowers at Montgomery.

"In the winter of 1860-61 your Uncle John and Wallace built the first Plano machine. This worked admirably after some fixing in harvest. It had the picker belt for taking up and accelerating the movement of the butts. We cut 164 acres in the harvest of 1861, and it did good work for a dozen years. Lewis told us to keep on using it in the harvests following so as to get experience in all the varying conditions of grain. Meantime we tried to get others enlisted, the Pitts brothers in Chicago and Adams at Sandwich. In the fall of 1862, George Steward, having come back from New Orleans, Lewis proposed that we should begin manufacturing on a small scale at Plano. We commenced on 50, got out 26 for harvest of '64, and sold every one of them. They gave good satisfaction, but they cost nearly as much as we got for them, and in buying machinery and material needed we had to get into debt. This scared us and induced us to sell a third interest in our patents to Champlin & Taylor, speculators, and through them to license the 6 best states to Easter & Gammon, then mere adventurers in the farm machinery business, which was done in 1864.

"With all that has been done since you are familiar.

Yours C. W. Marsh."

In 1900 he writes further:

"DeKalb, Ill., Jan. 13, 1900.

"Mr. J. F. Steward,
Chicago.
"Dear Sir:—

"Answering yours of recent date: Very naturally I feel proud of the position the Deering Harvester Company occupies among manufacturers of harvesting machinery, because of the fact that it is the lineal descendant of the concern founded by my brother and myself, in connection with Lewis and George Steward, in Plano in 1863, for the manufacture of the Marsh Harvester. Great credit is due to them and to the others who helped us develop the machine, for the struggle was long and bitter. Much printer's ink was wasted during this contest on circulars and other literature intended to convince farmers that grain could not be bound upon a machine, and that it would be impossible for two men to bind as much as the machine could cut. Notwithstanding all this, the saving of labor prompted farmers to take the risk, and they not only found that two men could bind the grain, but do it with half the labor involved in binding after a reaper. Their necessities being thus supplied, they clamored for luxuries. They wanted to work in the shade and we provided it for them. From the beginning we foresaw that bundles could be carried and deposited in bunches preparatory to shock-

ing, and a carrier was provided. At the time the Marsh harvester can
be said to have triumphed, inventors had been working 20 years to bind
grain automatically. They discovered early in the '70s that to bind
from the continuous swath delivered from the elevator of the Marsh
harvester seems promising, and its makers, prompted by their original
faith that automatic binding could be accomplished, furnished such inventors with machines at reduced rates. The makers of the Marsh were
foremost in aiding the successful development of wire binders in 1873
& 74 and in establishing them upon the market; and when William Deering in succession applied the perfected Appleby twine binder to the
Marsh harvester, a second revolution was promised and soon accomplished. The Story of the forty years can be quickly told: First the
machine; then a little factory and a little company—Steward & Marsh;
then enlargement of the shop and company—Marsh Bros. & Steward,
next further enlargement and Gammon & Deering and Steward; and
then in line Gammon & Deering, William Deering, William Deering &
Co., and the Deering Harvester Company.

Yours truly,

(Signed) C. W. Marsh."

As early as 1870 manufacturers began to see the handwriting on the
wall. The Johnston Harvester Company provided an attachment
consisting of a truck to be attached in rear of their reaper, and which
was provided with a foot-board, gavel receptacle and binding tables.
An automatic rake was designed to take the gavel swept from the
reaper platform and move it into the gavel receptacle of the attachment. The device, in part, copied the lines followed by Adams &
Gifford, which years before had been proved impractical.

CHAPTER XIV.

HEADERS AND STRIPPERS AND MOWING MACHINES.

The machine of Gaul, the first shown in this volume, may be considered to have been the first "header," as well as the first stripper. Strippers take the heads and leave all of the straw. Headers take the heads, leaving as much of the straw as possible. In the semi-arid regions, particularly of America, these machines are used, principally because of the fact that they can cut a wide swath. In order that they may do so they are pushed, as were the machines of ancient Gaul, of Bell, and those of other early English inventors. Bell "builded better than he knew." As the climate of northern England is very humid, it was thought necessary to permit the grain to lie in the swath, but it could have been made to do so by adding width and length to the various parts. In order that the grain might be delivered continuously Bell placed an endless conveyor back of his cutting apparatus and adapted it, by means of the gearing, to be moved in either direction at will. By this means he could begin at one side of the field and, by going back and forth, complete the work. It was in fact a right hand delivery or left hand delivery as desired. This accounts for the fact that he applied two dividers. His machine was adapted to cut low, as it was then and still is desirable to save all of the straw possible in Great Britain. Several of the early American machines were adapted to be moved before the horses. George Esterly was in the field, as were Schnebly & Schnebly. To Jonathan Haines, however, must be given the larger merit for the header as it finally came to stay; his patent was taken out in 1849. The machine differed from Bell's in that, instead of moving the grain deliveryward and depositing it on the stubble, it elevated it into a wagon having a large box. It was adapted to cut

257

high so that but little more than the heads need be taken, and the cutting apparatus could be raised and lowered by the operator, at will. The rear end of the push tongue was supported on a single truck, above which and behind the horses stood the operator, giving the proper direction to the machine by movement of a tiller that controlled the wheel. His reel was supported as Bell's had been, and his cutting apparatus was of the Hussey type. At the present day there are many thousand headers manufactured each year. The practice of manufacturers for a number of years has been to attach a short elevator and automatic binder to the machine. In order that the bundles may be properly bound these machines are adapted to be lowered sufficiently to give length enough of straw to make perfect bundles. It is proper to mention in this connection that Sylvanus D. Locke was one of the very first to make efforts to place a binding attachment upon a push machine of wide cut, but he was not successful.

About 1890 internal combustion engines, after a period of trial and error became available and dependable for many uses where much power with lightness was an object. Harvesting machines for many years had been constructed to be drawn by steam traction engines. The great combined harvesters and threshers of California reached the point of culmination in the line begun by Moore and Hascall as early as 1836. Successful attempts to place an engine upon a harvesting machine are comparatively of recent date. About 1860 Ausbert H. Wagner took out a patent showing a steam engine mounted upon the frame of a mowing machine. He did not meet with success, as he informed me, because of the fact that his engine was so exceedingly heavy. I know of no successful attempts to operate any form of harvesting machinery by power carried upon its wheels earlier than that made by George H. Ellis and myself, encouraged by Mr. William Deering, in 1894. That mowing machine seemed from the start to be a thing of life. This was followed by a mower of the Eureka type which has its cutting apparatus before the gearing carriage. No attempt was made to sell the machines as the time was not ripe for them, and, as far as mowing machines are concerned, it is not yet ripe. The placement of a small engine upon harvesting machines has been quite common since 1900, but, as far as known, I was first in placing an engine upon a header binder, as shown by the patent taken out by me in 1903. Be that as it may, I am willing to yield all the credit should it be learned that others anticipated my efforts. The frontispiece of this volume shows my so-called Tractor binder of 16 foot cut mounted on a gasoline tractor, the harvester portion and the tractor portion being placed back to back, the tractor being required to run backward in doing its work. This machine passed through two harvests in 1909, cutting at the rate of 50 acres per day of ten hours. As a further improvement in this direction an ordinary wide cut harvester and binder were so attached as to add to the 16 foot swath another 7 feet thus cutting and binding 23 feet in width and at the rate of 100 acres per day. The machine in its later stages is also adapted to receive a wide cutting apparatus and platform and, by means of an elevator, to operate as a header proper. The width of cut of a harvester carrying a binding attachment is limited to the capacity of the latter, which depends upon the size of the bundles. Sixteen feet of heavy grain is found to be as wide a swath as a binding attachment can take, but there is no limit to the width of swath that can be taken by a header proper, as it does not matter to what extent the straw is mixed on its way to the wagon box or "barge," as it is termed.

Mowing Machines

Early attempts of inventors in this art were directed to producing machines harvesting both grass and grain. In England large horizontal revolving discs were depended upon by Smith and others for cutting grass, and a few such machines were made and used in the United States. In Ogle's machine may be seen, to a large extent, the foundation upon which modern mowing machines are built; but we are not told that he intended to have his grain receiving platform removable in order that, in cutting grass, the latter might fall back and remain spread on the stubble. As but a single test of his machine was made, before it was destroyed by the workmen who feared its competition, it is presumable that he gave little thought to its possible use as a hay maker.

On May 3, 1831, a United States patent was granted to J. Manning, showing a finger bar with a reciprocating knife much like that used today. The fingers, or guards, however, were no advance over those of Gladstone, used in connection with his rotary disk cutter (except that they were below the knife) in that there was no part to aid the lower portion to hold the grass blades from yielding to the movement of the reciprocating knife. As shown in his patent, the machine was impractical because of the fact that the knife could only have been moved very slowly by the zigzag cam at the hub of the traction wheel. In those days models were often whittled out by the inventor, and many times he took short cuts to illustrate the embodiment of principles of devices that he was endeavoring to demonstrate.

To Hussey must be credited the first practical mowing machine. His reciprocating knife was practically that of Manning and, if we are correctly informed, that of Ogle as made by Brown and applied to the machine destroyed by the workmen; but the sections of the knife moved through slotted fingers and for the first time we find the grass properly sustained from movement with the cutting blades, or sections, as they are termed.

Hussey not only made his grain receiving platform detachable in order that he might mow with his machine, but hinged his finger bar to the gearing carriage in such a manner that it might rise and fall at its outer end to conform to undulations of the surface of the ground. Such was the origin of the hinged bar mowing machine. He thus fully laid the foundation upon which modern mowing machines are built.

Many of the early inventors of mowing machines depended upon a single traction wheel (as did Ambler, as shown by his patent of December 23, 1834), and from the gearing frame thereof they extended a rigidly secured finger bar. Some placed a small wheel at the outer end of the bar and others a mere runner. These machines for a time were popular because, having Hussey's removable platform attached, they could be quickly converted from a mower into a reaper. Hence the term "Combined Reaper and Mower," long used.

The first marked improvement on Hussey's mower was conceived by Lewis Miller and worked out by himself and a half brother, Cornelius Aultman. A patent was taken out by the young men jointly June 17, 1856.

Little description is necessary, as the reader may turn to any mowing machine of the present day and see at a glance the embodiment of Lewis Miller's conception. To the main gearing frame a coupling frame was pivoted and to the coupling frame the finger bar, in turn, was pivoted. The point of pivoting of the coupling frame to the main frame was substantially coincident with the axis of the crank shaft, which gave reciprocating movement to the knives, and the pitman, in turn, was pivoted to the knife at a point substantially coincident with the axis of movement between the coupling frame and the finger bar. The machine was a success from the start. The young men, then living at Germantown, Ohio, were already licensees and successful manufacturers of Hussey's reaping and mowing ma-

Aultman & Miller, Patent of 1856.

chine. Their business increased. New demands gave opportunity for advanced ideas and it is thought by the writer, personally long intimate with Lewis Miller, that no single inventor, after Hussey, did more in any branch of this art, as far as mowers alone are concerned, than Lewis Miller during his business career. From this machine, the original "Buckeye," there have been many deviations, but no departure from the foundations laid by Hussey and Miller.

Early attempts were made to take a portion of the weight of the cutting apparatus from the ground and sustain it on the main gearing frame. Various devices for the purpose are found in United States patents. So slow was the development, however, that special credit can be given to no one inventor, and no attempt will here be made in that direction. The records of the United States Patent Office may be depended upon as being substantially correct, no false claims to having invented the mower, as such, ever having been made.

During the years of the single wheel mowing machine various means have been adopted for raising and lowering the cutting apparatus, one of the earliest being that of E. Danford, patented September 17, 1850.

Danford's Mowing Machine.

Turning to the illustration, it will be seen that the seat is a very wide one. While the machine was mainly supported upon the traction wheel there was immediately in the rear thereof a large egg-shaped roller. The tongue was pivoted to the gearing frame, as the machines were put on the market by Mr. Danford, which left the tongue free in the neckyoke of the draft team, although the machine might be passing over very uneven ground. With the driver sitting at the grass end of the seat the cutting apparatus moved over the ground properly. Should he come to an obstruction, however, he moved sidewise to the stubble side of the seat, which caused the cutter bar to be thrown upward because of the oval shape of the roller beneath the seat. This was one of the first successful attempts to raise the outer end of the finger bar while at work, Hussey having merely so provided that the bar might rise and fall automatically to conform to the undulation of the ground. Ambler, as shown in his patent of December 23, 1834, had so provided that the cutting apparatus might be raised at its outer end, but this he accomplished by means of handles, as an operator would throw a plow out of the ground when walking behind it.

Aultman & Miller having led the way, by producing and putting upon the market in large quantities hinged bar mowing machines, it became a necessity for other manufacturers to follow suit, which they rapidly did, Cyrenus Wheeler being one of the earliest. Danford's machine was crude, but it served a good purpose, as the writer learned when a boy, having operated it for many seasons. So well did it serve its purpose that a second one was worn out on the same farm before Miller's Buckeye appeared to take its place.

Danford's machine was made at Elgin, Illinois, about forty miles from Chicago, in very large numbers. It was a brilliant success as a serviceable machine, although crude in construction. At that time, (1861), C. H. McCormick had no machine well adapted to mowing. His reaper seeming to be built on wrong lines for mowing, he turned to a successful competitor's machine for inspiration. His copy was an improvement, he thought, as it was so constructed that he might raise the finger bar at its outer end by shifting his position on the driver's seat, as Danford's operators had done, but he provided no supporting roller behind, leaving the cutting apparatus to ride wholly upon the ground, which was, of course, not thought seriously objectionable at that time. In order that he might raise the cutting apparatus at its inner end, he placed the seat in such a position that the operator, by hitching forward in it, or leaning forward, or leaving it and standing upon the foot-board, could throw the preponderance of weight in front of the axis of the supporting wheel, which gave the machine a tilt which moved the inner end of the finger bar some distance from the ground. The operation may be explained as follows: if the operator wished to elevate the outer end of the finger bar he moved to the stubbleward side of the seat, as in Danford's machine, and if he wished to raise the inner end of the finger bar he hitched himself forward in the seat, or shifted his position so that the preponderance of weight should be well forward of the axis of the traction wheel. In order that he might not lose his balance when standing upon the footboard a forwardly extending arm was secured to the seat, to which he could cling with one hand and thus be prevented from falling before the cutting apparatus.

The McCormick mower patent of 1861 added nothing worth while to the art of mechanical husbandry; indeed, I judge it one of the most useless imitations of a successful machine ever placed upon the market.

Strippers

About the middle of the last century inventors in Australia directed their attention to means for stripping the heads from the grain, and the first to succeed were little more than the machines of Gaul with a rapidly revolving beater, adapted not only to take the heads from the comb, but, by its rapid action, beat the kernels from the straw. In these machines the grain, with the chaff, is elevated to cleaning apparatus, from which it is delivered into bags upon a platform forming part of the machine.

As no disputes have ever arisen as to who invented the stripper, the patent offices of the various countries may be relied upon as showing where credit is due. Many thousand strippers are manufactured each year, principally in Australia and the United States, for use in semi-arid regions. My own stripper had the functional elements of a stripper harvester mounted upon an internal combustion tractor. Heretofore the swath taken by strippers has been six feet, with few exceptions. Modern strippers, like self-binding harvesters, cut a swath beside the line of travel of the team, and hence, a wide swath cannot be taken on account of excessive side draft if the width be too great. With the writer's tractor stripper the width of swath may be great, as the tractor is immediately behind the gathering devices.

CHAPTER XV.

Grain Binders

Very naturally the most abundant and cheapest material for making bands was straw; but although attempts were first begun in the early '50s, success has never been reached and probably never will be. While it is possible for man to devise mechanism that will handle a given condition of straw, the difficulty has so far been in manipulating the various conditions of straw with the same mechanical devices.

Attempts have been made to follow the hand method, that of uniting wisp to wisp of sufficient strength, passing the band material thus formed around the gavel, twisting and tucking the ends. Others attempted to twist a band from the butts of the gavel, by means of a rotating hook either traveling around the gavel or remaining stationary and the gavel turning adjacent to it. In fair grain, by this latter method, well worked out by Jackman, many good bands were made where the condition of the straw was favorable, but threshermen objected to bundles so bound because they had to be cut into many parts before they could be put through the machines. Not that the bundles were large, but that the straws that formed the surface of the complete bundle for an inch in depth, more or less, were so interknit that they could not be readily torn apart. Another attempt was made to separate a portion of the swath and direct it in rear of the grain-receiving platform to a twisting device and there form a rope by which the gavels might be bound. Still another, that produced by Fowler, consisted in crocheting a band of straw, near the middle of the gavel, by means of a needle which drew from the bundle the wisps necessary to form the loops, each through a preceding one. The difficulties encountered were these—unless the gavel was fully compressed, during the crocheting operation, the resulting bundle was so loose as to be valueless; and if the gavel were compressed before

265

the operation of crocheting began not so much as a single stitch could be taken because of the fact that the straws, under such compression and resulting frictional resistance, could not be rapidly drawn out to form the loops. The most successful effort substantially in this line was made by Walter A. Wood, whose corps of inventors devoted much time to producing a small rope of grass by means of which bundles were bound very successfully. The plan failed, however, because it was found more expensive to make the band material of the slough-hay, which was preferable, than to use the various coarse fibre twines, manila and sisal, for the purpose.

As early as 1850 John Heath produced a semi-automatic binder. A folding arm was adapted to lie in a groove on the grain receiving platform, upon which the cut straws could fall. The operator reaching out grasped the arm and brought with it the gavel, lying thereon, to the stubble side of the platform and there with a semi-automatic twine knotting device completed the band carried by the needle by tying a knot therein. This was found to be impractical because still manual.

In the Patent Office at that time as examiner was Edward S. Renwick, a born mechanic, and, later, one of the ablest patent experts in the country. I estimate his ability by the binders he, with William and Peter H. Watson, patented, and also by having contended with him, as a patent expert, in the courts. He it was who examined the Heath application and allowed it. It was no doubt his association with Heath in this matter that turned his mind in the direction of the patents patented to him and his associates. No machine was constructed under this patent, but the model embodied nearly all of the principles, broadly considered, found in the machines which now bind the grain of the civilized world. These inventors conceived the idea of binding from a continuous swath; of dividing off gavels therefrom as required; of stopping the flow of the incoming grain while the gavel was being bound; of compressing the gavel into bundle form, placing the band therearound and automatically tying the knot. At the same time they provided for a supplemental squeeze to the gavel, which should produce sufficient slack in the twine from which to form the knot. The completed bundle was then ejected, the band carrying devices withdrawn, and the gate opened and straw for the succeeding gavel permitted to enter the receptacle. Not only this, they were first to propose elevating the grain over the main supporting wheel and delivering it to the binding attachment. Furthermore, they recognized the fact that grain grew of varying heights, and that a perfect bundle should have the band near the middle of its length. Between the endless platform conveyor and the supporting wheel and extending upwardly they provided two series of belts between which the grain straws might be carried. By a very ingenious contrivance, well shown in the patent, these conveyors were adapted to be swung at their upper ends, in order to deliver the straws centrally into the receptacle of the fixed binding mechanism. The method of elevating by means of double conveyors did not come into use, however, until after 1868, when it was experimentally applied by the Marsh Harvester concerns to their hand binding machines. The shifting of the elevator to direct the swath of grain into the binding receptacle so as to be bound centrally has never proved practical, although attempted by Flenniken and McGregor for N. C. Thompson. The better course, now universally followed, is to shift the binding attachment, as a whole, to such a position that its band placing and band uniting devices may operate upon the straws practically at the middle of their length. It is possible that if Watson & Renwick had made a working machine and persisted in their efforts the automatic binder might have come before the Marsh harvester, which, as previously stated, wrought a revolution and placed the reaper far in the background. Watson, Renwick & Watson later went so far as to make a model of still another machine adapted to cut and bind grain, but no one of its elements has persisted. The special novelty was adjustment of the cutting apparatus relative to the binding devices, which were placed adjacent to the traction wheel, thus achieving regulation of the position of the gavel relative to the out-drawn band material. In the two models mentioned these inventors foreshadowed clearly the longitudinally adjustable binding device of today. Instead, however, of moving the binding mechanism relative to the swath of grain brought to the attachment, they changed the *direction* of movement in one case, and the *line* of movement of the swath of grain in the other, so that the band became centrally placed around the gavel preparatory to having its ends united. Not having embodied their conceptions in operative machines, they are entitled to credit merely as builders of air castles, so to speak, but the proposed embodiment of the ideas was so clearly shown, both in their models and drawings, and so carefully described in the specifications of their patents, that they nevertheless enriched the art to a very important extent, not only in the matter of central binding, but in a large number of the actual requirements necessary to make an operative semi-automatic binder. Later inventors did not follow the specific forms of construction shown by these inventors, but nevertheless the generic ideas had been exemplified and made clear to those who followed.

Later, during the '50s, many efforts were made, usually merely on paper, to bind the gavels of grain by the use of wire as a band material. No success was then reached, however. The earliest and fairly promising results were due to the efforts of William W. Burson who, early in the '60s, mounted a binding device upon the line of machines manufactured at Rockford, Ill., by the Manny interests. By means of this device, after the gavel had been raked to position by an operator, the band could be carried around the gavel by another operator and, by the turning of a crank, the ends of the band united, after which the bundle could be kicked endwise by the second operator out of position and the place thus made ready for another gavel. Too much labor was still required and although a few of the machines were sold and operated fairly, they soon ceased to exist. Both wire and twine were at times used by Mr. Burson as band material; the patent records show him to have been very fertile in ideas until a late day.

Early in the '60s Jacob Behel, also of Rockford, began his efforts to produce a grain binder. Upon the platform of the Manny reaper he mounted band placing and band uniting devices. His basic idea was embodied in his so-called ring carrier, a rotating ring into which the gavel might be thrust endwise by the raker and having, traveling therewithin, a carrier to place the end of the band around the gavel. The carrying movement was accomplished by means of a crank operated by the attendant. The crank also gave motion to the band uniting devices at proper intervals. The latter part should receive more than passing notice, as the broad principles embodied have persisted, and will probably continue to benefit man until his end on earth is reached. The knot tier consisted of a shaft supported in suitable journal bearings and having upon one end means for giving it a single rotation; upon its other end, a radial termination forming the fixed part; to this was pivoted another member, the whole comparable to the bills of a bird. The strands of twine to be united were placed across the bird's-bill-form device and the rotation not only wound the twine that was to form the bight of the knot around it but caught the ends between the jaws. The device, considered as a knotter solely, was defective. Not only was the stress of the twine depended upon to open the jaw, in order to take that portion of the twine to be drawn through the bight, but, in turn, the same stress closed the jaw in order that the portion thus grasped might be drawn through the bight.

I do not think that Behel borrowed the idea embodied in his knotter from the boy Appleby, nor from Locke, although the latter was working on the same lines about the time. Behel's home had for years been in Rockford, Illinois, and near Rockford, in southern Wisconsin, Appleby lived, in 1858, the lad who furnished to a gunmaker practically the knotting device of today. John F. Appleby, at that time, was eighteen years of age, but of him and his substantial achievement later. Suffice it to say, that the Appleby general idea may have become sufficiently known to meet the approval of other inventors and to prompt them to undertake its successful development. During the early harvest of 1858 the boy's employer purchased a reaper, which, one bright morning, was put in successful operation. It was to be followed by the farmer, the boy and others, who were to bind the gavels automatically delivered therefrom. The farmer was pleased with the operation and, nudging the boy, asked him what he thought, of *that,* receiving a reply that it worked finely. "But," said the boy, "I believe I can make a binder." The surprised farmer replied "Oh, you little fool! You couldn't make anything." Over twenty years later, after several manufacturers had been induced to take up his binder, Mr. Appleby had become superintendent of the Minneapolis Harvester Works. Driving to his home one evening he was halted by his old employer, then a teamster, who said that as winter was approaching he had concluded to get an indoor job for himself. Mr. Appleby instructed him to go to the factory in the morning.

However, Behel must be given full credit for one important step in the development of the modern automatic binder, a step further

than the boy had then gone. In order that the knotting hook, as it
is usually termed, may have the twine which is to form the knot placed
properly across the jaws, the first portion by the withdrawal of the
band carrying device and the second portion by the return movement of the band carrying device, it is essential that the two parts of
the twine be retained in a definite position between the knotter and
the gavel, and that the holder also be so located not only that the bight
of the knot may be properly formed, but that the ends to be drawn
through the bight be grasped by the jaws while still in the grasp of
the holding mechanism. This relative arrangement was carefully
worked out by Behel and, although his specific forms of construction
have not been followed, the generic idea was amply demonstrated.
He was first to bind bundles of grain in the field with twine.

The boy Appleby should not be charged with laches, as he was
without means. Behel was devoting his whole attention to his semi-
automatic binding attachment while the boy was following the flag
of his country in the war for the Union. A wide difference in political opinions existed between them which left Behel free to remain
at his work; he demonstrated, to a small extent in the harvest fields
and to a still larger extent at fairs, that it was possible to place twine
around a gavel of grain and complete a bundle by tying a knot in
the ends of the band.

The necessities of the great wheat fields of northern Illinois and
southern Wisconsin, more than elsewhere, inspired inventive young
men to reduce the labors of the harvest. At Janesville, Wisconsin,
Sylvanus D. Locke was one of the first to reach promising results.
His early efforts, like those of most others, had been directed to accomplishing the result by placing a semi-automatic device upon the
platform of the reaper, as Burson, Behel and others had done. He
had failed to reach perfect success, as had all others, but he later
conceived the idea of making a binding *attachment* that could be
placed upon the Marsh Harvester, which had then been about ten
years on the market. A rotary arm sweeping over the gavel receptacle
of the Marsh harvester was adapted, not only to carry a band of wire
around the gavel, but, having a twisting wheel and holder therein, to
there twist the ends of the band together, thus completing the bundle.
Like many others, he early abandoned the attempt to use twine al-

though, taking the Appleby-Behel idea, he constructed one of the most ingenious cord knotters up to that time.

During the early '60s James F. and John H. Gordon turned their attention to semi-automatic binders. Wire was in all early cases used by them as band material. While their interests were as one, they worked independently to a large extent. Many attempts were made by the Gordon brothers; the records of the patent office show nearly all that was done by them. Only so much, however, of the modern automatic binder as should be credited to them needs be mentioned.

Watson & Renwick had allowed the grain straws to fall in a mass into the binding receptacle. Later inventors, in attempting to operate upon the grain delivered by a rake, had compressed the gavel only as the rake had forced the grain straws against the outdrawn band material. John Gordon was first to demonstrate, in the field, the practicability of packing the straw wisp by wisp against the outdrawn band, as Spaulding had done in his little shop, thus encircling it and then completing the operation of binding. Gordon also provided means for checking the flow of the swath of grain straws during the operation of binding the already accumulated mass. The invention, thus demonstrated, was imperfectly embodied in the model illustrated by the drawing of his patent of 1872. The efforts of James Gordon, although many and extending over several years, resulted in no definite contribution to modern automatic twine binders, his attention having been devoted mainly to the use of wire.

In 1865 George H. Spaulding, a returned volunteer soldier, found employment in the so-called "Reaper City," Rockford, Illinois. After devoting much time in attempts to improve the Marsh harvester, in which Emerson, of the Manny Company was interested, he conceived the idea of so modifying the machine that a binding attachment could be placed where the men for the purpose of binding had ridden. Because of insufficient means he did not succeed in getting his binding attachment into the field, but he did get it before the public in the form of the patent granted to him in 1870. In this first machine he utilized the grain elevating devices for forming the gavel wisp by wisp, but in the second he employed crank-carried packers for the purpose. As far as mere conception and embodiment of the idea may be considered, he was first to do so, but as John H. Gordon preceded him in demonstrating in the field the practicability of the method of

John H. Gordon packer binder of 1874 and 1875 as modified for the harvest of 1876.

compacting, it seems to the writer that much credit should remain to Gordon.

To Spaulding goes the credit of making the binder wholly *automatic* in its action; a triumph to be considered later.

James Gordon took out his first patent in 1868. During that season, and, in fact, in the harvest of the year before, he had tested it. By means of an automatic rake the gavel was swept against the outdrawn band near the supporting wheel at the stubble end of the grain receiving platform. It was shown, in litigation, that the machines had operated fairly well. The band carrying arm was supported upon a shaft, or, rather, a shaft consisting of two parallel parts, and by them rocked in doing its work. The carrying arm was adjustable along those shafts and the band uniting devices were also adjustable longitudinally on the shafts which supported them and gave them movement. In the patent is found a claim covering the band-carrying arm adjustable in the direction of the length of the grain with a twisting device also adjustable. After grain binding attachments had become practical the two Gordons and D. M. Osborne & Company, each a third owner of the patent, brought suits for infringement of that claim. A long drawn legal battle, resulted in defeat; the court conferred a verdict of "non-infringement." The court held substantially that as defendants moved the whole binding attachment relative to the grain cutting and delivering devices, they followed Renwick and the Watsons, and that because of the constructions found in those early patents the Gordon claim was limited to so arranging the binding mechanism that it was only necessary to move the parts directly concerned in the operation of binding, and not the whole attachment. Early inventors had anticipated the coming necessities so many years before grain binders became practical that all means essential for central binding had become public property. The Gordons later devoted some attention to binding with twine, as the records sufficiently show, but, as with Locke, no element essential to the *modern* binder, aside from the use of packers, as stated, was invented or improved by them.

Early in the '70s Charles B. Withington, of Janesville, Wisconsin, came into the field. He made some valuable improvements which persisted as long as wire binders held their own. Spaulding's first and second binding attachments were adapted to move toward the binding receptacle, carry the band around the grain straws and complete the bundle while retreating. McPherson was early in the field in this line, the Gordons and others following. Withington embodied the idea in his binding attachment and accomplished one of the best of its day. It was taken up by C. H. and L. J. McCormick, and, about the year 1877, began to do successful work. The experiments of '76 showed but few improvements necessary. These were added by Withington, L. J. McCormick, William R. Baker, Lambert Erpelding, and others.

James Gordon, about 1872, came from Rochester, N. Y., to the Marsh Harvester Works at Plano, Illinois, with his experimental binder adapted to move bodily toward the receptacle, place the band around the gavel there accumulated and complete the bundle while retreating. The machine worked fairly well. Locke, in the employ of the Walter A. Wood Mowing & Reaping Machine Company, at Hoosick Falls, N. Y., was already well along with his experiments. His best success was with a Marsh harvester, of his own construction. The little company at Plano, in which Mr. William Deering first became interested, encouraged inventors by furnishing them Marsh harvesters at cost prices, and the Gordons, particularly, at each returning season bought a machine to be tested. S. D. Carpenter had given up the race and devoted his attention to other lines. William H.

Payne had met with some success. In 1873 John H. Gordon's machine promised a success to such an extent that several were made for the harvest of 1874 and sold. The fact that Mr. Gordon, although later than Spaulding, was before Gorham in packing the gavel was conclusively proved by the McCormick Company, which made itself a party defendant in Deering vs. Winona Company. (See Record.) For the same reason Locke built three machines, which were sold. In the year 1874 the manufacture of John Gordon's machine was taken up at the Plano works for the harvest of 1875. Walter A. Wood had met with sufficient success in the Marsh Harvester field to warrant him at that time in undertaking to put the Locke binder on the market. While Steward & Gammon had given some encouragement to inventors, William Deering, who had become an important factor in the business, urged the placement of the Gordon binders, in their then condition, upon the market. William Deering, though not a mechanic, was a merchant born and foresaw future commercial possibilities. He insisted that at least a hundred Gordon binding attachments be put out in the West for the year 1875 even though, as one of his partners later put it, they should ultimately

From an old cut.

Twisting holding and cutting device of the Deering-Gordon binder of 1876
The simplest one produced.

find their way into the Mississippi river, his thought being that the public should know that his concern had reached success sufficient to warrant them in taking risks, at least. The machines were made, but failed because of many imperfections in design and were returned. The Wood Company had met with better success, although its machines proved, in the end, to be far inferior. Its band carrying arm was rotary and often carried the completed bundles around with it, with destructive results. The 113 Gordon binders that were put out in '75 were all returned, as stated, and upon the writer fell the duty of rebuilding them for the season of 1876. As reconstructed, with new holding and twisting devices and several other improvements, all were resold, as well as many hundreds in addition, and from that time wire binders were put out by the Plano Marsh harvester concern, Gammon & Deering, until waived aside by the Appleby twine binders, in turn first successfully put out by that Company, in large quantities.

CHAPTER XVI.

Knot-Tying Machines

Early in the '70s C. H. and L. J. McCormick saw that the Marsh harvester had come to stay, and during the year 1874 they perfected a form of Marsh harvester belying the immense amount of printer's ink they had paid for during the ten years in crying up their reapers and denouncing Marsh harvesters. For the harvest of 1875 they had built many thousands of the latter, using the double canvas elevating devices demonstrated by Steward and Marsh in 1868, and adopted by Marsh licensees at Massillon, Ohio. The printed matter issued by them, exploiting their new machine, avoided any word that might hint that they were new in the Marsh harvester business.

The machines worked well. During the year '74 that company made an arrangement with James Gordon, who had applied his binder to a Marsh harvester, whereby they might operate under his patents, the royalty being ultimately placed at $10.00 per binder. The Gordon binders had been demonstrated at Plano and Gammon & Deering had already entered into tentative agreements. This, if nothing more, was sufficient to spur the imitators of the Marsh harvester, hence the McCormick license from Gordon.

Withington, however, later entered into an arrangement with the McCormick Company and his binder was chosen in preference to Gordon's, the first attachments being put on the McCormick Marsh harvester for the season of 1876. The Withington binder was a good one. Although much more complicated than Gordon's, ultimately it operated better. Not better, however, than the much simpler John Gordon machine, as rebuilt for that year. The method first shown to be practical by Spaulding, that of moving toward the gavel receptacle and taking the accumulation therefrom, was availed of by James Gordon in 1874 and a very successful machine made. The

276

binding attachment, as a whole, however, did not move to and from the gavel receptacle, but its arms swung as those of a crane. In order to balance the harvester and binder as a whole on the main supporting wheel, Gordon had placed his attachment near the rear of the machine, its arms extending forward. The improvements placed by the writer upon the John Gordon binder had proved so valuable that he was instructed to modify the Gordon crane binder, which he did, leaving the axis of movement at the rear, where Gordon had placed it. No binding device has ever been made, and it does not

Withington Wire Binder attached to McCormick Marsh Harvester

seem possible that one can ever be made, half so simple as that attachment. It was not only simple, but the draft was so light that no arming of the traction wheel was necessary, and the John Gordon form was abandoned in 1877 for the James Gordon form thus reconstructed.

Withington had placed his binding attachment upon the harvester in such manner that its arms extended from the front rearwardly to the center of the grain to be bound. The result of this placement was that when the gavel was grasped to be moved outwardly in the operation of binding the heads of grain were separated as far as

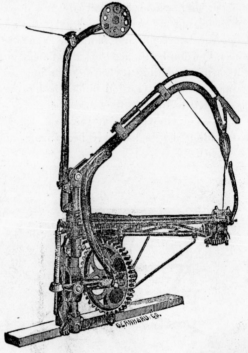

From an old wood-cut.
Deering wire binder attachment of 1878 as improved by Steward.

other portions of the straws forming the moving swath. With the Gordon crane binder, just mentioned, the swinging action was such that the heads of the grain straws were not separated, resulting in frequent entanglements to such an extent that several bundles might hang together. The Withington machine reduced entanglement.

Charles B. Withington died late in the year 1909. An obituary published in the Chicago Tribune, one of the editors of which is Medill McCormick, a nephew of Cyrus McCormick, referred to Withington as the "inventor of the first automatic grain binder," but the fact is that, although he invented means whereby he could use from two spools of wire in 1870, he did not get a machine into the field until 1876, three years after Locke and John Gordon had each sold wire binders. The McCormick Company put out six Withington machines, experimentally, in 1876. They promised well. In

1877 Lambert Erpelding improved them by adding a device adapted to tuck the wire into position to be engaged by the twisting pinion. The machines of '77 gave much trouble until this improvement was made, failing to tie as many as half the bundles in fluffy grain. The machines of 1878 were the first that worked well.

On December 13, 1909, previous to the unveiling of the portrait of Cyrus H. McCormick in the so-called Hall of Fame at the Illinois University of Agriculture, the statement above referred to appeared. While Mr. Withington was a very ingenious, respected, and able man, nothing in our art invented by him has persisted.

Locke's rotary binder, although pushed by the Wood Company, did not meet with the approval of the farmers to the extent the wire binders did that were put out by Gammon & Deering and the McCormick Company.

Aultman, Miller & Co., of Akron, Ohio, put out one form of the John H. Gordon binder, but, as they were new in the Marsh harvester lines, mistakes in both the binder and harvester ultimately defeated them. The Marsh harvester was taken up by other manufacturers by whom wire binders were also manufactured, but with little success.

The arrangement made by the McCormick Company with Mr. Gordon was unfortunate in that it required, as before stated the payment of $10.00 royalty to Gordon and his associates, one of whom was D. M. Osborne & Co. Before many seasons had passed the Gor-

Locke binder attachment applied to W. A. Wood Marsh Harvester.

don interests brought suit against the McCormick Company for non-fulfillment of the license contract. A strenuous defense was contemplated and many of the most eminent lawyers consulted, one of whom was Benjamin F. Thurston, who later stated to the writer that General Leggett and George Hardin had been consulted and had advised a fight, while he, Thurston, advised the settlement which was finally reached out of court by payment by the McCormick Company of $240,000.00 (stated by Casson in his "Romance of the Reaper" to have been $250,000.00, possibly correctly). The information here given was from the lips of Mr. Osborne and John H. Gordon, who stated that, although they requested a check, they were forced to take cash or nothing, and that the counting of which occupied them to near midnight, and after that late hour they were obliged to carry the amount in an old satchel to their hotel through the ill-lighted streets of the city of Chicago.

Many of the facts of the McCormick-Gordon affair may be found in the record of the suit brought by David M. Osborne, James F. Gordon and John H. Gordon against Cyrus H. McCormick and others in the Circuit Court of the Southern District of New York. The record was printed but very likely never filed, as the case was settled out of court as stated. Previous to the McCormick transactions the Gordons had been, during several harvest seasons, at the Marsh Harvester Works at Plano, modifying and improving their machines as experience proved necessary. The tests were made for and by the little company with a view to taking a license, which license was duly put in black and white. After the tests of 1874 (see record of Gordon et al vs. Warder et al, U. S. Circuit Court, Southern District of Ohio) machines were sent to Canada and there, in the fields, were seen by Cyrus H. McCormick. On April 5, 1884, James Gordon testified in regard to his dealings with Cyrus H. McCormick, and we find that the latter met him in the fields in Canada; that subsequently, in October of 1874, a license was granted. $20,-000.00 was agreed upon as advance royalties and notes given for a part of the amount. In a short time Gordon was notified that his patent had been thrown into interference with an application filed by Charles B. Withington, which application was owned by the McCormick Company. Fearing unfair treatment, and, quite likely for other reasons, Mr. Gordon sold the note. I quote from his testimony at the trial of the suit:

"Q. 30. Were you not advised that it would be to your interest not to pass the notes out of your possession before maturity? A. I was not. I did not need advice on that subject. The McCormick's reputation was such that I thought I had better get the money."

"Q. 33. And you passed it out of your possession for fear that Mr. McCormick might refuse payment? A. I passed it out of my possession because I wanted to use the money."

"Q. 35. Can't you tell me whether that was your motive or not in parting with that note? A. Well I was aware that the McCormick's were working against me, that they were trying to get an extension of the Reynolds' patent and that they were backing Withington in the interference and trying to divest me of my rights and I did not know but that they might try to divest me of my rights in this note."

"Q. 38. You did know at that time that McCormick was opposing you in the Withington interference? A. Yes. I knew a long while before that he was opposing me in the Withington interference, but I did not take the pains to go to Chicago to get the notes cashed because I thought they were legitimate and for an honest debt."

"Q. 39. Did you not know that he had repudiated that contract of yours? A. I did not at that time."

"Q. 40. Did you not so reason from the fact that he was assisting others contrary to your interests? A. I knew that he had under the contract the right to use various other improvements of mine which I considered of more importance than the particular one he was trying to divest me of my title to, and therefore was not very much afraid that he could set up any defense or lack of consideration against the notes."

Ans. to X. Q. 54. "I discovered McCormick was operating against me through Reynolds and Withington a long while before I disposed of the notes."

There was evidently much bad blood between the parties, which accounts for McCormick's refusal to draw a check in lieu of requiring the parties to count so large an amount of money and carry it at midnight through the streets.

The story of the wire binder is not a long one, as its day was so soon closed. Few were put out after the year of 1881 by any manufacturer. The efforts to bind with twine began with Heath's machine and the dream of Edward S. Renwick and the two Watsons. The model in the United States Patent Office made by these men shows knotting devices, but devices of a type that has never succeeded. The boy Appleby had produced a successful knotting hook in 1858 and had made partial models of binders, but, financial aid failing, he was forced into delay for the time.

Appleby's efforts, at that early day, are mentioned in what follows:

"I, Horace H. Houghton, resident of the town of LaGrange, Walworth County, Wis., being duly sworn testify that in the months of May and June, A. D., 1858, while at work for me as a farm hand at this place still my residence, John F. Appleby, the well known inventor of Grain Binders, then eighteen years of age, was making experiments on automatic grain binders and that his main efforts were employed on the knotting mechanism although other parts of the machine were built. —That this work was done under the direction of the said John F. Appleby at a gun shop in the village of Palmyra, Wis.—That the old appearing mechanism with the metal parts attached was made at said gun shop at the time and place above mentioned, also the knotting hook (now made bright), and made within the time mentioned; i. e., months of May and June, A. D. 1858.—That these models were in the possession of my father, in the house here occupied by him, from 1858 to about 1870, when he delivered them to the said John F. Appleby who was at that time at work on Grain Binders at Beloit, Wis.
Subscribed and sworn to before me
this 25th day of May, A. D.
1907.

(Signed) Horace Houghton.

William Greening,
Justice of the Peace
In and for the County of
Walworth and State of Wisconsin."

Jacob Behel successfully tied knots early in the '60s, but had not accomplished a commercial twine binder. Locke a little later approached the Appleby knotter very closely, but he did not succeed in producing a successful twine binder until long after the Appleby binder had been fully developed. His last effort, like that of others, did not compete successfully with the type produced by Appleby.

Marquis L. Gorham was a resident of Rockford, Illinois, the "Reaper City." He was inventive but, judging from the binder he made, he had not the faculty of embodying his ideas in good form and seemingly was not a skilled mechanic. His attention had been principally devoted to tillage lines. Various inventors in the harvester and reaper line living in Rockford were intimately associated and frankly and freely discussed their ideas. The inventive fever is contagious, and, no doubt, from Burson and Behel, the earliest workers in that vicinity, the fever spread. Mr. Gorham undertook the manufacture of a twine binder attachment to be mounted upon the harvester, and in 1874 had a crude machine in the field. In it was embodied the Spaulding principle of automatically sizing the gavels as well as the slightly modified form of the packing devices of Spaulding's second but unpatented machine, which he, Gorham, carefully studied. As will be seen by the patent, later taken out, Gorham did not pack against a yielding element which element could continue to move and permit the completed bundle to pass it, as Spaulding had done, but, on the contrary, hinged the outer portion of his binding receptacle in such a manner that it could be swung away bodily and let the completed bundle drop out through the gap thus made. In his knotting devices he attempted to follow Appleby and Behel, but instead of making use of a pivoted jaw in his knotter he preferred to grasp the held end of the twine by a bent finger, its spindle moving axially within the knotter shaft and adapted to grasp the ends of the twine that were to form the bow and draw them through the bight. This L-shaped finger was moved by a cam, but the time of rotation of the knotter was most uncertain because of the roundabout way of communicating motion from one part of the mechanism of the machine as a whole to the other. He attempted to remove the completed knot by a relative movement of the twine controlling element adjacent to the knotter, but not as Behel had successfully done. With the Behel device the bight of the knot was laid by a complete rotation of the knotter, and the portion of the twine to form the bow simultaneously grasped, after which the knotter was moved laterally relative to the notch which maintained the position of the twine between the knotter and the bundle. In short, Behel awaited the complete shaping of the knot before he attempted to strip it from the knotter; that is, he completed the knot as one step and then forcibly drew it from the knotter, practically as on all binders of the present day. Gorham, however, not seeing the desirability of making the two operations successive, attempted to move the stripping device by means of a cam on the knotter shaft, with the result that the knot was not always completely laid before it was stripped from the knotter. His knots, such as resulted in good bundles, were drawn from the knotter as they were pulled away. This method caused many failures to tie.

· Spaulding, in his second machine, built in 1870, had placed cranks at the middle of the drum which carried the elevating belts, and on the wrists of these cranks had mounted toothed bars the teeth of which when thrust up through the table, would engage the grain straws moved up by the elevating belts at the middle of their lengths, and force them, wisp by wisp, against the yielding metal plates, shown in his patent of 1870. (See page 297.) The toothed bars were supported at their stubble ends by guides. The machine was never patented. Waldron, who was to furnish the necessary means, became unable to carry on the work. A model of the machine as made is shown in the accompanying illustration, and the model from which the photo engraving was taken is in the Museum of Arts in Paris.

The facts in regard to this machine were gathered by the writer when preparing defenses in a suit brought by the Gorham-McCormick interests against various manufacturers of the Appleby binder, the blacksmith who made the forgings; Mr. Waldron, who supplied the means; Mr. W. D. Stapelin, and several others stating, in the form of affidavits, fully as to the construction of the machine.*

Spaulding's unpatented Binder, having packers and his patented
automatic sizing device.

* The proofs thus procured became lost at the time of failure of Aultman, Miller & Co., the defendant in the suit.

Waldron was anxious to get into the market with some kind of a money making machine, and was too impatient to await the development of a binding attachment, and so the machine went out as a new form of Marsh harvester. In the Aultman suits, Stapelin, McCormick's witness, testified that the automatic bundle sizing devices worked successfully, as shown by the printed record, page 549.

The facts brought out are that the "grain was elevated by metal teeth upon either canvas or leather belts, the grain being kept against the teeth by a float." "It elevated the grain to the top of the elevator and pressed against the overhanging plates which were mounted upon a rock-shaft like this in the model (of Spaulding's machine) and by such pressure elevated those plates so as to cause the rocking of the shaft upon which they were fastened."

Stapelin's Testimony

"X.Q. 29. When the arm, that is, the binding arm, came back—I mean from the cutting side of the machine toward the other side—it gathered a bundle from the harvester deck, or receptacle, did it not?
"A. It did.

"X.Q. 30. And it carried the binding material so as to place the bard around that bundle, did it not?
"A. It did.

"X.Q. 31. And the binder-arm carried that binding material into the knotter or twister, did it not?
"A. It did.

"X.Q. 32. And it there bound the bundle, did it not?
"A. It sometimes bound the bundle and it sometimes did not.

"X.Q. 33. But there seemed to be some difficulty about cutting the cord after it was bound or knotted; that is right, is it not?
"A. It was either a difficulty in cutting the cord or in tying the knot, knotting the cord; I cannot say which.

"X.Q. 34. And, so far as you remember, or have any knowledge, this was the only difficulty experienced in the operation of this machine; is that right?
"A. Of the binding machine; that is all I know concerning any difficulty concerning the binding machine."

In the lower court Judge Jackson had a copy of the Spaulding machine before him and held that the Gorham patent was not infringed. The machine was not before the Supreme Court.

Spaulding's workshop was Waldron's barn, in a portion of the upper story of which Mr. Waldron conducted his real estate business, and it also served as a loafing place for his friends on rainy days. All of the many comers passed through Mr. Spaulding's room in going to the stairway. Mr. Gorham was one of his interested visitors, and at one time, particularly, sat upon a lumber pile beside Spaulding's machine, listened to explanations and witnessed its operations. After he had concluded to undertake the task himself he borrowed Mr. Spaulding's patent of 1870 and studied it in order that he might embody its automatic feature in his prospective machine. As Mr. Spaulding had also built several harvesters of the Marsh type Mr. Gorham consulted him and borrowed certain parts. This story is in part told by Mr. Spaulding in his letter to the writer, soon to follow. It is believed by this writer, as often stated by Mr. Spaulding, that Mr. Gorham was an honorable man and, feeling that he was indebted to others for a knowledge of many of the broad principles embodied in his machine, he drew specific claims accordingly, as found in his patent of 1875. John Gordon's packer binder finished the harvest of 1874 near Rochelle, Ill., about twenty miles from Gorham's home, and Gordon was one of the many interested spectators who kept in touch with the tests.

During various interference proceedings in the Patent Office it was shown that Mr. Gorham's machine did some work in 1874 and considerably more work in 1875, but I am by no means convinced that his machine as modified in 1876 accomplished any results worth mentioning. That his machine could never have succeeded, continuing in his specific lines, is apparent by reference to the illustration, page 297, which delineates a false "tooth path" of Gorham's packer. (Page 271 of complainant's record in McCormick Co. vs. Aultman et als.) The present writer was shown the binder of 1876 by Mrs. Gorham, the widow, and given an excellent opportunity to study it. He had already had much experience in the art and was able to size it up correctly, as shown in the records of litigations afterward begun. The width of the machine as a whole was excessive, although the maker had attempted to shorten it by substituting for the inclined grain elevators of the Marsh harvester vertical ones following the Spaulding machine. Notwithstanding this, the binding attachment was so large and heavy as to more than over balance the grain end of the machine. To prevent the machine, as a whole, from tipping over stubbleward a large part of the grain divider was made of cast iron. The only result of the Gorham inventions was troublesome suits brought by the purchasers against nearly all manufacturers of the successful Appleby binders after the last revolution in the art of harvesting had been wrought. Mr. Gorham had sold rights to N. C. Thompson, a small manufacturer of reapers in Rockford. Thompson's superintendent, William McGregor, and principal mechanical engineer, Theodore M. Flenniken, after seeing Mr. Appleby's machine in 1876, attempted to embody some of the Gorham principles in a small machine. McGregor and Flenniken made this author, with machine present, perfectly familiar with it. Many were put out by Mr. Thompson, contributing to his business failure. Sterritt & Gibbs, of Corry, Pa., had been licensed to build machines under the Gorham patents, but soon failed. The writer saw machines of the Sterritt & Gibbs manufacture, but as they failed in the field, he never had an opportunity to see them in practical operation. This would be the end of the Gorham efforts but for the litigations. The size of the binder proper may be judged by the fact that its cutting apparatus was five feet in length.

Mr. Appleby never lost faith in his ability to produce a binder. On his return from the Civil War to his Wisconsin home he found that much had been done by inventors of that region, in efforts to produce binders using wire as band material during his three years absence. Stephen D. Carpenter, of Madison, Wis., beginning in the early sixties, had reached a certain degree of success and Appleby, finding that wire could be successfully handled had again taken up the task, thinking that by the use of wire success could be more quickly reached. He turned his thoughts to wire as band material for a time, and produced a successful binder. Through the middle seventies, however, he devoted his attention anew to binders using twine as band material, and for the late harvest of 1875 embodied in an attachment to the Marsh harvester, as then made by Parker & Stone, most of the devices found in the Appleby binder of to-day, the deft steel fingers of which tie the grain of the civilized portions of the world. His own story, soon to follow, will give details.

The Parker & Stone Reaper Works, as early as the year 1864,

began making Marsh harvesters for the Marsh association and continued for a year or two and later put machines on the market for itself. Thus thoroughly familiar with the Marsh harvester, they were willing to enter into an arrangement with Mr. Appleby to apply a twine binder to a machine of that type. The efforts continued until the ultimate failure of Parker & Stone.

CHAPTER XVII.

The Appleby Patents

Early in 1878 the writer and Mr. William Deering were invited to visit the factory of Parker & Stone at Beloit, with a view to an arrangement to undertake the manufacture of the Appleby binder, the prospective success of which they had been informed by E. D. Bishop in 1877, a party in interest. A tentative agreement was entered into and for the harvest of 1878 two binders were shipped to the works of Gammon & Deering, at Plano, Illinois, and followed by that company to Texas, where I made field tests during the harvest of that year. Soon after the close of the harvest Messrs. Parker & Stone had reached the conclusion that they were not strong enough to develop the machine and continue its manufacture and sale. Hence they entered into a formal license agreement with Gammon & Deering, dated November 29, 1878. The license fee mentioned in the agreement was $10.00, but in view of Gammon & Deering being one of the first to take up the task a reduction of fifty per cent was made, the clause relating thereto reading:

"And in consideration of the said *Gammon* and *Deering* being one of the first manufacturers of said machines, their services and experience being in the future diligently given to introduce said machine and bring it before the farmer and manufacturer, *pioneering* it through the coming harvest and giving other manufacturers who may see fit to adopt it in the future the benefit of their experience the remaining *Five Dollars* ($5.00) royalty on each of said machines so manufactured by them shall be considered to be paid therein."

The machines were by no means perfect, but before the close of the harvest of 1879 many of them had been made to work quite well. The success was sufficient to create a great demand, and for the harvest of 1880 William Deering, then sole owner of the business, was

289

led to put out 3,000 machines considerably improved, all of which showed their true mettle in the harvest fields. Mr. Appleby, while engaged with Mr. Deering in perfecting the binder during the winter of 1879 and 1880, had proposed reversing his binding attachment so that it should over-reach the grain receptacle from in front and, under a verbal arrangement with Mr. Deering, at Plano, had made patterns for what he termed a front geared binder, as distinguished from the leading form, which differed only in that the latter reached *forward* over the heads of the grain to the middle of the binding receptacle. Castings were made for metal patterns which he took with him to Esterly's factory and then to the Minneapolis Harvester Works, with which factory in the meantime he had become engaged, and there for the harvest of 1880 binding attachments were made by him from the original Deering wooden patterns, one of which was sent to the St. Louis Fair in the autumn of 1880. This binder was there purchased ostensibly by a farmer, and sent to the McCormick factory in Chicago. The late E. D. Bishop, well known to me, said:

"The machine sold at St. Louis had for a sample was a complete harvester and binder, ready to go into the field and do regular work. I had authority to sell it from their Gen/1 Mg/r, Mr. Jones, a brother of the Plano Jones, to some farmer if I could find such a purchaser. I sold to a man that represented himself as being a farmer that lived a few miles from St. Louis, for, I think, about $250., and received the currency from him, and gave him a receipt in the company name, and reported the sale to them. No one connected with the Minnesota Company at that time knew or had any intimation till weeks after, except myself that this farmer was buying it for Pratt, the McCormick agent, and I did not know it for a certainty until afterwards. Colahan arranged the matter, and you know his method of doing such business. He was there talking with me when asked if I was going to ship the machine to Chicago. I told him I had orders to sell to a farmer if I could, and deliver on the ground, and told him what I would take. This man came around and offered me the same price. That made me think Colahan and Pratt had a hand in it, and Pratt told me so afterwards.

"I also had orders from Jones to sell the Chicago machine after the exposition was through, but I was taken sick and hired Peter Mill, who was afterwards one of their Gen/l Ag/ts, to attend the machine, and he sold for about the same price to a man at Washington Heights, or near there."

The following throws light on the Bishop story: Pratt gave the information that he was ordered to buy the Minneapolis Appleby binder and ship to Chicago.

The above tells how the Appleby binder made at Minneapolis was procured, as well as the "Chicago" machine, the Deering, which was sold under the instructions of William H. Jones, an agent for Mr. Deering, and was sent to Washington Heights, a suburb of Chicago. The Deering binder had been very successful. Beardsley, a McCormick agent, manager in 1880 for the McCormick Company, said:

"I don't believe in a 'packer binder' size or no size the bundle; a compressor is *the* thing to make a bundle with—in my opinion."

Very naturally the Company, being about to take up the manufacture of the Appleby binder, needed help, and an agent said, in substance:

About experts, I hired a feller who worked last year for Deerings, and sent him down to Minn. Harv. Works, and he spent two days there and is now setting up one of ours for Shatto. I had a call yesterday from a man who has been here a month working in Harv. Shop under promise that they would send him on the road. He told me he and chum and bro. were all going to quit this Saturday unless the M. H. Co. did by them as they agreed to. I will hire *him* if he does quit them. I told him *I* wouldn't nor you wouldn't hire anybody away from another firm and all that kind of high morality talk, but if two or three good men came along in about a week, if they understood the twine B. I could find places for them.

Nevertheless, mechanics of the McCormick Company, the principal two of which were the late Henry Pridmore and the late William R. Baker, were put to work copying the two machines, selecting, however, the front geared form. Mr. William Deering, while still associated with Mr. Gammon, had reached an understanding with Mr. Appleby and his associates that he should have the exclusive right to manufacture in the state of Illinois under the Appleby patents. Mr. Appleby later informed me that conversation with Mr. Gammon had led him to believe that the exclusive license idea had been dropped. Mr. Deering informed this author that he, finding the McCormick Company were encroaching upon his rights as he understood them, approached Mr. Appleby, only to have it explained that the McCormick Company had said they should build his binder at any rate, but offered him and his associates $25,000.00 for a license. What followed immediately is found in the testimony of Henry Pridmore in the suit brought by William Deering against the Winona Harvester Company, in which the McCormick Company made itself interested, a portion of which reads as follows:

"X. Q. 20.—Before you began to make drawings for the Appleby binder, had you ever seen any Appleby binders?

"A.—I had.

"X. Q. 21.—Whose manufacture have you seen?

"A.—The Minneapolis, the Deering, or so, I suppose.

* * * * * * *

"X. Q. 24.—Where were those two machines?

"A.—At the factory of the McCormick Harvesting Machine Co.

"X.Q.25.—You used them as samples or guides in making the drawings for the defendant's machine, did you not?

"Objected to as irrelevant to direct examination.

"A.—The Minneapolis was the only one I used to take measurements from or refer to for strength.

"X. Q. 26.—When did you first see an Appleby twine-binder of the Deering make?

"A.—I believe it was in the exposition building of Chicago, in the month of September, 1880, or thereabouts."

Under oath two of McCormick's employees swore that the first McCormick twine binder had been copied from a Deering and a Minneapolis machine, in the autumn of 1880, from patterns, as stated, originally made at the Deering factory.

William Deering's feat of building 3,000 twine binders was the feature of the 1880 harvest and caused a furore among his competitors. To offset the Deering advantage the McCormick Harvesting Machine Company took up the Appleby binder, and made an arrangement with Mrs. Gorham, whose husband, although he had died nearly five years before, was said by Casson to have built for the McCormick Company its binders for the year 1881. Evidently the Minneapolis Appleby binder had served its purpose to such an extent, as sworn to by Mr. Pridmore, that the first "McCormick Binder" copied from it was completed before the 14th of February, and seemingly it was desired that Appleby pass judgment on it, although Bishop had been present during its making; still they wished Appleby to come, but he was busy and it was difficult for him to get away.

Then another effort was made to get Appleby to come to the works, although Casson assures us that the ghost of Gorham—it must have been his ghost since Gorham was dead—assisted in making the copy of the Deering Appleby Minneapolis binder. Evidently he could not aid them in the matter of twine and they depended upon Appleby, who informed them that Manilla twine could be produced from 700 to 800 feet per pound as Deering had used it on nearly all of his binders in 1880.

The Appleby binder first made, or possibly, as rumor had it, the one purchased at St. Louis, was mounted on the McCormick copy of the Marsh harvester and sent to England. In the McCormick circular for the fall of 1881 the machine so sent was said to have won the Derby prize, and from that circular I quote: "This sort of good generalship and management on the part of McCormick has helped to keep his machine where it has stood for the last thirty-five years —in the lead of all others." Aside from the fact that it has never led, I agree with the words of the quotation, "such has been the good generalship and management on the part of McCormick." The facts, as stated to me by McCormick employees, are that in order to get this machine off in time for the Derby show the simpler castings were taken from the binder attachment bought at the St. Louis fair and put directly into the sand, only the more complicated parts having been duplicated in wood for the purposes of molding.

The situation in which the McCormick Company was placed by Mr. Deering's success in making and selling the Appleby twine binder in 1879 and 1880, in addition to thousands of wire binders, is made clear by the words of Mr. E. K. Butler, long associated with the McCormick Company, as follows:

"In order to get L. J. McCormick and his son, R. H., his partners, and practically the shop managers, out of the way, Cyrus H. brought about the organization of a corporation, which gave him control. Deering's success had shown them the necessity of moving quickly, but they found the management so weak that as late as February, of their first season of twine binders, 1881, they had practically shipped no machines. Cyrus, then holding a majority of the stock, had become master, and he called me in and gave me the general management."

After the harvest of 1880 William Deering was approached by the owners of the Gorham patents in an effort to make a sale to him. An able patent lawyer, Mr. Joseph G. Parkinson, was called in counsel. Meantime, I had spent much time in Washington looking over the records. Mr. Parkinson and I agreed that no invention covered by Gorham's 1875 patent was found embodied in the Appleby binder. The price asked for an exclusive right under the patents was $100,-000.00. This proposition was promptly turned down.

Gorham's agents soon went to the McCormick Harvesting Machine Company and entered into a combination, the two parties pooling their interests and placing them in the hands of an able lawyer, William Lathrop, the intention being to bring suit against all manufacturers of Appleby binders for infringing the Gorham patents and a number of worthless patents put into the pool by the McCormick Company. Bills were duly filed, and it then became my duty to make investigations. Naturally the first thing was to determine by what rights suits were brought. Mr. Gorham had died in 1876, and reference to his will in the archives of the County Court showed this author that he had placed his patents in the hands of his wife as *trustee* for herself and the two children, one of whom was Mrs. Harrison, of Boston, Mass. Mr. Orange Gorham, a cousin of Mrs. Gorham by marriage, and Mrs. Gorham herself, suspected that she was not being fairly dealt with by Thompson, Lathrop, and the Mc-Cormick Company. At her instance I consulted with one Brazee, an attorney of Rockford, Ill., who was retained in her interest. Mr. Orange Gorham and I then called upon Mrs. Gorham, who showed the papers that had been drawn, and furnished a copy, the original of which is found of record in Liber Q-27, page 126, of Transfers of Patents in the United States Patent Office. The signature showed to this author that she had only parted with her individual interest, and the deal was immediately taken up with Mrs. Harrison, who had also become suspicious that her interests, as well as those of her mother and sister, were likely to be seriously affected by the pretended deal. The matter was put into shape so that Mr. William Deering was given a power of attorney by Mrs. Harrison in order to protect her rights and incidentally those of her mother and sister, the instrument reading as follows:

"KNOW ALL MEN BY THESE PRESENTS: That I, Alice M. Harrison, of the City of Boston in the State of Massachusetts have made, constituted and appointed, and by these presents do make, constitute and appoint WILLIAM DEERING of the City of Chicago, County of Cook and State of Illinois, my true and lawful attorney for me and in my name, place and stead to commence and prosecute to a conclusion or dismiss a suit in the United States Circuit Court in and for the Northern District of Illinois, or any other court or courts against William Lathrop, Norman C. Thompson, McCormick Harvesting Machine Company, and any other person or persons or corporations to set aside a contract between Helen M. Gorham and said William Lathrop, Norman C. Thompson and McCormick Harvesting Machine Company concerning United States Patents numbered respectively 159, 506, 160, 879, 218, 377, 233, 089, and other property, dated October 20, 1881, and an assignment of said patents and other property dated October 31, 1881, referred to in said contract, and also a certain other contract between said Helen M. Gorham and Norman C. Thompson, concerning said patents and other property, dated January 3, 1879, and to apply for leave to amend, and amend any paper, pleading or proceedings and to do any act or acts concerning said suit or suits or the subject matter thereof as he may deem necessary or proper, and to do or perform any act, or defend, commence, dismiss or prosecute to a conclusion any suit or suits or other proceeding or proceedings relating to the patents, devices, inventions or improvements possessed by or belonging to Marquis L. Gorham, deceased, at the time of his death; giving and granting unto my said attorney full power and authority to do and perform all and every act and thing whatsoever, requisite and necessary to be done in and about the said property, suits or premises, as fully, to all intents and purposes, as I might or could do if personally present at the doing thereof, with full power of substitution, hereby ratifying and confirming all that my said attorney, or his substitute or substitutes or employes shall lawfully do or cause to be done by virtue hereof.

"IN TESTIMONY WHEREOF, I have hereunto set my hand and seal this sixteenth day of December A. D. 1882.

Signed, sealed and delivered in presence of—The word 'irrevocably' first stricken out before signing.

Elijah George

Alice M. Harrison (Seal)

———————— (Seal)."

In this way William Deering became, in effect, a party in interest and, in fact, the rights he represented were practically equal to those

of the members of the pool. A meeting of defendants was soon
after held, at which, it was thought best to encourage respect for
patents rather than attempt to destroy them, and Mrs. Gorham, advised by her cousin and Mr. Brazee, readily agreed to a new arrangement, this time with the defendants, the builders of the Appleby
binders having agreed as follows:

"The agreement made this Sixth day of October 1882 by and between
Helen M. Gorham, Executrix of M. L. Gorham deceased, of the first
part and ——————————————————————— is to be deposited with
E. A. West, with the understanding that the same or a copy thereof
shall be submitted to   Brazee, Mrs. Gorham's Atty.,
of Rockford, for his approval, and if in his opinion the same is not sufficient to protect Mrs. Gorham Executrix to the extent contemplated by
the written proposition submitted to Mr. Deering dated October 4— (except as to the sum to be paid, as to which exception shall not be taken)
then said Brazee may prepare a contract based on such proposition the
sum to be paid to be as in the contract, that is to say $100,000 & ex-
penses of legal proceedings—and if the parties of the second part accept such contract drawn by Mr. Brazee, it shall be signed by all parties
and be substituted in place of the contract deposited with said West
which shall then be cancelled—And if the parties of the second part decline to assent to the contract which may be so drawn by Mr. Brazee,
then the contract so deposited with said West shall be cancelled by him
whenever instructed in writing by William Deering, or it shall be so
cancelled by said Deering. A copy of said contract to be mailed to said
Brazee by said West and he shall within five days from this date notify
said West whether the same meets his approval as attorney for Mrs.
Gorham—and if it does not shall prepare and submit a new contract
before the twelfth day of the present month, October 1882.

Aultman, Miller & Co.	The Johnston Harvester Co.
Geo. W. Crouse, Treas.	F. S. Stebbins, Treas.
C. Aultman & Co.	The Plano Mfg. Co.
Jacob Miller, Supt.	by G. W. Chamberlin, Secy.
	Geo. Esterly & Son
Dennett H. M. Co.	Minneapolis Harvester Works
per H. M. Conger, V. P.	by S. S. Murdock Gen. Mangr."

But Mr. Lathrop getting wind of the meeting, brought about a
more satisfactory arrangement with Mrs. Gorham, which induced
her to close a proper deal on October 20, 1881, when the McCormick
Company was made sole assignees of the Gorham patents.

Previous to this time Mrs. Gorham had applied for a patent covering certain improvements on the Gorham machine of 1875, the application for which patent was thrown into interference with the patent granted to Appleby. The subject matter of the interference was covered by claims which called for a specific shape of the tripping compressor,—that is, the metallic arm against which the gavel was compacted was curved in form so as to give confirmation to the outer portion of the bundle. George Esterly, one of the first licensees, not only avoided the Gorham patent which resulted from the application, but demonstrated the fact that the shape of the compressor cut no figure, he having made and used it without curvature. He demonstrated, in fact, that it was the completed band which gave confirmation to the bundle, as, by the expansion of the compressed bundle the latter assumed a rounded shape. In this interference, involving a trivial matter, Mr. Appleby was defeated, which fact explains certain clauses in the license to the McCormick Company. We find:

"Said first party is licensed to build under said patents, at a price not to exceed Three Dollars and Fifty Cents, which is to be the sum total for the patent fees for each machine as above; which is to be estimated or arranged as follows: One-third (1/3) of the sum to be paid in advance to said party, and the remaining two-thirds (2/3) to be retained by said first party as a contingent guarantee fund against the claims that may be substantiated by the Gorham patents, owned or controlled by Thompson and others, at Rockford, Ill.; it being well known that said Gorham or Thompson's claims control certain features in said Binders, and that said first party is to be protected to the extent of the reserve fund named above against the claims of said Gorham or Thompson or the owners thereof.

* * * * * * *

"It is understood that said Appleby patents are not as strong as they ought to be, and said first party are to advise and assist in strengthening the same. It is also understood that in case said second party desire the assistance of said first party to defend and maintain said patents so far as said action may make them dominant over the Gorham patents they are to exert themselves through their agents, whose duty it is to attend to these matters in defending and maintaining said patents.

"The peculiar feature of invention in controversy relates particularly to the automatic feeding device in connection with the automatic trip in sizing or regulating the dimensions of the bundle by said Appleby, and as prior to said Gorham as stated and shown in the records at the Patent Office in Washington—when these questions shall be satisfactorily adjusted or decided then the balance of said fee is to be paid."

After William Deering had proved the value of the Appleby inventions by putting 3,000 machines on the market in 1880, and it had taken a license, the C. H. McCormick Company seems to have seen a new light, and in the later arrangement with Lathrop, Thompson and Mrs. Gorham will be found a clause reading as follows:

"The parties of the second part hereby mutually agree to and with each other that they will in all matters pertaining to this contract act in absolute good faith and to the best of their ability strive to secure the best possible returns and income from the use of said patents or the infringement thereof and the said McCormick Harvesting Machine Company especially promises and agrees that persons and attorneys within its employ while so employed shall not be enlisted or arrayed against the patents or any of them so conveyed to the party of the first part or against the carrying out in good faith the objects and provisions of this contract."

The Appleby twine binder, with one exception, was the only one then or since manufactured, and hence suits for infringement could only be brought against Mr. Appleby's licensees, as the excepted binder, invented by Holmes, used rotary packers. The C. H. McCormick Company, as above shown, obligated itself not to be arrayed against the Gorham patents, although it had already agreed, on November 3, 1880, *to* array itself against the Gorham patents. On May 30, 1882, the money was paid and a release drawn reading as follows:

"Chicago, Ill., May 30, 1882.
"Received of the McCormick Harvesting Machine Company thirty-five thousand dollars ($35,000) cash in hand, paid in full for all dues or demands which have or may here-after accrue under the within contract or license dated Nov. 3, 1880, relating to the construction of grain binders under the Appleby patents so-called, as specified in said contract, during the entire term for which said patents have been granted.

John F. Appleby,
Parker & Stone,
Gustavus Stone,
Charles H. Parker,
    per L. H. Parker,
E. D. Bishop."

(McCormick Harvesting Machine Company vs. C. Aultman & Company, et al,—Defendants' Record.)

The state of mind in which the Gorham-Thompson-Lathrop-Mc-Cormick agreement placed Mrs. Harrison is shown by statements made by her in a bill prepared by her directed to set aside the agreement from which the following is an extract:

"Your oratrix further shows unto your Honors that neither she nor her said sister, Lillian, ever consented to or acquiesced in the execution of said contract with the said Norman C. Thompson nor did the said Helen M. Gorham, as such executrix, or otherwise, have any right, power, or authority to make said contract; that the same was and is in direct violation of the rights and duties of said Helen M. Gorham as trustee under said will and testament of said Marquis L. Gorham, deceased, nor authorized by law or by any court as an act by her as such executrix, and wrongful, prejudicial and illegal as against your oratrix and her sister, Lillian, and the said Helen M. Gorham herself.

"Your oratrix further shows unto your honors that the said Helen M. Gorham at the time of the execution of said pretended agreement with the said Norman C. Thompson, was wholly inexperienced in regard to contracts and business of that kind, and in dealing with and meeting in business negotiations and transactions the said Norman C. Thompson who was and is a man of keen business perception, adroit and successful in manipulations for his own benefit and pecuniary profit and of large practical capacity and experience in business matters, or with any other person of his influence, sagacity or ability; and that for the purpose of obtaining the execution of the said contract on the part of the said Helen M. Gorham the said Norman C. Thompson employed counsellors at law to assist him in persuading her to sign the same, and the said Thompson did greatly deceive the said Helen M. Gorham in regard to the facts and did intentionally misrepresent to her the facts in regard to the value of the said patents and inventions, and the rights and duties of said Helen M. Gorham under said will and testament and in relation to the value of the consideration he pretended to part with by said contract. That for the purpose of obtaining the execution of said pretended contract on the part of said Helen M. Gorham the said Norman C. Thompson and his employees by his direction and assent, willfully and intentionally misrepresented that the said patents and improvements belonging to the estate of the said Marquis L. Gorham, deceased, were only of a value much less than their actual value; that they were not original or useful and that said estate could not be protected under them nor receive any benefit therefrom; that the said Helen M. Gorham was fully authorized and in duty bound under and by virtue of said will and testament to execute said contract, and that the value of said consideration named in said pretended contract, to be given by said Thompson was largely in excess of its real and actual value. And your oratrix charges that is was solely in consequence of the inex-

perience of the said Helen M. Gorham and the misrepresentations made
to and deceit and fraud practiced upon her, as aforesaid, she was persuaded to sign the said pretended contract with said Norman C. Thompson and to ignore her duties under and by virtue of said last will and
testament of said Marquis L. Gorham, deceased.

"Your oratrix further shows unto your Honors that since the execution of said pretended contract the said Norman C. Thompson has wholly
failed and refused to keep or perform the provisions thereof to be kept
and performed by him, and that he has neglected and failed to pay over
or account to the said Helen M. Gorham any profits or proceeds resulting from the said patents and inventions or the business thereto
appertaining.

"Your oratrix further shows unto your Honors that after the execution of said pretended contract the said Norman C. Thompson having
failed to make it available or being desirous of obtaining other different
or greater privileges from the said Helen M. Gorham, on or about
September 1st, A. D. 1881, began to importune her to make and execute
another contract with him, and the said defendants, William Lathrop,
and the said McCormick Harvesting Machine Company, and in this
effort was greatly aided by the said Lathrop and by one C. H. McCormick, President of said McCormick Harvesting Machine Company, and
others, and that on or about October 31st, A. D. 1881, the said Helen
M. Gorham, Norman C. Thompson, the McCormick Harvesting Machine Company, and William Lathrop executed a pretended contract in
words and figures as follows: To wit:"

Here reference is probably had to one of the contracts that resulted in putting the title to the patents in the McCormick Company,
no doubt of record.

The assignees of Mrs. Gorham, forestalled by Mr. Deering's and
the author's action, offered to give Deering a license under the Gorham patents, which they had acquired by the later agreement, through
an assignment properly executed by Mrs. Gorham as *trustee,* for the
rights which he had also purchased from Mrs. Harrison. Still the
way was not clear, as the title by Mr. Deering's act, as explained,
and otherwise, was clouded. After consulting with William N.
Whitely and others he refused to join, stating that he had friends
to take care of, which friends were all of the alleged infringers. An
offer was made to grant licenses to the other defendants at certain
figures. This Mr. Deering stated to this author he could not recommend, but told them that if they would cut those figures in half he
would advise defendants to join and not attempt to defeat the patents.

All acquiesced but Aultman, Miller & Co., who decided to stand suit, and finally defeated two of the five claims of the 1875 Gorham patent sued on.

The McCormick Company did not become interested in the Gorham patents until Mr. Deering had refused to take them, as stated, and, in fact, until after Mr. Deering had been testing and manufacturing the Appleby binder for three years, and one year after the McCormick Company had begun building their copy of the Deering-Appleby binding attachment, mounted on their appropriation of the Marsh harvester patents. Notwithstanding all this, in various publications the C. H. McCormick Company claims to have been instrumental in originating the modern twine binder. At a prominent exhibition was placed a series of models. Among others one of the Gorham binder, put there by that Company, as made and patented by Gorham, upon a Marsh harvester as developed by William Deering and his predecessors, but differing in certain impractical details. Upon that model appeared a card with these words:

"MODEL
of the
FIRST TWINE BINDER THAT BOUND GRAIN IN THE FIELD.

"Marquis L. Gorham, in the winter of 1873-4, built the first automatic cord binder, and with it successfully cut and bound, during the harvest of 1874, fifty acres of grain, and during the harvest of 1875 sixty acres of grain.

"This binder was the first to bind grain with cord, and also the first to automatically bind bundles of the same size. It had, as shown in this model, two reciprocating packers, moving the grain forward at its center between the deck and breastplate against a trip, so that when a certain amount of grain had accumulated, a clutch would be thrown and the binder started. John F. Appleby saw this machine in the field, and after again closely examining it in a shed at Thompson's works at Rockford, Ill., began to build his cord binder. He first tried it with Gorham's trip, but without packers, in 1875, and then in 1876 with one packer, but before it would work he had to put in two and take Gorham's entire plan. Gorham's health failed in 1875 and he died in 1876. Appleby got his binder to working nicely in 1878, and Parker and Stone of Beloit, Wis., were the first to build them, and they sold 115 for the harvest of 1878. Hoover and Gamble, of Miamisburg, Ohio, were the second to take a license, in the fall of 1878. Others followed during 1879 and 1880, all copying the Parker and Stone Binder. The Spaulding machine (of which the McCormicks bought a half interest in 1874) was inoperative; Mr. Spaulding could not make it bind a bundle in the shop and it was never put in the field.

"The McCormick Company bought the entire interest in the Gorham patents and also a shop right in the Appleby. Under the Gorham patents shop rights were sold to all makers of binders in the United States with one exception, against whom a suit is now pending by the McCormick Company."

CHAPTER XVIII.

William Deering and the Binder.

At the Paris Exposition of 1900 a small book was distributed under the title of "La Compagnie MacCormick de Chicago a l'Exposition de 1900."

"Lieuse automatique a corde.

"La lieuse à corde se développa pendant les années 1874-1878. Monsieur le marquis L. Gorham pendant l'été de 1874 fit travailler avec succès une lieuse à corde dans un champ près de Rockford (Illinois). Ce fut la première lieuse à égalisateur de gerbes construite qui put lier pratiquement une botte dans le champ.

"En 1874, John F. Appleby, vit cette lieuse en opération et, alors, commenca à construire sa machine."

"Gorham mourut en 1876 et Appleby continua le developpement de son lieur."

Translation

The string binder was developed during the years of 1874-1878. Marquis L. Gorham, during the summer of 1874, successfully operated the string binder in the fields of Rockford (Illinois). This was the first binder constructed which was provided with a device to equalize sheaves and by which sheaves could be bound right on the field.

In 1874, John F. Appleby saw this binder in operation and then started to construct his machine.

Gorham died in 1876, and Appleby continued to work on the development of his binder.

The above can be understood in various ways. It seems to me, that the impression the author seeks to convey is that the development of the twine binder began in 1874 and continued to 1878, and that Appleby saw Gorham's twine binder in 1874 and commenced to build a machine, but that Gorham having died, Appleby continued the

303

development of the binder that Gorham had begun. In the book referred to there is no statement of the efforts of Watson and Renwick, who had conveyed the grain into a receptacle, there compressed it, gave a final squeeze to the gavel to provide slack for knotting the twine; had provided means for binding centrally and ejecting the completed bundle. Nor does it say that Behel, one of Gorham's neighbors, had bound bundles in public in the fields and at the fairs, tying the twine with the knotter which Gorham followed, and had held the twine substantially as Gorham later did; nor does it refer to Spaulding, who packed and self-sized the bundles in Gorham's presence and for his inspection. The author of the book fortifies himself by limiting previous operations to actual field work, ignoring all that had been done to enrich the art by the one hundred and sixty-seven inventors of binders before Gorham (as shown by patents granted), and does not mention the fact that of all the mechanical elements found in Gorham's binder only the co-operation of three was held to be original with Gorham, and that they were only specific in their nature, but broadly following the Spaulding basic idea. The author states that the Walter A. Wood Company took a license under the Gorham patents, but leaves the reader to infer that the Wood machine used some of the Gorham devices, which it did not. The only part of the Gorham patents sustained by the courts related to the use of reciprocating arms moved by cranks which the Wood Company, building the Holmes binder, never employed but packed the grain into the receptacle by rotary means, as John Gordon had done.

The clauses above quoted from the French book were submitted to Prof. Charles M. Andrist, of the University of Minnesota, long a resident of Paris, with the following result. He says:

"It seems to me from the reading of the last paragraph—'Gorham mourut en 1876 et Appleby continua le developpement de son lieur'—the writer, whoever he was, could only have had one object in view, and that was, to convey the idea that Appleby continued the development of Gorham's binder, else why any mention of Gorham's death? I am, further, inclined to this opinion, because in the preceding paragraph the statement is made that Appleby saw the Gorham binder, after which he began to construct his machine. The expression 'son lieur' is ambiguous as it might mean either Appleby's own machine or Gorham's.

"Had the writer wished to say that Appleby continued the development

of 'his own binder' he might have expressed 'own' by the French word
'*propre*' thus 'Gorham mourut en 1876 et Appleby continua le developpement de son *propre* lieur.' However, it seems to me that the meaning
of the writer was that Appleby continued Gorham's invention after the
latter's death, since there would have been no need of mentioning Gorham had he meant otherwise."

The exact facts in regard to the Spaulding, Gorham, and Appleby
machine will be found in this volume. The alleged facts, stated in
the card quoted in the last chapter were never matters of proof, and,
although attorneys for the McCormick Company in the Aultman,
Miller & Co. case had Appleby, Bishop and McGregor on the witness stand and were thus given every opportunity, by cross-examination, to bring out the facts, they did not attempt to do so. In the
litigation just mentioned McGregor and others testified that the reciprocating packers of the Gorham machines were failures, and gave
that fact as the reason for adopting packers mounted upon a crank,
substantially as in the Appleby machine, and also following the
Spaulding packers of his second machine, as embodied in the model,
of which an illustration is presented on a previous page. The facts
regarding Spaulding's second binder and Gorham's familiarity with
it, were not availed of in the Aultman & Miller case, as the attorneys
for the defendants had full faith that the Spaulding patent of 1870
would limit Gorham's claims to specific forms of construction not
found in defendant's binders, as the lower court, in fact, held. The
Mr. Hoover mentioned was second to acquire rights from Appleby,
Bishop, and Parker & Stone. (Printed Record. McCormick Harvester Co. vs. C. Aultman et als, page 255.)

The attention of Gammon & Deering was brought to Appleby's
inventions by a letter, now in the author's possession, received by
J. D. Easter & Co., an associate in the Marsh Harvester interests,
owning territory adjacent to that controlled by Gammon & Deering.
The letter reads:

"Mazomanie, Wis., Sept. 5, 1877.
"J. D. Easter & Co.
   "Chicago, Ill.
"Gentlemen:
   "I have an interest in the Appleby or Beloit String Binder, which I
am anxious to associate with some good substantial Co. that have a har-
vester already established. We have done splendid work as far as we

have operated on the Beloit harvester this season, especially the last of it, as you could learn by enquiring of your agents at Hammond, Wis. or Owatonna, Minn., or what would be better still, of examining the machine yourselves at Beloit, or at the State Fair at Milwaukee. I would be satisfied to make such connections for a year as would give you full and satisfactory trial with but small expense. Please inform me by return mail if there is any chance for encouragement from you, and if so when you would like a further conference in the matter. Hoping to hear that you will examine into the merits of the machine, I remain,

Yours respectfully,
E. D. Bishop."

Unbounded faith in the ultimate results of human ingenuity, so characteristic of Mr. Deering, had led him earnestly to hope that twine already tied by Behel's knotting devices early in the sixties, would soon be successfully used in binding grain, and he was alert to Mr. Appleby's accomplishments and words expressive of high expectations. Ever watchful, he listened with characteristic attention. The result of the visit is well known; it was Mr. Deering's eagerness to abandon wire as a band material and come to the use of twine, with the manufacture and sale of which he was perfectly familiar, that soon led his most progressive competitors "to sit up and take notice."

The various types of wire binders had become quite satisfactory, as far as handling the cut grain was concerned, but the coming twine binders were seriously defective in that they did not tie the bundles sufficiently tight. The Appleby binders made for the harvest of 1879 at the Deering factory, improved over the two furnished by Parker & Stone in 1878, did fair work. For the year 1879 the Walter A. Wood Co. purchased ten of the Appleby binders made at Beloit, but at the close of the harvest judged them less satisfactory than the experimental Holmes binders they had tested. Although Mr. Wood had the courage to put out the Holmes binders for the harvest of 1880, he lost out in the end as they could not compete successfully with the Appleby binder, the latter at that time having become thoroughly practical. (Testimony of Parsons, David M. Osborne, James F. Gordon, and John H. Gordon vs. Cyrus H. McCormick and others.)

Mr. Abel Hoover, of Hoover & Gamble, with Mr. Deering and his men, followed the machines made for the latter through the harvest of 1878, the former intending that his company should take a license if the machines succeeded so well as to induce Mr. Deering to take up the manufacture, following Mr. Bishop's offer and, as his tentative agreement early in 1878 contemplated, after he and the author had accepted Bishop's invitation to visit Beloit. The first *formal* license was granted to Hoover & Gamble, the royalty being at the regular rate, but Deering had made a verbal agreement previous to that time, for exclusive rights for the state of Illinois.

CHAPTER XIX.

GORHAM AND SPAULDING CLAIMS.

Neither the C. H. McCormick Company nor any inventor or person associated with it, did a stroke of work upon the Gorham machine, nor did it embody a single McCormick idea. The Marsh harvester had been put on the market, many thousands per annum, for over twelve years before the McCormick Company took it up, and the Appleby twine binder had been upon the Marsh harvester from the first machine made for 1875 until the close of the harvest of 1880 before being taken up by that company. Such are the facts, and a comparison of the facts with the card previously quoted, shows how flimsy is the myth that C. H. McCormick invented the Reaper.

In the first deal with Mrs. Gorham the McCormick Company had contributed their half interest in the Spaulding patent, which they tried to reissue with basic claims, and which was worth little to the pool because of the fact that the Osborne Company, who owned the other half, refused to join. On the contrary, Osborne was licensing under it all comers. The patent to Paschal and Newell Whitney and that to Greenhut were what are called merely paper patents. No successful operative machines had ever been made by those men, as Mr. Greenhut told me. On the other hand, the pool considered the Gorham patents and others in which Mrs. Gorham was interested of great value. Indeed, the McCormick Company paid Mrs. Gorham $100,000.00 for them and lesser rights. In the litigation with Aultman, Miller & Co., involving several of the patents, the complainants were in the main defeated. One-half interest in the Spaulding patent was owned by D. M. Osborne & Co., and that Company took sides with the various parties licensed who were building the Appleby binder. The patent to Paschal and Newell Whitney was utterly

308

worthless unless, possibly, as proof that Gorham had borrowed the feeding device from those inventors. The patent to Greenhut showed an incongruous, crude and worthless machine. The first patent mentioned, granted to Behel, had already expired. The second one had less than a year to run, and cut no material figure; the third was valueless and the fourth had expired.

In April, 1881, the Gorham interests attempted to reissue the patent of 1875. While the original patent as accepted by Gorham had but thirty-two modest claims, the reissue application, filed several years after the inventor's death, contained seventy-six claims, the added ones largely being broad in their terms, and so formulated as to read upon the details of construction of the Appleby binder, which machine was evidently before the specification writer when the claims were drawn. Nearly all of the claims were rejected by the Patent Office, with the result that on September 21, 1882, Parkinson & Parkinson, attorneys for the McCormick Company, wrote as follows:

"To the Hon. Commissioner of Patents,

"Sir: The above application, having been refused, we request that the original patent may be returned to us in accordance with the provisions of the law."

The law left it optional with them whether to take out the reissue or withdraw the original. They found they could not do better, and demanded the return of the patent. In the Aultman, Miller & Co. case the Court of Appeals held that claims three, ten and eleven, of the original patent were infringed, holding some of the elements of the Appleby binder to be the equivalent of the elements forming them, differing but in form. This accrued after the claims had been rejected by the Patent Office, when considering the reissue application.

The question was raised whether complainants had the right to proceed on these rejected claims, and the matter was certified up to the Supreme Court of the United States, in the following form, as worded by the defendants:

"Where a patentee voluntarily resubmits his patent to the examination and revision of the Patent Office, and then acquiesces in the rejection of claims, or in a construction which narrows or restricts them, the same principles apply as in the case of acquiescense in rejection on original proceedings."

The Supreme Court decided in the negative and held that the complainants acted *within their legal rights.* Such was the new law and thus ended an absurd attempt to enlarge a patent by reissue. (See cut of Gorham's packing device, page 316.)

It will be seen that the teeth of the Gorham packing devices are reciprocated bodily, and have a rocking motion on a pivot, at their own sweet will, merely, by means of which pivot pin they are connected to the segment, while Appleby's packers have the necessarily positive orbital movement. A study of the Paschal and Newell Whitney feeding devices will show that Gorham's form more nearly followed theirs; Gorham's were not moved upwardly positively, as were Appleby's packers (although the orbital movement was not strictly circular). The latter more nearly followed the orbitally moving packers of the John Gordon binder as put on the market in 1874, the packers of which had been patented by him in 1872, and which imitated closely in action the packers of the second Spaulding machine, with which, by the way, Mr. Gorham was perfectly familiar. The fact that Mr. Gorham was familiar with the Spaulding machine, and that the claims of his original patent were specifically drawn, convinces the writer that he did not believe himself entitled to broad claims. (The position taken by the writer hereof, in regard to the Gorham patent, may be found in the record of the suits brought by the McCormick Company against C. Aultman & Co., and he still stands by the opinion therein expressed.)

After a half century in this art, spent in inventing and perfecting harvesting machinery, the writer puts himself squarely on record by saying that although the Gorham packing device may have operated as a feat, that it can never be made practical because of the fact that the pivoted teeth left to erect them, or *permit* them to become erected; all of the reciprocating movement that cause the erection of the teeth is motion lost. McGregor, Carter and others, in the above suit swore that they failed to operate well, which fact led to their abandonment and the substitution of packers carried on cranks, by Mr. Flenniken.

Description of the efforts of Mr. George H. Spaulding, as known to me, may well be prefaced by extracts from a letter written by Mr. Spaulding, March 25, 1897, just previous to his death. I knew Mr. Spaulding for years. He was in the employ of the Deering Company, with which he made some deals, and also made deals with the McCormick Company involving his inventions and executed the reissue application of his 1870 patent. By all he was respected as a man possessing a keen sense of honor, and a lovable man. He writes:

"During these years, Mr. Jacob Behel, and Solomon T. Holly were at work upon different forms of grain binders, both in the employment of Mrs. Manny, and both thoughtful and skillful mechanics. They were each working upon an attachment for the Manny Reaper, and both had decided that twine was the proper material to use in binding grain, but each used different devices for tying the knot, Mr. Behel using that patented to him in 1864 and later, which is substantially that used today on all binders.

"Mr. Behel had moved to Rockford during my absence and I soon became acquainted with him, after my return,* visiting him often, and talking over his and my ideas of harvesting machinery. So thorough and skillful was he as a draughtsman and mechanic, that I received much aid from him in making models. Mr. Holly used often to call on Mr. Behel, and there I met him many times, where we talked over our various schemes. Mr. Holly often loaned me tools that I was not financially able to purchase.

"It is proper to say here that in Rockford, while I lived there, were Mr. Behel, Mr. Holly, Mr. W. W. Burson, Mr. Marquis L. Gorham, Mr. T. M. Fleniken, and a number of others, who between 1864 and 1875, were engaged in inventing harvesting machinery, and I can do the gentlemen no greater justice than to say that there was the utmost harmony and freedom among them. Neither seemed to possess the least suspicion that his ideas might be appropriated by others, and as a result, we conferred as frequently as we met.

"In 1861 I made a model of an improved harvester of the Marsh type. The difference between this and the Marsh machine was that in my arrangement the grain was not elevated as on the Marsh harvester, but thrust directly into a receptacle and bound there by the attendants. The men stood upon each side of the receptacle, one on the platform side of the machine and the other between the driving wheel and receptacle. I built a full sized machine on this plan, with some variations, in the summer of 1869 and it was quite successfully worked in the harvest of that year. It was my first experience at binding grain upon a ma-

* Mr. Spaulding was a soldier in the war for the Union.

chine and I remember what hard work it was to me as well as to others who tried it, inexperienced as all were, as we were cutting in very heavy, green oats. It was there and then that I resolved the next machine I should make would be one that would bind its own sheaves of grain. I had even prior to that time studied out the plan upon which I resolved to work; so, in the latter part of August of that year (1869) I commenced to construct a model doing the work as best I could with little time, no means and but few tools. This model, when finished, was sent to the Patent Office, with the application that ripened into my patent granted June 30, 1870. Soon after a favorable report from the Patent Office I began to build a full sized machine, having made an arrangement with Mr. John Waldron for financial aid, and in his barn, temporarily fitted up with a vice and bench and supplied with a few tools, I began with strong hopes that I should be able to complete my machine in time for the following harvest; but, alas! the nearest machine shop was a mile away. For every bit of forging or in order to bend any piece of iron it was necessary to go very far to find a fire. The grain fields of the west had been captured by the Marsh harvester and Mr. Waldron, anxious to realize, took little interest in my automatic binder, and the harvest time of 1870 fast wearing away, I was obliged to remove my nearly completed binding attachment, and, in order to satisfy him, go to the field with the Marsh binding tables and receptacle in the place fitted for them as I had so constructed my machine that it could be used as a manual binding machine or automatic.

"Now, returning to my struggles with the binding attachment when fully completed as designed, testing it upon straw, I found many difficulties to be overcome. The first one was that the elevating devices carrying the swath of straw directly upwards caused it to impinge upon the tripping compressor so nearly at the axis of movement as to produce bundles of various sizes; and furthermore, I found that the needle in its movevent to lay the band around the gavel, was thrust too nearly through the mass of grain that had accumulated, and furthermore I found that there was a tendency to clog at the top of the elevator. In order to overcome these difficulties I removed the drum which carried the elevating belts and placed instead thereof a shaft having double cranks at the middle of the grain passage-way, and both in front and in rear of said cranks applied a short drum adapted to carry the elevating belts. Upon these cranks were supported two toothed bars provided with long teeth adapted to be thrust upwardly through the binding table, and in fact some of them into the straw being delivered by the elevator and force the swath not only through the throat but carry it well upward toward the extremity, and finally against the tripping fingers. The needle was adapted to move between these two feeding devices. The machine as changed is correctly represented in the model I made for you about 15 years ago. So changed there was no more clogging and no more irregularity in the working of the automatic self sizing devices. Tried upon straw I found the operation perfect; but there was not sufficient time to apply the finishing touches, and, in order to test the practicability of my machine as a whole, I was obliged to go into the field at the end of the harvest. Naturally being then still young and somewhat enthusiastic, I took pleasure in explaining my machine to all comers and was glad to do for all interested what so many members of the coterie of inventors in Rockford had done for me, freely giving their judgment as to what I proposed. The temporary shop became a chosen resort, on rainy days, for those suffering from enforced idleness, as a result of which visitors were many, but, as inventors find no idle moments, the visits of those interested were not so frequent.

"Mr. Burson's twine binder of 1865 impressed me as being so promising that I was somewhat doubtful as to the ultimate adoption of wire binding material. Nevertheless, as time was short, means limited and the accomplishment of my object was shorter by undertaking to use wire, I applied a wire twister to my machine.

"In Rockford lived Mr. Marquis L. Gorham, a man possessing a keen sense of honor, gentlemanly, and one whose friendship was lasting. He took much interest in my work and when I had the machine sufficiently completed to operate upon straw, he examined it very carefully as was his custom when anything new was to be seen. He expressed a very favorable opinion and stated he believed that there were features embraced in that machine which were excellent, and that if a successful grain binder were ever made the principle of self sizing the bundles would have to be used, for the reasons, as he stated, that it would always give the binder the same amount of straw to operate upon, and hence, the working parts the same amount of work to do; consequently always take the same amount of power to bind it, thereby saving the chance of clogging the machine in heavy crops of grain. The automatic self sizing feature, he thought also to be important on account of the fact that there would be a great saving in band material, as such a machine would waste nothing upon small bundles, and besides, the labor of stacking and shocking would be somewhat easier and better results generally attained. My backing having failed me I could not apply for patents upon my improvements, but as I believed that my patent already covered the principle of self-sizing bundles, I was glad to learn, later, that other inventors appreciated the value of my invention.

"Some time in the year 1872, if I recollect rightly, I met Mr. Gorham and he then informed me that he had concluded to try his hand in making an automatic grain binding harvester. I said to him that I was glad to know it and wished him every success and that I hoped to be financially able to complete my machine, in all its details, and do much better than it had already done and accomplish better results than ever. He expressed himself as desirous of consulting me from time to time while making his experiments, which he did, and I gladly gave him advice and information. His work had been mostly upon other classes of agricultural machinery and was free to admit to me that he was entering a new field and that my judgment would be superior to his. While he was building his machine, we frequently met and he pretty nearly always had some little detail in regard to which he desired my opinion as to construction, etc. He often consulted in regard to my invention, that of self-sizing the gavel—and told me he was going to use that principle in his machine. We often talked over the matter on the best means to make the binder trip in fluffy, and consequently light, straw, and I urged upon him the necessity of using packers that I had found to be useful so as to force the straw positively against the tripping and compressing fingers. He quite agreed with me in this. Mr. Theodore M. Fleniken, a mechanical engineer, who was at that time working for Mr. Gorham, consulted with me frequently on that point as well as many others. He used to stop at my house evenings when through with work and have, oftentime, long talks as to what I thought

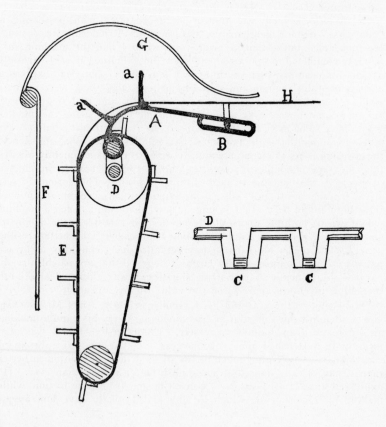

would be best to do, as he had had but little experience in harvester building. My judgment in those matters he submitted to me and the suggestions I made seemed to be satisfactory to him. He called at my house one evening and asked to see my patent as Mr. Gorham wished to look it over. I think it remained in his possession about half a year. When Mr. Gorham's machine was finished and tried in the harvest it was found defective in its operation. He, however, remodeled it for the next season, improving it somewhat but it still showed defects when tried in the field. I think there were a few of them, as modified by Mr. Fleniken, built by M. C. Thompson for the harvest of 1877, and possibly placed on the market. I had frequent talks with those who were sent out as experts to start the machines in the field and run them in practical service. The experts reported that they gave poor satisfaction to those who purchased them on condition that they should work properly. None of them, so far as I ever heard, were in fact sold. After this the machine was entirely remodeled by Mr. Fleniken, who, I believe, received patents for improvements he had made upon Mr. Gorham's machine, Mr. Gorham having died in 1876. When the improved machines were tried, however, they were found very defective."

The packing device of the second Spaulding machine, explained to Mr. Gorham by Mr. Spaulding and embodied in a model that was exhibited at the Paris Exposition, and is now found in what may be considered to be the French equivalent of our Patent Office, may be understood from the accompanying illustration, which is a sectional elevation of the working parts having to do with packing the gavels. A represents one of the packing arms having the teeth, a, a, pivotally supported at B. C, C, represents the cranks formed on the shaft D. E. represents the vertical conveyor and F the co-operating wall adapted to hold the swath of straw in contact with the elevating devices. G represents the trip arm, as shown in the Spaulding patent of 1870 and also embodied in the second machine. This arm was operatively connected to the clutch whereby the rising movement of the arm G put the binding mechanism into operation. The bundle was then engaged by the needle, not shown on the sketch, and moved along the table H, the ends of the band being united during the passage, as in the Withington, James Gordon, and several early wire binders.

As an insight into the methods followed by certain of the manufacturers of harvesting machinery, it is thought proper to disclose, in connection with the Gorham matter, the Spaulding application,

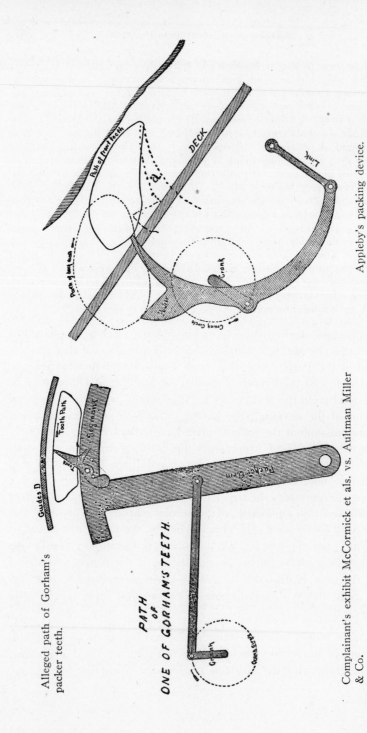

Alleged path of Gorham's packer teeth.

PATH OF ONE OF GORHAM'S TEETH.

Appleby's packing device.

Complainant's exhibit McCormick et als. vs. Aultman Miller & Co.

prepared by the C. H. McCormick Harvesting Machine Company, for a reissue of the patent of 1870. (The last mentioned company, it will be remembered, purchased, in the fall of 1880, an Appleby binder made by William Deering, and also one made by Mr. Appleby for the Minneapolis Company from patterns which, under an arrangement, had been made at the Deering factory.) On March 21, 1881, in the interest of the McCormick Company, the application was prepared and immediately thereafter filed by Jacob Behel, a patent solicitor and inventor, of Rockford, for a reissue of the Gorham 1875 patent, notwithstanding the fact that in the smothered Spaulding reissue application, previously made, the following claims were among those that had been prepared by the attorney of the McCormick Company covering the same subject-matter:

"1. In a grain-binder the combination with the binding apparatus of mechanism automatically producing gavels of uniform size for its action.

"2. In a grain-binder the combination with the binding apparatus of automatic mechanism tripped by the gradual accumulation of the grain for throwing the binding apparatus into action.

"3. In a grain-binder the combination with the binding apparatus of a tripping arm against which the grain is packed in a constant increment to start said apparatus by the accumulation of gavels of uniform size.

"4. In a grain-binder the combination with the band-carrying arm and band-uniting mechanism of a tripping compressor against which the incoming grain is gradually fed and packed, whereby they are started by the accumulation of gavels of uniform size.

"5. In a grain-binder the combination with the grain receptacle and binding devices of a compressor normally closing the exit side of said receptacle, a rake which feeds the grain and packs it gradually against said compressor and tripping mechanism intermediate between the compressor and binding devices whereby said binding devices are automatically thrown into action by the yielding of the compressor.

* * * * * * *

"14. In a grain-binder the combination with a compressor of a rake that packs the grain there against by a constant increment.

* * * * * * *

"17. The combination of the compressor, its rock shaft, the arm projecting from said rock shaft, the shipping lever and clutch, and the crank whereby the binding mechanism is actuated.

* * * * * * *

"20. A gavel discharger that is automatically thrown into gear through the raising of the compressing fingers by the accumulation of the gavel, substantially as described."

It will be observed that all of these more or less generic claims have to do with automatically packing and sizing the bundles. The attempt seems to have been to make both the Spaulding and the Gorham reissues cover the Appleby binder, but in order to make the Spaulding claims read on the Appleby binder some also read upon the Gorham. The writer feels warranted in saying that any patent expert familiar with the art of harvesting and binding grain taking up this subject will reach the following conclusion. The attorneys feared that, in view of the Spaulding patent, they could not succeed in efforts directed to sustaining themselves in court against the Appleby binder, should they place a broad construction on the Gorham patent, an interest in which patent their clients owned. Therefore they prepared the Spaulding application, which clearly subordinated the Gorham patent. They did not file the application, as the joint owner would not consent, but a printed copy of it was given me by one of complainant's attorneys, from which the above quotations are made.

CHAPTER XX.

John F. Appleby's Story.

The accomplishments of Mr. Appleby, in a large part by means of financial assistance rendered him, may be considered to have culminated in the third and last revolution in the methods of harvesting grain. His story, kindly furnished to the writer, reads as follows:

"I was born in the state of New York, Oneida County, town of Westmoreland, in 1840. My parents were English born, married in this country and settled down as farmers in Oneida County, N. Y. At the age of four I came to Walworth County, Wis., and lived in Wisconsin up to 1858 and was there at the time that I started to work on self-binders, being then 18 years of age. I first contemplated the building of a twine binder and the knotter was the first part of the invention that I gave my attention to. There was nothing then known to me in the art of reaping machines except hand-raking and self-raking machines. Gathering what little knowledge I could from the reaping machines then in use I went to work to devise means for attaching a binder, following in main the construction of machines then in use. The one with which I was most familiar at that time was the Esterly reaper, or the Falvey & Reiley reaper, which were similar. I decided on a plan for the knotting device. This mechanism was built at the gun shop of one Mr. Pearce in Palmyra, Wis., I furnishing the wooden patterns and models for the construction of the mechanism as we proceeded with the construction of the machine. The wooden patterns included those of the knotter followed by him in copying the parts and putting them in metal form. In the interference proceeding involving the curved compressor arm Mr. Pearce stated that he invented that part of the model made by him for me. Such is a common mistake of mechanics in thinking that to *carry out* ideas advanced is to invent. This was in the summer of 1858 while I was at work on the farm, taking occasionally a day off to attend to my mechanical work. Having no means to carry on this work I got a young man by the name of Houghton interested with me, taking part in my interests for the money necessary to carry on the work. After expending about $50 in experimental work, having succeeded in making

319

a good knot-tying device and also building portions of the harvester to which it was to be attached in a crude manner, he concluded not to continue work any longer as it was quite expensive, and thinking that it would take more money than he could supply to complete the construction of my invention withdrew from it and left it to me. I continued to work at farming for some years afterward, keeping in mind my invention and improving it in plan and design from time to time, but did no more toward the construction until during the war. During the war and at the siege of Vicksburg I put in a little of my leisure time in mechanical work. I then made a wooden model of a magazine repeating fire arm which I took out patents on and after the war sold to Thomas W. Lane of Boston, Mass., for the sum of $500. One half of

the patent was sold shortly after to Valentine Fogerty for $7000, as I was told. While stationed at Vicksburg during the siege I constructed the model of a self-binding machine or so much of it as pertained to the self-binder but had not an opportunity of completing it at that time, having to move away from there on the march and so did nothing about it until 1865 after the war, and when I had received my money for my magazine fire arm patent I went to work from that to build a binder.

"I constructed a binding mechanism which operated well and interested one William Thompson of Mazo Manie, Wis., he taking part in it and defraying the expenses of construction of machines, which we tried in

the field. At that time it was the opinion of the public that wire binding would be preferable to that of twine binding so my efforts at that
time were in the direction of wire binders and the first binders that I
built were of wire binding mechanism.

"In 1869 I took out my first patent on binders and in that year built a
machine and put into the harvest field which did fairly good work. I
improved it in 1870 and still continued to work on it at Mazo Manie,
Wis., until the spring of 1872 when, in the month of March, 1872, I
went to Beloit, Wis., and made arrangements with the Parker & Stone
Reaper Company there to build a self-binder experimentally for the
coming harvest. This machine was built on the reaper plan, that is,
with self-rake raking the grain rearward and transversely to the binder.
The binder was a wire binding mechanism. This we had in the field in
1872 and again in 1873 I reconstructed it and operated it in the field
again. At this time we got the machine to work, as we thought, perfectly. When we were at work about three miles from Beloit in a field
owned by a man by the name of Dayton, he having a Parker & Stone
self-raking reaper and men binding after it by hand, we did much cleaner
work and made better bundles than was done after the self-raking reaper
and when we had worked during the forenoon before starting to the city
mentioned to Mr. Dayton that we would come back in the afternoon
and cut again. Mr. Dayton objected to our coming back again, saying
that each bundle was bound with an iron band. Admitting that we did
better work than he was doing with his machine and binders, he requested that we should not come back again but do our experimenting
somewhere else as he expected to use his straw for fodder and his
grain being bound with wire he feared it would kill his stock and preferred that we should not bind any more of his grain with our binder.
Up to this time we all thought we had made a grand success of the
binder. Messrs. Parker & Stone and Mr. F. A. Dennett and Holdon
Parker were all present and up to the time that Mr. Dayton requested
that we should not do any more work for him, thought we had the
greatest success in the world. On going back to the city we consulted
in regard to what should be done and the verdict was, as given by Parker & Stone, that they would not build a machine that farmers would
not use and that for the time ended the experiments on self-binders.

"In the fall of 1873 I bought an interest in the Webber Reaper Works
at Rockford, Ill., four miles from Beloit, and there we built some reapers
and some fanning mills. Also built a self-raking reaper in the summer
of 1874. Having perfected that and found that I could organize a company for the building of a reaper at Mazo Manie, Wis., I went there
and started to build those reapers. I then went to Parker & Stone again
at Beloit and made arrangements with them to further experiment on
self-binders, convincing them that I could build a binder that would
tie with twine, they having concluded that they would never attempt
to build a wire binding machine. In the summer of 1875 I built a binder

and put onto a Marsh harvester which they were building that season
and operated it in the field near Beloit. This was a binder which sized
its bundles automatically and tied with twine. It was late in the harvest when I had finished it and only operated it one day in the field.
While working the machine the binder worked well so that we considered that we had made a success of the binder, but one part of the
harvester did not work well in connection with the binder and required
some alterations in order to make the binder work to advantage. That
binder was practically the same in its general construction as binders
now generally in use. This binder I built in the winter of 1874-1875.
In 1876 I reconstructed the binder and put it to work early in the season
in green rye before the harvest was ready. As we entered the field it
began to rain but as we had blocked out a piece of grain in which to
try the machine we finished the piece without missing a bundle and the
machine worked to the entire satisfaction of Parker & Stone and all
those present and before leaving the field they got me to agree to build
three other binders for the coming harvest which I did. One of them was
taken to Madison and from there north to a railroad station, De Forest,
where we operated it in the cutting of wheat all of one-half day, doing
splendid work and never missing a bundle. One of the machines went
to St. Charles, Minn.; another one to West Mitchell, Ia.; and one went
to Mankato, Minn. All worked in the field and did good work.

"On my return from the field I took my model and went to Washington, making applications for patent. I went by the way of Philadelphia where at the time the Centennial Exposition was in progress.
Before going east I had made my contract with Blanchard & Arnold
of Milwaukee to go to West De Pere, Wis., they being the proprietors
of the West De Pere Agricultural Works. There we started to
build binders, I taking the patterns from Beloit to work from. Blanchard & Arnold became embarrassed that winter. They being
manufacturers of pig iron, owning furnaces and there not being sale
for iron, concluded not to build any binders. Though we had already
built six, they concluded to stop so I returned again to Beloit in the
summer of 1877 and took the four machines which I had built the year
previous, making some improvements on the harvester in the way of
driving the binders and put them out into the field again. Took one to
Salina, Kas.; one was taken to Waseka, Minn.; others worked about
Beloit. We had then made sufficient improvement on the machine to
make it work successfully, having added the butter or grain adjuster
now known as the Appleby-Bullock patent, and after working the machines successfully and satisfying the Parker & Stone Reaper Company
that it was a successful machine to build we started out to build self-
binders for the harvest of 1878. We built 115 binders for that season,
some of which were, in accordance with a previous arrangement,
shipped to Gammon & Deering, Plano, Ill., by whom they were shipped
with this Company's machines, to their agents, Robinson & Perry, of

Austin, Texas. The machines sent to Austin, Texas, were worked through the harvest and did fairly good work—worked so well that we established an agency with the Gray Brothers to whom we sold the binders. Gammon & Deering's representative, Mr. J. F. Steward, spent some time in the field with them. Several of our machines built that year went to Marissa, Ill., and worked in the harvest fields there. The only binders with which we had any contention in the early part of the harvest was the Walter A. Wood wire binder, known as the Sylvanus D. Locke. While at Marissa we had a field trial in which the Walter A. Wood self-binder and our Beloit twine binder participated and we sold all of our twine binders on the ground and it was proclaimed to be far superior to the Walter A. Wood wire binder. I think about thirty of the Parker & Stone twine binders were sold in southern Illinois that harvest, the rest going further north into the Minnesota harvest. That year was a difficult season for harvesting grain, the grain being killed by hot sun in the early part of harvest and the grain falling down and the straw was of that weak and fluffy nature that any binders then known could not successfully bind the grain with the exception of our Beloit twine binder. This binder having the advantage of the packers or feeders and working automatically, first packing its sheaf and sizing it uniformly before binding, successfully bound that difficult condition of grain. This probably more than anything else made a successful beginning in the era of the twine binder known as the Appleby binder.

"In the fall of 1878 we licensed the firm known as Hoover, Allen & Gamble, or Excelsior Reaper Works at Miamisburg to build our binders; also the firm of Gammon & Deering, then manufacturing harvesters and binders at Plano, Ill. Having made arrangements with Hoover, Allen & Gamble of Miamisburg I went there in person and built their machine,—harvester and binder, furnishing them patterns with which to build the machines for the coming year. I also went to Plano, Ill., having also made arrangements with Gammon & Deering for the manufacture of the same and assisted them in the construction and the attachment of the binder to their harvester. Began building binders at the Gammon & Deering manufactory in the winter of 1878 and 9 and I assisted them in the building of 75 twine binders for the coming harvest of 1879 and assisted them in experting the machines through the harvest. Those machines built by Gammon & Deering were successfully operated through that harvest and with slight changes they have built them ever since.

"In the winter of 1879 and 80, having licensed George Esterly of Whitewater to build our binder, I went there to build a machine, including harvester and binder and completed the building of the machine with patterns, preparatory to the manufacture of that known as the 'Esterly self-binder.' The pattern for the binder frame I took from the shops of the Gammon & Deering factory at Plano, by consent, it being a front geared binder, the first of the kind ever built, one of which

I had built for Gammon & Deering at their shops, but trying it on the Gammon & Deering harvester found that it was not built so that the machine balanced well with a front geared binder.

"This style of binder I also took to Minneapolis and used in the construction of the harvester and binder known as the Minneapolis Harvester Co., including harvester· and binder and got it so far complete as to build 80 of them for the harvest of 1880 and the machines worked successfully. The latter part of the harvest at Fargo, N. D., we had sold several of our binders, the Minneapolis binder, and I had made some improvements in the way of a swinging cord holder and a tucker for the knotter, those being the essential improvements over the previously built binders for that year.

"While there I found C. H. McCormick, Withington, Storle, and Jenkins working in the field with experimental machines,—I think three different binders, of their own make.

"There I met George Carver, then experting for Deering, operating the Deering machines, of which they had a great number and were all working well.

"During the summer of 1879, while operating the machines in southern Illinois and Minnesota we found a little difficulty in the clogging of the binders at times because of too great an accumulation of grain in the binder, and the compression being rigid made it very severe on the compression of the bundle. This led to the construction of the device known as the elastic compressor which has been employed on all Appleby binders since that time. We were at that time using a smooth drive wheel on the harvester. We put lugs on for future use.

"On my return to Minneapolis Mr. Charles Colohan came to me and wanted to enter into an agreement for the manufacture of my twine binder to be attached to the McCormick harvester. At that time I refused to enter into an agreement with him in behalf of the McCormick Company, feeling interested in the protection of other manufacturers, but later on they came to see me again in regard to a license and declared that they would build the machine anyway as they had a right to do, I having established a price as royalty and for that reason I concluded it was best to license them to build the binder. We entered into a contract and they built the first year, on royalty, and they seeing that they would have to build this binder in order to compete with other manufacturers, several of whom were then engaged in the manufacture of my binder and had ceased to build other binders known as wire binders, concluded to buy a shop-right as it would cost them less than to build on royalty. We licensed them to build, giving them a shop-right for the sum of $31,000 having the right to build all they pleased. Up to the time of licensing the McCormick Company the Parker & Stone Reaper Co., the Excelsior Reaper Co., the Gammon & Deering Co., the Esterly Co. and the Minneapolis Harvester Co. had all been building the Appleby binders, all of which were successful. Then fol-

lowed the McCormick, building the binder identically as the two floating disc binders built by the Minneapolis Harvester Co. were for the
harvest of 1881.

"In 1881 the Ohio Champion Co., known as Whitely, Fassler & Kelly,
at Springfield, Ohio, were building a twine binder of different construction, very complicated, but very perfect and mechanical in its construction. This, however, proved a failure and Whitely, Fassler & Kelly
concluded to buy the residue of the Appleby patents and acquire the
whole right to the patents, with the exception of licenses and shop-
rights already granted, and to assume the rights accruing from all licenses not settled for by shop-right. Some companies were licensed to
build Appleby binders after Whitely, Fassler & Kelly had acquired the
patents pertaining to the Appleby binder, so called. While associated
with the Minneapolis Harvester Co. for eight years I continued in the
improvement of binders, taking out many patents, all pertaining to harvesters and binders.

"In my first talk with Mr. Deering in regard to a shop-right for the
manufacture of my binder it was agreed that he should have an exclusive right to the state of Illinois, the consideration of which was to
be a greater sum than was finally agreed upon, the original price being
fixed at $10 royalty for each machine, but later on in consideration of
the efforts made by Messrs. Gammon & Deering in pioneering the machine and being early in the beginning of the manufacture of the same,
and dropping from out of our agreement the exclusive right of the
state of Illinois, the figure was placed at $5.00, as Mr. Gammon pre-
ferred to make the contract in that way, saying that he did not care
who else built the machine and did not care for the exclusive clause in
the contract.

"In my experiments I first used a soft twine, flax, a small twine that
would run, say, about 1100 feet to the pound. We used some hemp that
was hand spun at Davenport. The next was some manufactured at
Xenia. It was a 2-ply hemp, I think, made from the tow of hemp and
would run about 700 feet to the pound. The next was Manila twine
brought to the factory of Gammon & Deering at Plano by Mr. William
Deering, who obtained it from Philadelphia, I think it was. The introduction of the Manila twine was an item of great value in making
provision for the supply of the best material possible for the automatic twine binder.

"In the summer of 1875, just at the end of harvest, I had been operating my twine binder with self-sizing devices, in the field, to demonstrate the working of them; they worked well except that a portion of
the harvester to which the binder was attached was found defective in
its elevator, but when the machine elevated and delivered the grain to
the binder it worked well. I only made a short trial during that one
afternoon and the harvest was over in the vicinity of Beloit. I had
heard, while building my machine, that at Rockford some one had built

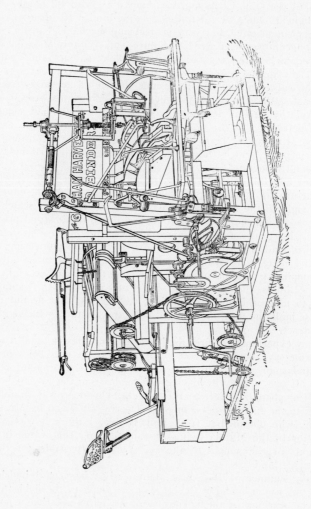

a machine known as the Gorham, and I went down there to see it work, and, calling at the factory of M. C. Thompson, I enquired where I could see Mr. Gorham's binder work. Having received instructions where to go I proceeded to the field and found Mr. Gorham with his large machine; the size of it surprised me, as I supposed it was a smaller machine. I found him and others in the field, cutting a piece of oats. It was nearly all out when I got there, but Mr. Gorham showed me the working of his machine. I told him that I had been operating a grain binder in the field and related to him to what extent I had succeeded. He taking an interest in me showed me all about his machine and I saw it operate in the field. The grain leaning, he had to cut it all one way. It was a very ponderous machine and could only cut and bind about two feet of the grain. After he had got through cutting I went with him to his house and took supper, had a very pleasant visit and that was the last and the only time that I ever saw Mr. Gorham, or his machine. The binding mechanism of this machine was very large and projected so far from the drive wheel that in order to balance the machine to keep it from tipping, the grain wheel plank, as it was usually called, was made of cast iron, two inches thick by about ten inches wide and about four feet long. It required about that weight to make the machine balance on the drive wheel.

"In my '58 binder I conveyed the grain with an endless apron, the same as in general use to-day, except that it was toothed, though it was constructed with chains running over sprockets back of the sickle in the platform. This conveyed the grain to the side of the machine in the usual way of the side delivery into a receptacle which I called my bundle former. This was made with tines that were put through a timber rocking shaft and they were bent at right angles so that the grain, when forced into this bundle former, rocked the latter and threw the binding mechanisms into gear, so sizing the bundles automatically by the accumulation of a certain quantity of grain sufficient to fill the bundle former.

"In the testimony of E. D. Bishop a witness for the complainant in the McCormick Harvesting Machine Co. against C. Aultman & Co. and Aultman, Miller & Co., Bishop testified in answer to questions 9, 10, 12, and 13 as follows:

'Q. 9. State whether or not you remember at any time of going to Rockford, Illinois, and seeing a twine-binder there; if so, when you went, who accompanied you, and whose binder you saw?

'A. I did. I went in August—near the first of August, as I recollect now, in company with John F. Appleby, and I saw the Gorham binder. I meant in the year 1874.

'Q. 10. Who was with you when you saw the Gorham binder?

'A. John F. Appleby, and it is my recollection now, but I am not positive, that it was Mr. McGregor and Mr. Gorham was present during part of the time.

'Q. 11. What Mr. Gorham do you refer to?

'A. The inventor, or the man who claimed to be the inventor.

'Q. 12. Where was John F. Appleby living at this time?

'A. He was living at Rockton, I think, in Illinois, about five miles from Beloit.

'Q. 13. Did you or did you not go from Rockton to Rockford with Mr. Appleby at that time?

'A. I did.'

(Dr. E. D. Bishop was, off and on, in the employ of the McCormick Harvesting Machine Co.).

"The answers to these several questions are entirely wrong, for I never at the time mentioned, or any other time, ever made a trip to Rockford with E. D. Bishop, to Rockford or any other place, to see the Gorham Binder or any binder whatsoever. Mrs. Gorham in her statement in the same suit is at error when she states that it was in 1874 that I went to see the Gorham Binder. It was in 1875 and after I had built an automatic grain binder of my own at Beloit in the Parker & Stone Reaper Works.

"In 1877, while I was with the Beloit Reaper Works at Beloit, Wis., we sent one of our machines to Waseka, Minn., and there operated it in a piece of barley near the town of Waseka and while there Mr. Holmes and son of Owatonna, who were then experimenting on a grain binder but had never succeeded in making one work in the field, as they admitted to me, went over from Owatonna to Waseka to see my machine work. It worked successfully in a heavy piece of barley. This was done to show the feasibility of the attachment of a binder to a harvester, having many of the harvesters without the binder attachment in the market that year. Holmes and son were interested in seeing the machine work inasmuch as they were making some efforts themselves in the direction of a grain binder. Later in the season I had the same binder at Owatonna, Minn. It worked in a wheat field where Holmes and son were again permitted to follow my machine. I operated my binder for several days in this wheat field, it working nicely. Holmes and son followed it each day. Up to that time Holmes and son had never built an operative binder and had never attempted the automatic sizing of bundles and the compression of bundles by mechanism other than the twine with which they tied it. This, we may conclude, was the starting point of what was known as the 'Holmes Binder' built for several years by the Walter A. Wood Company at Hoosick Falls, N. Y."

At a time that the question was raised as to who was first to take up the Appleby binder after it had been proved to have merit by machines put out by Parker & Stone, Mr. Appleby wrote as follows referring to Gammon & Deering:

"It is but fair to this Company to say that it was first of all existing companies to investigate into the merits of the Appleby Binder with a view to arrangements to work under the patents. Hoover & Gamble, Esterly & Son, the Minneapolis Harvester Works, The Plano Mfg. Co. and others soon followed."

The threat made to build the Appleby binder with or without license, notwithstanding the verbal understanding with Mr. Deering for exclusive rights for the State of Illinois, was told the author both by Mr. Appleby and Mr. Deering very soon after it was made, and I have before me the written statement of Mr. Deering to the effect that when calling on Mr. Appleby at a hotel in Chicago he found him in conference with C. H. McCormick, Jr., Dr. Bishop and a stranger. I quote:

"I inferred that they were in negotiations for some rights under the Appleby patents, and charged the same upon Mr. Appleby upon the first opportunity that presented itself, I think at my office, when McCormick was not present, and he admitted that they were in treaty with McCormick. I charged upon him the want of good faith, was exceedingly indignant and he stated in justification that McCormick stated he should build the Appleby twine binder with license if he could procure it and without if he could not. Mr. Appleby stated that he had no choice in the matter and was forced to enter into the treaty with them."

In the progress of every revolution there are "Valley Forges" and "Waterloos," whether the revolution be a political or an industrial one. The boy Appleby began with high hopes and had his ups and downs. As a farm hand he could earn but little more than necessary to satisfy ordinary wants. His ingenuity led him into various mechanical employments, but he could not earn enough to carry out his ideas, and hence must depend upon outside assistance, which he obtained from time to time. His binder of 1875 promised well. He made others, adding improvements. During the harvest of 1878 his machine operated so well as to induce Gammon & Deering to undertake their manufacture. For the harvest of 1879 over fifty machines were put out by the last named company. They worked as well as, but probably no better than, the machines sold by Parker & Stone for the harvest of 1878 until near the close of the harvest after a few improvements had been made. The winter of '79 and '80 was indeed a "Valley Forge." All were discouraged but William Deering.

That he was not discouraged, that his foresight and unbounded confidence in human ingenuity was well founded, is shown by the fact that for the harvest of 1880 he built 3,000 Appleby binders, somewhat improved, all of which were sold and gave such eminent satisfaction that other manufacturers "fell over each other," as it were, in efforts to take up the Appleby binder. A number of years after while in a retrospective mood Mr. Appleby wrote:

In William Deering of Chicago, Illinois (formerly of the firm of Gammon & Deering) I found a man far sighted enough to see the importance of my inventions. To him belongs the credit of forcing my binder on to the market with sufficient energy to convince the farmer of its practicability. His demonstration of the practicability of the inventions soon led other manufacturers to adopt it.

John F. Appleby.

The inventive mind is said never to rest. Such is certainly true of Mr. Appleby, and he fancied after the bright days and the dark days of the harvest of 1879 that he could make a better binder than the one that, soon having received its finishing touches, now binds the grain of the civilized world. Approaching Mr. Deering on the subject the following agreement resulted:

"MEMORANDUM OF AGREEMENT between William Deering, of Chicago, Ill., and J. F. Appleby, of Beloit, Wisconsin, WITNESSETH THAT:

"WHEREAS, said Appleby is an inventor and has given attention to invention of self binders for grain using twine for bands; and whereas he believes he has invented and can produce a very simple and efficient binder differing from and superior to any he has heretofore invented and different from any other; and whereas said Deering desires such a binder,

"Now it is agreed between parties hereto that said Appleby shall make such a binder within next two months and deliver same to said Deering with the patterns for same, and said Deering is to pay therefor five hundred dollars. It is further agreed that said Deering shall be entitled to take out patents on all the inventions on same subject to patents on said machines and become the full owner of same, with all the rights possible to be conveyed to him by said Appleby and by said patents on the further payment of the sum of Five Thousand Dollars, on the following conditions and manner:

"If after said Deering shall have seen and examined and tried said sample binder he judges he shall wish it, he shall then pay said Appleby the sum of One Thousand Dollars, which shall entitle him to use of the machine during harvest of 1880. If it then works well and said Deering concludes to adopt and build it, he shall pay said Appleby the further sum of Four Thousand Dollars, which shall be in full. Should not said Deering conclude to pay more than the first $500. provided for in this agreement, then ownership shall revert to said Appleby of the binder in question.

"If at any time hereafter said Appleby shall be able, by suggestion or otherwise, to aid said Deering in improvements to said binder, he agrees to do so, provided he is not put to unwarranted expense or that it does not deprive him of rights in other inventions to his special loss.

"Witness our hands this 11 Nov. 1879.

(Signed)   William Deering.
J. F. Appleby."

Mr. Appleby's estimates of the value of his inventions were, during his early life, exceedingly moderate, of which fact the above agreement may be considered proof. It is seen that he would accept $5,000.00 for a better binder than the one produced, and in addition was to aid in improving it in so far as he could do so without unwarranted expense, etc. He set his own price. The binder was made and inspected by the writer, with the result that its future was stated, in his opinion, to be less promising than the one now known as the Appleby binder. It was adapted to self size the gavels as they accumulated in the receptacle, and from the receptacle they were taken by the binding devices, which moved crane like toward and from the receptacle, following somewhat nearly the Gammon & Deering wire binder of that date. Mr. Appleby's own opinion as to the merits may be gathered from a letter written to Mr. Deering January 13, 1880, from which I make the following extract:

"I presume you would like to hear of the new Binder. I have got its movements all complete and it works just as was designed. I think it the simplest & cheapest Binder ever made. I cannot make it wholly complete without a Harvester to attach it to as I shall drive the feeders for automatic sizing from the Harvester rolls. I have to work at every conceivable inconvenience, as there is but one shop in town that does jobbing work and that runs only evenings as the proprietor works in the Reaper shops. I have kept the Binder at my house and it has not been seen except by the help I have employed to work on it."

The following is copied from a list showing dates of beginning of placing on the market various types of harvesters. This was compiled by me in 1897, and represents the development as it transpired

	Deering Company	Wood Company	McCormick Company	Aultman, Miller & Co.	Osborne Company	Champion Company	Johnston Company
Marsh Harvester, upon which two men did the binding	1863	1870	1875	1880	....	1867	....
Marsh Harvester having wire binder attachments in place of the stand for the men	1874	1874	1877 (six in 1876)	1880	1875	....	....
Marsh Harvester with modern twine binder	1878	1880	1881	1882	1882	1882	1882
Light Marsh Harvester with modern twine binder	1183	....	1884	....	....	....	....
All-steel Marsh Harvester with modern twine binder	1885	....	1887	....	1885	....	....
Light all-steel Marsh Harvester with modern twine binder....	1889	....	....	....	1892	....	....
Roller bearings	1891	....	1894	....	1897	....	....
Bevel geared Binder..	1890	....	1894	....	....	....	....

This will no doubt be disputed by those who are perpetuating the McCormick legend, but I was active in field, factory and market all those years, and know whereof I speak.

On August 8, 1881, a trial was held at the Derby Show in England, and on the 13th an article appeared in the *Chicago Evening Journal,* containing these statements:

"We learn by special cable message that the McCormick machine was declared the winner in this great race for popularity, being awarded the society's gold medal.

"This is the second time within three years that the McCormick machine has been entered for competition before the Royal Agricultural Society, and on both occasions it carried off the highest honor—a gold medal. But then this is nothing new for the McCormick machine, for since the first World's Fair ever held, in 1851, in London, down to this last brilliant victory, the McCormick machine at every important contest has not only REAPED all the honors but THRASHED all competition."

The vessel upon which the machine was shipped was wrecked on the Irish coast.

"The machine was given up as lost, and another machine was shipped . . . but in spite of all that could be done, it was clear the latter machine could not reach the trial in time. But Cyrus H. McCormick was not to be beaten, and so he cabled his English agent to get the original machine from the wreck of the Britannic, and do the best he could with it. And it was with this half-drowned, rusty machine . . . that Mc-Cormick outdistanced his thirty competitors, and really snatched victory from the jaws of defeat. *This sort of good generalship and management on the part of McCormick has helped keep his machine where it has stood for the last thirty-five years—in the lead of all others."*

The facts are that this machine was a Marsh harvester which McCormick had begun building after having fought it, as a competitor, many years. It had upon it an Appleby binder attachment copied from one of the patterns which were made at the Deering factory, the sample attachment itself having been made from those patterns by Appleby at the Minneapolis factory and bought for McCormick at the St. Louis Exposition.

First refusing to admit that Cyrus McCormick's machines were ever in the lead as to quality, and oftentimes not so in quantities, the writer, having a knowledge of C. H. McCormick's business methods, long ago was confirmed in the belief held by many others, that *"this sort of good generalship and management on the part of McCormick has helped keep his machine where it has stood for the last thirty-five years—in the lead of all others."* In this connection I will further say that a list was published in the same Fair Catalogue of 1881 enumerating sixty-one gold, silver, and bronze medals and decorations claimed to have been won by Mr. McCormick and his company between the years 1851 and 1881. The number is not a large one when compared with lists of medals taken by other large manufacturers, but, in the same catalogue we find: "It is a well recognized historical fact that the McCormick is the type and pattern after which all other reaping machines are modeled," and besides, as so many times stated in advertising circulars, that C. H. McCormick is to be credited with all modern methods of harvesting grain.

Now, considering the list: The medal taken in 1851 was for a machine that embodied no element acknowledged by the courts, the Patent Office, his relatives and those versed in the art, to have been invented by Cyrus H. McCormick. This is equally true of every machine that won medals for him.

His self-rake reaper which won medals was the same old 1851

machine but with a raking reel, to make which he bought rights of McClintock Young, years after his competitors had adopted better self-raking devices.

The mowing machines that won medals were founded upon the inventions of Hussey, Nishwitz, and others.

His combined reaping and mowing machine that won medals was founded upon the inventions of Hussey, Nishwitz, and Young, first put out in 1869.

The harvester that won medals for him was the Marsh harvester taken up by McCormick after it had been constantly put on the market over twelve years by a competitor. The wire binder that is alleged to have won him a decoration was the Marsh harvester with Withington's binder mounted upon it, improved, somewhat, by William R. Baker and Lambert Erpelding, employes, and Leander J. McCormick. The twine binder claimed to have won him a medal at the Derby trial, in 1881, was the Marsh harvester, long fought by him as a competitor, having the copy of an Appleby twine binder bought on the market.

In all the machines, from first to last, there was not one element invented by Cyrus H. McCormick in any of them. See "Memorial of Robert McCormick," page 58, from which I shall soon quote.

(I offer a sample brick from the monumental falsehood. A full generation after Hussey had invented and patented his reaper, embodying the flexibly affixed grain-receiving platform, and his licensees and others had embodied the invention in their machines for many years, McCormick adopted it. I refer to the McCormick Annual Catalogue for 1871, page 8, *"ADVANCE REAPER AT WORK." "ITS HISTORY." "ITS FIRST APPEARANCE IN 1869."* In 1910, at a meeting at the McCormick Theological Seminary, opened with prayer, the fulsome historian and biographer tells us that McCormick invented "a platform to receive the falling grain, flexibly affixed so as to accommodate itself to the irregularities of the surface" of the ground passed over. This parallels Casson's story of Gorham's ghost, called back to build a twine binder by McCormick, for the harvest of 1881).

"He never invented or produced any essential elementary part in any reaping or harvesting machine from first to last. These assertions are broad, but absolutely true. They stand squarely upon the records and the history and state of the art. C. H. McCormick or any one for him, cannot deny them with proofs, therefore he is not entitled to recognition as the man who 'had done more to elevate agriculture than any man the world has produced,' because of his supposed inventions in this line; but, on the contrary, that the development of Western agriculture has elevated him, and that he has more money, and received more honors, 'than any man the world has produced,' by appropriating the brains of others, and the credit due them as inventors, are propositions much more defensible."

The medals were, many of them, no doubt, due him as a large manufacturer, and we should not criticise but for the hints, and in many cases positive statements that he was the inventor of the machines, and was acknowledged by the judges of awards as such.

Another quotation from a newspaper found in the 1881 catalogue ends with: "When McCormick got up the wire binder he beat himself, and now he has a twine binder—well, that beats the devil." The publication of this statement is but one of the many directed to misinform the public as to inventions that have led up to modern harvest methods.

The bibliography of the alleged invention of the reaper by C. H. McCormick is extensive, but mainly in the form of posters and annual catalogues published by McCormick. All references to the matter, outside of those that cannot be traced directly to claims made by Mr. McCormick and his own family, are antagonistic to his claims. All transactions in the Patent Office, in the courts and in Congress, dispute his claims. Casson's book will not be here considered further than to say that every one of the multitude of statements giving McCormick the credit of having invented the reaper, or any part thereof ever used by any competitor, or long used by him; or any part of a harvester or any part of an automatic binder, are unqualifiedly false. McCormick never led.

Let us recapitulate. The methods followed by C. H. McCormick seem to have been continued by his successors. His exceeding conservatism made him money, as he spent comparatively little in experiments. He adopted what others had proved to be valuable. He did not apply a seat to his machine until he was obliged to, as his machine could not compete with Hussey's and others having seats for the raker. He did not apply a practical self-rake to his machine for many years because it would involve a reorganization.

He wasted much printer's ink in attempts to down the Palmer & Williams, Seymour & Morgan and other self-raking machines. It is probable that the J. Atkins self-raking reaper, a wonderfully practical and ingenious machine, patented in 1852, had more to do with convincing Mr. McCormick that he was far in the rear than anything else. The writer remembers the Atkins machine well. A neighbor had owned a McCormick, which he termed a "horse killer," and substituted for it an Atkins self-rake. When a boy the writer followed it often, watching it, in its almost human movements, sweep the grain from the platform in neatly compressed gavels.

McCormick, as stated, finally adopted the McClintock-Young reel rake, as it had been already so adapted to his special reaper as to require little change in the latter. He attempted to make his reaper a combined reaper and mower more than twenty years after combined reapers and mowers had been placed on the market. He did not come to a two-wheeled mowing machine of the Hussey type until Hussey, Lewis Miller, Nishwitz, and others had fully developed the floating finger bar machine of the present day. He did not make that two-wheeled machine a combined reaper and mower a practical success until early in the '70s. He did not take up the Marsh harvester until it had been in public *use* more than fifteen years and was driving reapers from the field. He did not apply a wire binder to his Marsh harvester until three years after Osborne, Walter A. Wood and John Gordon, succeeded by Gammon & Deering, had put out binders meeting the approval of the public. He did not take up the Appleby twine binder until it had been three years on the market as made by competing manufacturers. He did not adapt a reel, adjustable in both essential directions, until after many other manufacturers had proved its value. His successors did not build an all steel machine until John Harris, D. M. Osborne, and William Deering had proved the value of steel as material for the same. His successors, who claim so much enterprise for him, did not build a rotary corn shocker until five years after the Deering Harvester Company had begun its development, and two years after it first put them out. The machine had been fully perfected by its competitor and fifty had been put out for tests with instructions to the agents not to sell them; as they could not purchase one to copy, men were sent into the field to make measurements, photographs were taken, and the Mc-

Cormick Corn shocker resulted and was put on the market. For six years after the Deering Harvester Company had made an automatic mower, the invention of the present writer and George H. Ellis, and five years after two more were made; it did nothing in that line, until early in the spring of 1900, when it learned that the Deering Harvester Company had one at the Paris Exposition, when it undertook to produce a similar one; and succeeded in getting it to Paris in time to go into the field test. (The success of the McCormick self-moving mower was widely advertised.) It did not apply the falling-tooth bundle carrier until two or more years after it had been put on the market by the Walter A. Wood Company, and the Deering Harvester Company. It did not seriously attempt to make a low-down binder until apparent success had been reached by others. These are only samples of the imitations McCormick and his successors practiced, and they are mentioned here for the purpose of showing how unreliable may be considered the claims made as to Cyrus H. McCormick having been first to produce a successful reaper, and to show how unreliable are the proofs adduced to make the public so believe. C. H. McCormick and his successors have been noted, from the beginning, as having made good use of printer's ink, and its claim to have driven many hundred manufacturers out of business is but a fair sample of the exaggeration. Its claims to having won so many victories are to a great extent victories on paper only. Its machines were heavy and not up to date until recent years and could not speak well for themselves, hence the resort to extensive advertising. Victories were claimed at trials although the machines had failed.

Let the reader of this volume turn to Casson's work and compare the statements therein found with those found in this volume, backed by court decisions, decisions of the Patent Office and the Records of the Patent Office, and judge for himself.

The fact that Casson's statements are unreliable is well shown on pages 116 and 117 of "Cyrus Hall McCormick, His Life and Work." Referring to William Deering, he says:

"And in 1880 he staked practically his whole fortune upon the making of 3,000 twine self-binders, and won.

"Cyrus McCormick saw at a glance that the wire self-binder must go. It was his policy to give the farmers what they wanted, rather than to force upon them an unpopular machine. So he called to his aid a mechanical genius named Marquis L. Gorham—one of those who had been lured into the quest of a self-binder by the insistence of 'Pump' Carpenter. Gorham's most valuable contribution was a self-sizing device, by which all bound sheaves were made to be the same size. By the time that the grain stood ripe and yellow the following season, Gorham had prepared a twine self-binder that worked well, and McCormick, yielding to the sudden hostility against wire, pushed the Gorham machine with the full force of his great organization."

Simmered down this means that after the year 1880 McCormick *"called to his aid a mechanical genius named Marquis L. Gorham.*** By the time that the grain stood ripe and yellow the following season, Gorham had prepared a twine self-binder that worked well, and Mc-Cormick*** pushed the Gorham machine with the full force of his great organization."** The facts are that Gorham had died nearly five years before, and the McCormick Company did not begin dealing with his widow until about five years after his death. Casson knew this, as the writer had submitted to him all of his very many documents, and Mr. Appleby, Mr. Whitely and Mr. Deering had talked the matter over with him repeatedly. That any member of the C. H. McCormick family and that Company allowed such a statement as the above to be made either shows unwarranted carelessness or a willingness that the public should be deceived in order that the great fraud in reaper history, so early initiated and so deeply at heart, might be perpetuated.

I here present an old cut of the first McCormick twine binding attachment (applied to the Marsh harvester) and one of the Minneapolis binding attachments, built by Mr. Appleby from patterns made by him at Mr. Deering's works. The attachment, as already stated, was bought at the St. Louis Fair, copied by McCormick and put out in large quantities. Compare the machines with the Gorham binder, again shown, as left by Gorham at the time of his death— the reader is permitted to judge as to the reliability of the statements in "Cyrus Hall McCormick, His Life and Work."

*The writer of the above tells us, in "The Romance of the Reaper," that Ralph Emerson (with whom the present writer was long indirectly associated) said of McCormick: "His enemies have said that he was not an inventor, but I say that he was an inventor of ability." Query: Is this statement of Casson as true as his that Gorham arose from the dead and built a binder for McCormick?

One of the most important litigations, involving harvester patents, brought against manufacturers, was on patent 77,878, granted to James F. Gordon, in 1868. If sustained by the courts, this patent would have controlled the binding of bundles centrally, relative to the length of the grain; the court, however, held:

"1st. That in view of the proceedings which took place in the Patent Office, before said Letters Patent No. 77,878 were granted, as disclosed in the File Wrapper and contents, showing that the patentee was required to, and did narrow and limit the broad claim of his first application covering and embracing the broad feature of a binding device or mechanism capable of adjustment in the direction of the length of the grain in order to bind the bundle of gavel at or near the center, by confining and restricting said claim as finally allowed to

" 'the binding arm H capable of adjustment in the direction of the length of the grain, in combination with an automatic twisting device, substantially as and for the purposes set forth;'

"and in view of the state of the art as shown in the prior patents to Watson, Renwick & Watson, No. 8083 dated May 13, 1851, of Watson & Renwick No. 9930, dated June 6, 1853, of S. S. Harlbut, No. 7928, dated February 4, 1851, of A. Sherwood No. 21540 granted Sept. 14, 1858, and of Allen Sherwood No. 25308 issued Aug. 30, 1859. Said first claim of said Letters Patent No. 77,878 alleged to be infringed by defendant, must be limited and confined to the specific combination embodied therein and described in the specification, including the Rake as an element of said combination, and cannot be properly enlarged or broadened as a pioneer invention as urged by counsel for complainants so as to cover any and all binding devices or mechanism which are made adjustable to separate and independent Harvester Machines.

"2nd. That if not so limited and restricted said Letters Patent No. 77,878 were anticipated by the patents above mentioned, and therefore void.

"3rd. That as limited and confined to the specific combination therein described said first claim of said Letters Patent is valid, but complainants cannot under said claim invoke in behalf of this patent the doctrine of equivalents, or the liberal construction allowed to pioneer inventions, so as to broaden said claim and thereby practically make it cover what the Patent Office had once rejected with the patentee's acquiescence.

"4th. That under this view of the proper restrictive construction to be placed upon said Letters Patent or the first claim thereof, it neither anticipates the S. D. Carpenter patent nor was it anticipated by said Carpenter's patent. Said Carpenter's patent and inventions embodies

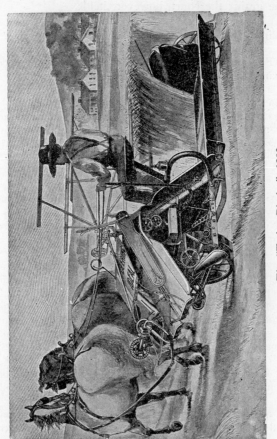

The "Twine Binder", 1900.

Deering Marsh Harvester with Twin Binder, 1880.

Minneapolis Appleby Binder of 1880.

First McCormick copy of Deering and Minneapolis Binder as put out in 1881.
Does it look like the Gorham binder?

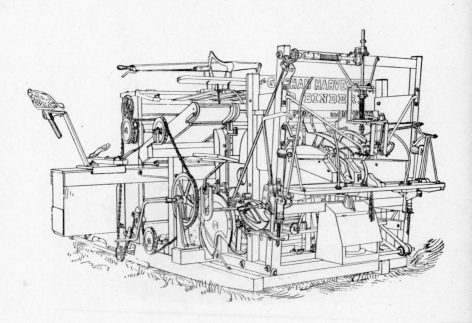

the adjustable and independent binding mechanism such as defendants generally use and employ in connection with their grain Harvester.

"5th. That the defendants binding machines, which are entirely separate and independent and distinct from the grain harvesters, although so constructed as to be attached to said harvesters and made adjustable so as to bind the gavel centrally, do not when so used infringe the first claim of complainants said patent No. 77,878.

The adjustable feature of certain parts of a single combined machine or grain harvester, cannot, in the light of the art as disclosed in prior patents, be treated or regarded as the same, or substantially the same thing as an independent binding mechanism adjustable as a whole with all its parts fixed and unadjustable, simply because said binding device is used in connection with grain harvesters.

"6th. That the Bills in the above entitled causes should each be dismissed at complainants costs, and it is accordingly so ordered and adjudged.

Howell E. Jackson, Circuit Judge.
George R. Sage, District Judge."

CHAPTER XXI.

TWINE DEVELOPMENTS.

"For as ye sow ye are like to reap."

The success of binders of the present day, all of which are Appleby binders, depends largely upon the quality of twine, and that was true with the Holmes binder, until recently to a small extent and for a time manufactured by the Walter A. Wood Mowing & Reaping Machine Company, as well as all experimental binders that have come and gone.

Mr. William Deering, to whom must be credited the initial moves that have resulted in the present great binder twine industries, when a boy was an apprentice in a woolen factory. He finally became owner of the little factory and eventually of other factories and later still drifted into the mercantile business for the purpose of disposing of the product of his factories, taking in also cotton goods, twines and cordage. He may be considered to have been, practically, a "natural born" fibre expert. Flax, hemp and cotton fibres had been used with indifferent success in the earlier Appleby binders, and he foresaw that he should have trouble with his 3,000 twine binders for the harvest of 1880 unless he could get a better twine. He knew the better qualities of hemp and sisal fibres which had been used for rope yarn and visited many twine factories in the United States, endeavoring to induce those having rope machinery to produce a yarn sufficiently fine for use with his binders. None would undertake the task until he approached the late Edwin H. Fitler, of Philadelphia, who thought it possible to spin finer yarns, but did not care to undertake the experiment unless Mr. Deering would take the risks of failure and could give an order for a ton at least. When told that he was ready to give an order for many carloads if he could be shown a good sample, Mr. Fitler was greatly surprised, and at once sent for his superintendent and gave instructions how to proceed. In a few days sample balls were sent and a very large quantity of twine ordered. It was the writer's good fortune to test the first ball of Manila twine in the field, and the result of the test was a telegram simply reading: "Manila splendid."

On July 19, 1892, Mr. Fitler wrote a letter to the Cordage Journal in regard to twine. It reads:

"Yours of the 6th only reached me today. I have been away from home and being pretty well run down, worn out with politics and business, and it was concluded that my business should not follow me.

"The article you sent me I had read before. It was written no doubt by Mr. Balch, who was formerly with the N. C. Co. (National Cordage Company). Of course it will make the cordage manufacturers smile, those that know all about machinery; and as to the claim of Good making the first Binder Twine, it is simply absurd.

"Single-thread Binder Twine never was thought of or heard of until our firm made it for Mr. William Deering, of Chicago. And permit me to say that the first ever made was spun on a Todd & Rafferty jenny.

"When the samples came from the factory to the store about 13 or 14 years ago I drew out one of the balls about a pound to keep as a sample and I now take pleasure in sending you some of it so that you can see that it was an A No. 1 Twine, strictly Pure Manila, for in that day cheating and mixing was not in vogue.

"Of course, we have improved in our mode of manufacturing since this sample was made, but there are a number of manufacturers that cannot beat it to-day."

CHAPTER XXII.

A Legend Analyzed

"The work of the farmer is not so hard as it was when I was a lad. Since Mr. McCormick, of blessed memory, gave us the binder, now made at prices less than dreamed could be possible, the harvest labor has been reduced to the minimum."—J. H. Gore, in "Wallace's Farmer," January 15, 1909.

The writer is familiar with the articles written by Mr. Gore, all well paid for. The reader of the preceding pages, should he turn to the files of the Patent Offices of the world, could find no mention of Cyrus McCormick's name connected with binders.

Mr. McCormick was only one of the thousands of successful business men of his time. P. T. Barnum, the show man, a contemporary, was equally successful. A large part of his success was due to resorting to the mysterious, because, as he frankly admitted, the public liked to be fooled. When Dan Rice was at his highest and Barnum only a small competitor, the latter inscribed upon his banner, so to speak, "The greatest show on earth." Similarly Mr. McCormick, as continued by his successors, took upon himself the credit of being "the inventor of the reaper." An effort has recently been made to place the name of McCormick beside that of Lincoln and claim equal honors. An attempt is also being made to place the name of McCormick in the newly established Hall of Fame. I quote from "The Voter" of March, 1909:

(The reference letters at the close of sentences direct to comments similarly lettered at the close of the article quoted.)

"One hundred years ago—February 12, 1809—there was born in a log cabin in Kentucky one who was destined to become the emancipator of the black man on American soil. One hundred years ago—Feb. 15—there was born in a log cabin in Virginia one who was destined to drive the specter of hunger from the world. Both came from the

South. Both followed the trend of empire to the West. Both wrought, each in his way, for the good of mankind. Both were adopted by Illinois and both found their last resting place in its soil. Abraham Lincoln—emancipator of men. Cyrus H. McCormick—emancipator of hunger. (a) Citizens of the same country and state, they are known to the peoples of all nations and their works will live long after the generations of today have passed.

"In a sense the destinies of the two men were intertwined. When McCormick was battling for his rights and patents, when the foremost lawyers of the country were engaged upon one side or the other, it so happened that Abraham Lincoln was retained in opposition to the McCormick contention. (b) The fee which he was paid—$1,000— served to finance his campaign during the famous Lincoln-Douglas debates. The debates led to the presidency and thus, indirectly, the man who invented the reaper and lessened the labors of the farmer, assisted in advancing to fame the man whom the nation honors as its martyr President. (c)

"During this great legal contest Lincoln and Douglas were on the same side. The leading counsel was Edwin M. Stanton, afterward Lincoln's Secretary of War, and his fee of $10,000 was considered enormous in those days. H. B. Davis, George Harding and Peter H. Watson were the other lawyers antagonistic to McCormick. In his behalf appeared William H. Seward, afterward Secretary of State in Lincoln's cabinet; Senator Reverdy Johnson and E. N. Dickerson.

"This was but one of the incidents of the days when competition was tragic; when legal battles in the courtrooms were followed by hand-to-hand encounters in the fields; (d) when the contest between 'Harvester Kings' was the great topic of the time, and when the victory was only for him who had the tenacity to stay in the fight to the end. In fifty years McCormick fought and vanquished two hundred competitors. (e) At the end perhaps a score of makers of harvesting machinery remained, and these, having learned the futility of the struggle that had been waged, finally combined. Today peace reigns where harsh words and ruthless methods were common and the great business of the International Harvester Company is the result.

* * * * * * *

"Cyrus Hall McCormick, son of Robert McCormick and Mary Anna Hall, was born at Walnut Grove, Rock Ridge County, Virginia, Feb. 15, 1809. His father, farmer and inventor, was of revolutionary stock. His great-grandfather was an Indian fighter in Pennsylvania, while still farther back in the line is the McCormick who fought against James II. at the siege of Londonderry. His mother was the daughter of Patrick and Susan McChesney Hall. With such Scotch-Irish Presbyterian lineage it is little to be wondered that Cyrus Hall McCormick possessed the energy, tenacity and perseverence which commanded the respect even of those who hated him. (f)

"On his father's farm of 1,800 acres young McCormick was educated (g) and equipped for the struggle which was finally to make him the foremost manufacturer of the world. (h) He learned the rudiments in a little field schoolhouse. With his father and brothers he worked with his hands in the farm carpenter shop and smithy. He hammered iron and shaped wood. He held the plow in the furrow. He cared for horses and cattle. He was schooled in those things which make for self-reliance and he was fortunate in being cast in the requisite environment.

"Robert McCormick, the father, was a man of inventive genius. He had fashioned a hemp brake, a clover huller, a bellows, a threshing machine and had essayed a reaping machine, which, however, proved impracticable. His ambition to perfect a reaper and his disappointment in not achieving was an incentive to the boy who early displayed an inventive ability which, in his case, may be attributed to both heredity and environment. The father lived to see the reaper of his dreams materialize in the handiwork of the son. (i)

"At the age of 15 young McCormick invented a grain cradle. At 21 he patented a hillside plow, which threw alternate furrows on the lower side, being thus a right and left hand plow at the will of the operator. (j) Two years later he built a self-sharpening plow and during the same twelvemonth was working on the details of his masterpiece.

"It is difficult in this age of machinery, to realize the crudity and insufficiency of the tools with which man labored before the nineteenth century. For ages agriculture, the leading industry of the world in all periods, had exacted from man the heaviest toll of toil. From the time of the Egyptians the man with the hoe had bent laboriously over the soil from which he was obliged to drag his sustenance. The tools used by the farmer in this country at the beginning of 1800 showed but little advance over those employed in the days when Ruth went forth to glean in the fields of Boaz. The wooden plow, the reaping hook, the hand sickle, the spade, the mattock, the crude hoe—these were the implements still in evidence when Cyrus Hall McCormick was born. (k)

* * * * * * *

"The growth of democracy foreshadowed the dawn of better things. While human labor was cheap, while serfs and slaves humbly did the bidding of their masters, there was no great demand for labor-saving inventions. The spirit which created a republic in this western continent and gave constitutional government to the old monarchies of Europe exalted the laborer, made his toil more valuable and led to inventions by which the tedious, time-wasting methods of feudalism were supplanted. The need of a machine to replace the sickle and the scythe had been recognized by others than the McCormicks. In England the Royal Agricultural Society of Great Britain had offered a prize for the invention of such a device. In this country Obed Hussey, seaman of Nantucket, was in 1833 granted the first patent for a practical reaper. (1) Two years before, in 1831, (m) Cyrus Hall McCormick had with his own hands fashioned every part of a reaping machine, which he exhibited to his neighbors in Virginia. (n) His patent was not taken out until 1834. Though many improvements have come, the fundamental principles of the modern harvesting machine are the same as those demonstrated by the youngster of 22.

"The machine drawn by two horses, tested in a field of oats, consisted of a vibrating cutting blade, a reel to bring the grain within its reach and a platform to receive the falling grain.

"During the years that followed the young inventor made many improvements, but realized nothing from his invention. Youth, poverty and inexperience all conspired to keep the knowledge of his accomplishment from the world. (o) He needed money and cheaper iron. With his father and a neighbor as partner, he built a furnace for the smelting of iron ore, but the panic of 1837 brought disaster to the enterprise. (p) The neighbor evaded his share of financial responsibility, but the McCormicks, father and sons, gave all they had, even mortgaged the homestead, that their indebtedness might be discharged.

* * * * * * *

"In 1841, ten years after the test in the Virginia fields, two farmers came and paid $100 each for reapers. In 1842 seven machines were sold. In 1843 twenty-nine, and in 1844 an order for fifty from Cincinnati showed that its fame had crossed the Ohio river. (q) This order demonstrated the limitations of his location. To fill it the machines were sent on wagons to Scottsville, down the canal to Richmond, by water to New Orleans, and up the Mississippi and Ohio to Cincinnati. The farm sixty miles from a canal and 100 miles from a railway was no place for the manufacture and sale of the reaper.

"At the age of 36, with $300 in his belt, McCormick started on horseback for the West, in whose development he was to play so great a part. From the hills of Virginia he rode to the prairies of Illinois. Here he felt was the natural home of the reaper. His prophetic vision saw the sun-burned grass blossom into fields of golden grain. His imagination was fired by the thought of the time to come when the trails would be main traveled roads, when the Indian would disappear before the white man, when the isolated clearings of the pioneers would become great cities, when the hum of water wheels would be heard along the banks of the streams. He pictured the world as it was to be. He anticipated the time when the wheat fields of the state of his choice should be known throughout the world. His fancy carried him to Europe and the Orient. He forecast the day when the pitiful cry for bread by the starving hordes of the old world would be heard in the land of plenty and the answer returned in shiploads of wheat and flour. He saw, as in a dream, the possibilities of agricultural enterprise, the supply of foodstuffs meeting all the demands of the hungry. And in the wake of such condition he had faith to believe that great industrial communities would be born and men and women and children come to people the wonderful land. In all this was the bright, particular star of his hope and faith and being—the reaper that he had invented, in which he believed and which he determined to force into universal use. And his dream came true. (r)

* * * * * * *

"He rode through Illinois, Wisconsin, Ohio, and New York. In Brockport, N. Y., he met Dayton S. Morgan, machinist, and William H. Seymour, storekeeper, who agreed to make 100 reapers on a royalty for the wheat producing section of New York. (s) At this time he regarded Cincinnati as his headquarters, although he was a resident of that town but a year.

"Convinced that Chicago was to be the great central market of the grain producing country which his machine was to bring into being, he settled here in 1847. He saw more than the village in a swamp without canal or railway. He possessed the gift of the seer. He chose Chicago because he knew and understood.

"McCormick came to Chicago a full-grown man. His waiting time was over. He had experimented. He had added to his patents. He had preached the doctrine of his ambition. He was convinced of the possibilities of his machine. A rugged, heavy-set, broad-shouldered, muscular, determined man, with thick black hair and steady eye, his was a convincing personality. His enthusiasm was of the dogged quality. He made others believe what he believed himself. He was entering into his own. He was about to reap where he had sown.

"In his first talk with Mayor William B. Ogden he so impressed the town's first citizen that he asked for a half interest in the proposed reaper works. The first year the partners sold $50,000 worth of machines. Then McCormick bought Ogden out.

"Within ten years the McCormick machine was known in every part of this country. In 1851 European farmers were made acquainted with its possibilities. At the world's fair in London the 'Grand Council Medal' was awarded to McCormick, and, although the London Times had at first ridiculed his invention as 'a cross between an Astley chariot, a wheelbarrow and a flying machine,' it later conceded that 'the McCormick reaper is worth the whole cost of the exposition.'

"At the Universal Exposition at Paris in 1855 the grand prize was again awarded. In 1867 Napoleon III. himself fastened the cross of the Legion of Honor upon the breast of the inventor. In 1878 he went to Paris for the third time to receive for his reaping and self-binding machine a grand prize of the exposition and to be decorated as an officer of the Legion of Honor. (t) In recognition of his 'having done more for the cause of agriculture than any other living man,' he was at this time elected a corresponding member of the French Academy of Sciences.

"He was not without honor in his own country. William H. Seward had affirmed that 'the McCormick reaper pushes the American frontier westward at the rate of thirty miles a year.' Edwin M. Stanton said 'the reaper is to the North what the slave is to the South.' (u) and Senator Reverdy Johnson, in an argument before the Commissioner of patents, declared that the 'McCormick reaper had already contributed an annual income to the whole country of $50,000,000, at least, which must increase through all time.' (v) The commissioner, though he refused an extension of the patent, said: 'Cyrus H. McCormick is an inventor whose fame, while he is yet living, has spread through the world. His genius has done honor to his own country and has been the admiration of foreign nations and he will live in the grateful recollection of mankind as long as the reaping machine is employed in gathering the harvest.'

* * * * * * *

"The years that brought prosperity and fame were not without strife. A consistent individualist, Cyrus McCormick would never brook competition. As other men came forward with similar inventions, the agricultural machinery world became a scene of battle. For years scores of lawyers were engaged in court by the warring harvester kings. Bitter rivalry developed. Salesmen and agents fought with each other. (w) Demonstrators came to blows and machines were wrecked in the fields. William Deering, Ralph Emerson, William Whitely, D. M. Osborne, the Gordon Brothers, Governor Asa S. Bushnell, Benjamin H. Warder, John J. Glessner, W. H. Jones, Lewis Miller, founder of the Chautauqua and father-in-law of Thomas Edison, Walter A. Wood, James J. Hill, Governor Merriam, the Marsh Brothers, John F. Hollister—these are the names of some of the men who fought in the campaign of the 'Harvester Kings.'

"But the day of competition is gone. The old individualistic theory and practice of Cyrus Hall McCormick has been superseded. Social forces, stronger than any individual, have brought the 'Harvester Kings' together. The sons of McCormick and Deering have forgotten the feuds of their fathers. Glessner and Jones have buried the hatchet. (x) The economic advantages of combination, the wastefulness of competition, have brought together warring interests of the past and welded them into the International Harvester Company, with an output of 700,000 harvesting machines a year, a revenue of $73,000,000, a capital of $120,000,000, a pay roll of nearly $22,000,000, an army of 70,000 employes, a square mile of factories, trackage of 12,000 cars at its 100 warehouses and six busy railroads of its own.

"Acres of coal in Kentucky, forests in Arkansas, Mississippi and Missouri, beds of ore in Wisconsin and a steel plant in which 2,000 Hungarians are employed are owned by the combination to keep its fourteen industrial plants in operation. All because of the dream of a boy on a farm in Virginia.

* * * * * * *

"In 1858, Mr. McCormick married Nettie Fowler, daughter of Melyar Fowler, of Jefferson County, New York. Her interest in all that concerned her husband was marked. She suggested economies of administration in the factory, supervised field tests in Europe, recommended that the factory be kept open during the summer and when after the great fire of 1871, he was advised not to rebuild, she encouraged him to continue the business.

"The McCormick family consisted of four sons and three daughters, two of whom, a son and a daughter, died in infancy. The three McCormick sons are principal officers of the International Harvester Company.

"While the dominant idea of Cyrus McCormick's life was the machine he invented, he was not unmindful of his obligations to the community in which he lived. He endowed the McCormick Theological Seminary, established the McCormick professorship of natural philosophy in Washington and Lee University in Virginia, and contributed generously to the Union Theological Seminary, Hampden-Sidney, and the college at Hastings, Neb. When the Interior, a Presbyterian publication, needed assistance he financed it and put it upon a paying basis. His heirs are still interested in the paper. The Young Men's Christian Association has known his benevolence and he was one of those who issued the call for the foundation of the Chicago public library.

"At one time Mr. McCormick entered the daily newspaper field. In 1858 he owned a Democratic paper, The Herald, which he consolidated with another Democratic paper, The Times, calling it The Herald and Times. The venture was not a financial success, and he sold his interest to Wilbur F. Storey, who dropped the name Herald and put forth his first issue of The Chicago Times, June 1, 1861.

* * * * * * *

"The story of McCormick is largely the story of Chicago. No man did more than he to make it great. No man was better equipped to aid in the fight for commercial and industrial supremacy in which the young city engaged and no one helped more to keep it on its course until achievement. When, May 13, 1884, in the fullness of years, he passed to his reward, his was the satisfaction of knowing that he had contributed his full meed to his country's well being and advanced the cause of civilization throughout the world."

A few remarks in regard to the above are pertinent.

(a) After even a cursory perusal of this book the reader is left to judge whether the hero of the above article was the emancipator of hunger.

(b) And Lincoln was on the winning side.

(c) Yes, the money, in effect, paid Lincoln for defeating McCormick's pretensions enabled him to win the presidency and save the nation. There was no parallelism; contradistinction separated the two men. One was the embodiment of loyalty; the principles held by the other may be gathered from his paper of 1858-1861, the *Times and Herald,* of Chicago, its chosen editor Ex-Governor McComas, of Virginia, and extreme advocate of state rights and "Exponent of Southern Democracy."

(d) Not often. Respectable competitors did not bring a lot of "husky" backers into the fields, as stated by A. E. Mayer, but let their machines fight the battles.

(e) No. Simply this: several hundred manufacturers have come and gone. McCormick was one of the many survivors. We know whereof we affirm, having recently completed the list of past and present builders of reapers, from which the writer of the above statement, having access thereto, could have got the full facts.

(f) It is true that competitors respected his perseverance, but they detested his methods.

(g) His father was an educated man and wealthy and, noticing the similarity of the early draft devices on the McCormick machines to those of the earlier English inventors, we are led to surmise that Loudon's Cyclopedia may have had a place in the library of the home.

(h) He may have been foremost at times, usually not. William N. Whitely was the "Reaper King" until about the time of McCormick's death.

(i) See "Memorial of Robert McCormick," by Leander McCormick.

(j) No record of their practicability is extant.

(k) Iron plows were in use to a small extent.

(l) A Nantucket boy, and hence, when young, a seaman. See Mrs. Hussey's letter, ante. As a man, he was a skilled mechanic and inventor of world-wide reputation. (Franklin was once a printer's devil; Vice President Wilson a shoe-maker; Lincoln a laborer; Edison a news-boy.)

(m) See "Memorial of Robert McCormick." Nowhere is conclusive proof that he did a stroke of mechanical work.

(n) Although there was a blacksmith shop in the farm factory, he could not make the experimental sickle there. (See John Mc-Cown's statement.)

(o) Not true. He published to the world by patenting; such is the purpose of granting patents. But the machine was faulty and could not speak praise in its own behalf.

(p) We have no proof but that his alleged experiments from 1831 to 1840 were confined to one machine. In 1840 he made two machines. They were the first sold. The writer of the article would have us believe that they incurred the expense of erecting the Cotopaxi furnace to make iron, in the middle thirties, for machines not yet practical and to remain so until 1846. (See testimony of W. S. McCormick, ante.)

(q) "Its fame had crossed the river." Is this true? His repeated statements, and that of his brother, show that the machine had no merit to win fame until the seat was first applied in 1846. Was it not the fame of Hussey's reaper that had "crossed the river?" That was being made near Cincinnati and at other places in the West; the first one twelve years before and, after he had returned to Baltimore, the machines there made were sent to the western states, where they created a demand for reapers, largely filled by small country shops.

(r) This clause reads well, but as a matter of fact the forty-eighters were late comers. Too late to see and come, they were only followers, or were carried on by the tide.

(s) Did he contract with a mere storekeeper and mere machinist to build 100 machines for the coming harvest? Seymour & Morgan were already manufacturers of agricultural machinery. Their history I know very well, in part from Mr. Morgan's own lips.

(t) At London in 1851 and Paris 1855 he had adopted Hussey's cutting apparatus, for which he later paid dearly, at the end of a law suit. In 1878 his alleged honors were won by his reaper, brought only partially up to date by the McClintock Young reel-rake, to make which he bought rights, and later by his copy of the Marsh Harvester, borrowed bodily and to which he had applied Withington's binder.

(u) Seward argued McCormick's case and lost. Stanton argued Manny's defense and won. Did Stanton refer to McCormick's reaper in the above statement when defending Manny and his reaper?

(v) Reverdy Johnson was arguing for the extension of McCormick's patent, but there was no proof of the ridiculous statement; the Commissioner did not believe it, and McCormick got but a few flattering words.

(w) Much overdrawn.

(x) They had no hatchet to bury. They were honorable business men, nearly all intimate personal acquaintances of the present writer.

The above *alleged* history, the "Romance of the Reaper," "Cyrus H. McCormick, His life and Work," school histories, "Cyrus Hall McCormick and the Reaper," are all edited by persons ignorant of the facts, and from the same heap of historic rubbish, the last above noted edited by Reuben Gold Thwaites, and published in the Transactions of the Wisconsin Historical Society, (1908). All contain the same old errors, simply rephrased.

CHAPTER XXIII.

BLOCKING THE GREAT PRETENSION.

One of the notices first to reach the public that the Treasury Department was about to perpetuate a grave error came in a private letter from the editor of one of our greatest weekly agricultural publications to the author. It reads:

"I do not need to tell you how unjust it would be to credit the invention of the reaper to any one man, and particularly to this man. My object in writing is to ask if you think this should pass without notice."

The attempt of the McCormick Harvesting Machine Company to get the portrait of its founder upon the ten dollar treasury note very naturally resulted in the protest against the use of a portrait that had been availed of so many years practically as a trade-mark. The discomfiture of the company, due to its failures, became so pronounced that competing manufacturers felt that it was their turn to laugh. The pages of "Farm Machinery," published at St. Louis at the time, supplied material for much merriment. In an early issue of that publication, during the year 1897, an article appeared entitled "Has Been Stopped." In this article statements were made similar to those found in the protests filed in the Treasury Department. Two clauses of the article were evidently considered by Mr. E. K. Butler, manager for that company, as constituting a severe arraignment. They read:

"In view of the prior art, it has been said, it seems very strange that his successors should claim that he ever invented any detail that has lasted, or, in fact, any that was ever used by any manufactory but his own, and by that for only a short time.

"As far as an investigation is concerned, it is doubted if one could

356

be forced onto the McCormick Company, for several have tried to shame it into an investigation—have practically defied, but have found the English language inadequate—its words too weak to anger the Company into an investigation, or to close their mouths in shame."

Very soon thereafter the editor received a telegram reading:

Chicago, Jan. 18, 1897.

"C. K. Reifsnider,
    "Editor of Farm Machinery,
        "506 Olive St., St. Louis.
"Unless your next issue contains statement of facts showing desire on your part to so far as possible undo the serious injury done us by your publication which carries the impression of an editorial we give you this notice that we hold you and your publication responsible.
                    "McCormick H. M. Co.
                    "By E. K. Butler,
                    "Secretary and General Manager. 6 p."

The editor replied to the above, closing with the following:

"Far from us be the thought of injuring any one. The article referred to in the McCormick Harvesting Machine Co.'s telegram was one headed 'Has Been Stopped,' and related to the controversy over Hon. Cyrus H. McCormick's portrait on the new silver certificate to be issued by the United States Treasury Department. It appeared as a reading article, far removed from editorial, and was in fact a paid advertisement inserted through our advertising department.
"Excepting a few paragraphs, disclosing the purport of the article, it was NOT read by anybody about the office of FARM MACHINERY except our proofreaders, but was accepted as advertising, as are all other matters relating to that department of our work, hailing from responsible sources."

The explanation did not seem to suit Mr. Butler and the editor felt called upon to make some matters plain, which he accomplished very thoroughly in a later number of "Farm Machinery." The above paragraphs were quoted in the "Farmers' Advance," published by the McCormick Company, but the last part, the following was never quoted into its columns:

"CALLING McCORMICK'S BLUFF
"It is well known to the reading public that since the Treasury Department at Washington discarded the idea of using the portrait of the Venerable Cyrus H. McCormick upon the new silver certificates, the

McCormick Harvesting Machine Co. has wept many bitter tears. Somehow, those now in charge of the McCormick affairs seem to think other harvester men are responsible for the change of heart on the part of the Secretary of the Treasury. Another authority suggests that Mr. McCormick was a 'Goldbug,' and from his exalted station in the higher life declined the use of his portrait for silver purposes, and that he threatened to haunt the Secretary and cause further decrease in the revenues and greater increase in the deficit that then haunted the Secretary and Grover, unless he desisted from his base purpose of prostitution. Neither the Secretary nor the ghost of Mr. McCormick has taken us into his confidence, and because we have never been in position to speak authoritatively we have refrained from discussing the subject in the columns of Farm Machinery. Nor do we intend doing so now, nor would we touch upon the matter at all but for the fact that some of the tears shed by the present McCormick defenders have flooded our office, compelling us to notice them.

* * * * * * *

"We clip the following from the March issue of the Farmers' Advance, published by the McCormick people. The subject treated of is Machinery.

"* * * The bravery of those who are only at the front when there is no danger, is well shown by the article that appeared in an issue of a St. Louis implement paper, on the 12th inst., which article was written in Chicago and inserted in the St. Louis paper as a paid advertisement. We know of no such betrayal of a paper as that practiced by a jealous builder of harvesting machines in Chicago who forwarded this article to the St. Louis paper and had it inserted during the editor's absence, thus securing its publication without signature, and throwing the responsibility upon the paper. * * * Read it and you will see the utter uselessness of our replying to attacks made by parties who are afraid to sign their statements.

The Editor replies:

"This is pure 'bluff' of the rankest race-track order. The article referred to was brought into our office by a responsible person who was known to us, and he did not hail from Chicago. It he knew who wrote the article or where it was written, he did not inform us, so neither we, nor any one about this office, knew then or know now where or by whom it was written. It may have been written at Chicago by Mr. McCormick himself, or by Mr. Swift, or by Mr. Armour, or by Satan, or by the president of the McCormick Theological Seminary, all of whom reside in or about Chicago. We simply don't know, and, since by this publication, the McCormick's, by implication at least, charge us with revealing knowledge we did not possess concerning the authorship, we think we may be pardoned for saying we don't care. Certainly some of the above gentlemen could plead guilty of being 'jealous builders of harvesters at Chicago.' "

The attempt to prostitute the Treasury Department, although treated lightly by the editor of *Farm Machinery,* was looked upon as a serious matter by those who filed the protests. To add to the force of words, the portrait of Cyrus McCormick and that of Lydia Pinkham, both long used practically as trademarks, were pinned to a two dollar treasury note side by side, in order that those to whom it might be shown, particularly Secretary of the Treasury, Carlisle, could see the impropriety of the proposed scheme; in fact, no words were necessary. It was a matter of such importance that the McCormick Company, on getting wind of the protests, sent its representative, R. B. Swift, to Washington, where he made himself very busy opposing the protests. No others favored such improper use of the treasury certificates and no others "shed tears" over the failure. The pretended propriety of placing McCormick's portrait on the silver certificate was founded on the claim that he had done more for the agricultural world, through his (alleged) invention of the reaper, than any other inventor in agricultural lines. Assuming that to have been true, and assuming that Lydia Pinkham was not a fictitious person, but had been the actual inventor of the remedies, why, it might be asked, should it not be equally proper to place her portrait by the side of McCormick's, her remedies having been used to such an extent by the overworked wives of the agricultural classes. The Secretary of the Treasury saw the point, and the plates already prepared, were destroyed.

The late William N. Whitely, an early inventor and manufacturer of harvesting machinery, and for many years the "king" of the reaper business, January 8, 1897, wrote to the *Farm Implement News* upon the subject of McCormick's portrait on the silver certificates about to be issued, as follows:

"Editor *Farm Implement News:*

"Having been informed that the bureau of engraving and printing was preparing new $10 silver certificates to be ornamented by the busts of Whitney, the inventor of the cotton gin, and C. H. McCormick, inventor of the reaper, I write you to say that it would manifestly be unjust to credit the invention of the reaper to any one man. Mr. McCormick does deserve great credit for his enterprise and business skill in the many years he was engaged in manufacturing harvesting machinery and we are pleased to honor his memory; yet so much has been done in bringing the reaper to its present state of perfection by the many thousands of inventors that our government would make a mistake in singling out Mr. McCormick from the many meritorious ones who have contributed so much to the reaper of the past and of the present day. We well understand that no effort has been spared for many years past in keeping C. H. McCormick before the American people as the inventor of the reaper by his immediate relatives and friends, and we have no right to find fault with such a course upon their part; but when the great government of the United States of America proposes to certify by the above mentioned course to the correctness of the claims made for C. H. McCormick as the inventor of the reaper, to the disparagement of so many other worthy inventors and co-workers upon the reaper, then those who know better should raise their voices against such an attempted recognition for any one man, of whom the best that can be said is that he was only one of the many.

"From 1831 to 1834, and for several years thereafter, two persons, i. e., Obed Hussey and C. H. McCormick, were striving to produce a successful reaping machine for cutting grain and grass, as were many others, before and since. These two men were contemporaneously in the field, and no doubt they both labored faithfully to accomplish the desired result. The invention of Obed Hussey, the features of which were embraced in his first machine in 1832 and 1833, included all the principles of a practical reaper. It was a side draft or side cut machine; that is, the cutting apparatus extended out to one side, the animals drawing the machine moving along by the side of the grain or grass to be cut. It had two driving and supporting wheels, gearing extending rearward with a crank and pitman therefrom to reciprocate the cutters, which were scalloped or projecting blades from a bar and vibrated through slotted guard fingers which held the stalks to be cut. The cutting apparatus was hinged to the side of the frame of the machine to enable it to follow the surface of the ground over which the machine was passing. A platform was supported by an outer and inner wheel. The operator was seated upon the machine and raked the grain into sheaves from the platform as it was cut. Over sixty years have come and gone, yet all the essential features of the first Hussey machine and all Hussey machines made thereafter (which were large numbers) employed substantially these devices. The machine was successful the first time it was completed, and ever after were the Hussey machines successful in harvesting grain and grass. The fundamental principles of all harvesting machinery of the world to-day were furnished by Obed Hussey's invention and patent of 1833; and while very many and valuable improvements have been made thereon for harvesting grain and grass, for which credit should be given to the worthy inventors who followed after Hussey, yet we must not ignore his valuable contribution, 'the reaper.'

"Cyrus H. McCormick's first patent was dated, in 1834. This was known as a push machine with a straight cutter, the operator walking by the side of the machine and raking the grain from the platform. Other modifications in after years were made on this machine by Mr. McCormick; and it may be said that the inventive genius of Obed Hussey and the business tact and skill of C. H. McCormick produced and brought into practical use the first successful reaping machine of this or any other country.

"Whatever might have been embodied in the first McCormick machine or in his experiments or machines for the first fifteen years of his efforts, the reaper of the present day does not disclose any principles contained in these early efforts of C. H. McCormick; but that cannot be said of Hussey. All reaping machines of the present day embody substantially all of the vital principles given by Obed Hussey in 1833 and at different periods thereafter. The Patent Office, as well as other sources of information, make good these statements.

"Passing, however, from the early history up to the present time, when the present mowing machines and grain binding machines are seen in operation, and taking into account the thousands of patents that have been issued to American inventors for various features that they have brought out, it would be but simple justice that all be recognized as contributors to the building up of such valuable and important pieces of machinery; and I cannot but repeat that it would be very unjust, unfair and un-American to single out one person, and that one Mr. McCormick, as a representative to be used by the government printing bureau, when it is so well known what he did and what he did not do in the invention of the reaper. It would be a false monument; it would only be respected by persons who are ignorant of the facts.

"If this should succeed, it would not be the first time, as likely it will not be the last time, in the history of mankind where those who did the work were soon forgotten and those who were more fortunate in being held up and prominently kept before the public by their friends or powerful allies received unjustly the credit."

The position taken by Leander McCormick is shown by the following interview, which speaks for itself:

October 23, 1899.

"On Saturday, the 21st inst., I visited Leander J. McCormick at the Virginia Hotel, Chicago, in response to an invitation to do so over the telephone. He is very much agitated over the misrepresentations of the McCormick Harvesting Machine Co., Swift, Mann and others, as having to do with the history of the McCormick reaper. He is preparing a great deal of material that he wishes me to have, but does not care to appear too anxious in the matter. He asked me to call and ask his servant for a quantity of papers lying on his table. He says the servant will hand them to me without any questions. I stated to him that I would not like to do so, but hoped that he would find a way to get them into my hands that would be above any suspicion.

"He says that his brother, Cyrus H., had nothing whatever to do with the reaper made in 1831, except to go to the blacksmith's for his father and get the straight sickle blade made. He says that his father, with the help of the mechanics, made the machine; that it was not at all like the picture that the M. H. Co. show, but on the contrary was an extremely crude affair, having even wooden gears. He says further that C. H. had nothing whatever to do with the machines patented in '45 and '47; that they were improvements on the original machine made by his father and himself (L. J. McCormick). He says that the arrangement whereby this seat was accomplished was his own invention. Upon returning from a contest in New York he says that he said to his brother, who was business manager for the family, that they would be out of the market unless they improved their machine; that it would have to be made to raise and lower in some good way. C. H. replied to him, he told me, by asking why he did not improve the machine himself. He then went to work and made the quadrant device for raising and lowering the machine, completing it entirely during the absence of C. H., who, upon his return, proceeded to patent it in connection with Leander J. and brother W. S.

"Mrs. L. J. McCormick informed me that she remembered clearly her husband's telling her of the invention of the arrangement whereby the seat was applied to the machine; that she found the drawings at the old home in Virginia and saved them, but they were destroyed in the Chicago fire. She remembers the latter and the drawings very well.

"Mr. L. J. McCormick further told me that the reason that C. H. McCormick took out the patents was that they did not understand patent affairs well, and supposed that he, C. H., being the assignee, had the right to take out the patents.

J. F. Steward."

In 1897 a book, written by R. B. Swift, was published (the ablest ever written setting forth the claims of C. H. McCormick). For credibility of this witness see Nettie McCormick vs. R. B. Swift, Illinois Law Reports. The above is recent testimony against his claims but it is hardly necessary to come further down the century than 1861, when the U. S. Patent Office passed upon Mrs. Hussey's request for an extension of the 1847 patent, her husband having died in the meantime.

The following is Examiner Peck's report to the Commissioner of Patents:

"United States Patent Office,
Feb. 23d, 1861.

"In the matter of the application of Eunice B. Hussey, Administratrix of Obed Hussey, deceased, for An Extension of reissue 449, 451, 742 — 917 of the patent granted to said Obed Hussey August 7th, 1847, for an Improvement in Reaping Machines.

"Hon. S. T. Shugert,
Acting Commissioner of Patents.

"In compliance with your directions and the provision of the law I have the honor to report:

"Obed Hussey obtained a patent for an improvement in Harvesting Machines in the year 1833, and subsequently made the improvements in said machine patented Aug. 7th, 1847. This patent was surrendered and re-issued in divisions. The original patent and the subsisting divisions (in printed copies), are hereto annexed for convenient reference. The invention embraced in the four re-issued divisions No. 449, 451, 742, and 917, was re-examined in view of the state of the art at the date of the original application, when they were issued. Since these patents were re-issued the invention has been investigated in the Courts, and proof is furnished that the novelty of the particular subdivision then under investigation was judicially sustained.

"The evidence and exhibits now furnished by the parties relating to the question of novelty have been carefully examined and I do not find any proof that the improvements embraced in the patent granted to Obed Hussey August 7, 1847, were first invented by another. Nor does there appear to be satisfactory evidence that this invention was in public use or on sale with his consent or allowance prior to the date of the patent. In this connection I would invite your attention to the testimony of Thomas J. Lovegrove, page 77 & 80 of applicant's evidence, and of John M. Leland, page 49, of A. J. Cook, page 41, of Benj. Hoyle, page 39, and of A. S. Foster, page 35 of opponent's testimony.

"It is not deemed necessary in view of the concise and specific description of these improvements as set forth in the specifications to enlarge upon their definitions. The several claims are limited by the clear and precise terms of the specifications, to which they expressly refer; and their construction cannot be enlarged beyond these terms. It may, however, be briefly remarked, that the leading object of the invention was to relieve the cutting apparatus of harvesting machines from the objection of clogging or choking.

"This improvement it appears resulted in a great measure from the use of closed guards and the scalloped cutter beveled on both sides of its cutting edges.

"The inventor sought to bring the cutting edges in nearer relation to the bearings or supports of the substance to be severed. The former mode of arranging the edges of the vibrating cutter so as to play centrally through the slot of the guard or finger, was supposed to be necessary to prevent contact of the edges of the cutters with the iron guards.

"The cutter when left comparatively free in their guides had a tendency to vibrate vertically and strike the guards. Among the improvements upon his invention of 1833, this inventor did not merely remove a part of the upper branch of the guard or finger for the escape of clogging matter, but he altered the construction of the upper branch with a view to greater strength and rigidity, and substituted a continuous guide bar placed above the rear edge of the cutter to hold it firmly down upon its bed, which, together with the upper branch of the finger held the cutter from vertical vibrations. These changes enabled the inventor to effect his purpose of bringing the edges of the cutter down flush with the lower branches of the guard fingers and cross bearings; the danger of striking the cutters against the fingers being also obviated. The use of a slotted guard finger whether open or closed with a scalloped cutter beveled on both sides could not be efficient to produce that incisive action in severing flexible fibrous substances supported only at one end, which would be ensured when the finger serving as a lateral support with its square corner, is brought in close proximity with the flush edges of the passing cutters. This near relation of these parts would prevent fine grass from being carried into the slots of the guards, by the reciprocating movement of the cutter, without being severed.

"There can be no doubt of the great value of an efficient cutting apparatus of the Harvesting Machine, as it lays at the foundation of this one of the most important of Agricultural Machines. The history of this branch of invention has established the fame of Obed Hussey as among the most meritorious as he was of the earliest of American inventors in the department of improvements. His persevering efforts for a long series of years in the improvement of Harvesting Machines resulted in success.

"The proofs show that the inventor has not been inactive or negligent in his endeavors to introduce the invention and to realize a remuneration from its sale and use.

"The account filed by the applicant is quite voluminous, and sufficiently in detail; and for its correctness your attention is invited to the deposition of John H. Bawdon, page 47, and of W. H. Poole, page 61, of Applicants testimony.

"Your attention is also respectfully invited to the reasons of opposition, and the abstract of the points of the Argument of Counsel in support thereof, together with the several exhibits which are parts of machines referred to in the evidence; for consideration in deciding this application.

Respectfully submitted,
H. P. K. Peck,
Examiner."

Threshing over old straw is indeed a tedious task and wearisome to the reader, but it has seemed a necessity. The accumulation of chaff and straw that have hidden the few kernels of truth so long needs to be swept away. In so far as I have succeeded in winnowing away the chaff, which constituted the bulk of the article "Who Invented the Reaper," by R. B. Swift, I trust that I have accomplished a little good, at least. The writer has heard just such talk for fifty years as he has been considering, and expects to until that Reaper, to whom no man claims priority, swings his scythe. Up to this time there have never been "800 different concerns building reapers." Rival reaper builders have not, as a rule, been defeated at great expositions, as stated by Mr. Swift; as many honors have been fairly won by others wherever medals and diplomas have been contended for. After the unfairness to Hussey at London in 1851 manufacturers have often refused to go into trials. Manufacturers who sell their machines on their merits require no exhibition medals. The claims that McCormick machines intimidated competitors to such an extent that they would not willingly contest have no foundation. Claims of superiority in advertisements and annual catalogues, from a business point of view, by some are not considered objectionable, but clearly advertising methods in compiling history are decidedly out of place.

The claims that other manufacturers have suffered defeats, etc., which has created antagonism, induces a smile on the face of every one who has lived through the last fifty years. Was Manny's machine defeated by McCormick's? Were the "New Yorker" and the Palmer & Williams self rakes defeated by the hand raking reaper that McCormick continued for ten years later to build, solely? Was the Ketchum mower defeated by McCormick's mower that came nearly a decade later? Was the Marsh harvester, that was fought by the McCormick reaper for nearly fifteen years, defeated? Why did he then defy patents and put it out extensively? Was the wire binder already put on the market for two years, defeated by McCor-

mick's copy of the Marsh harvester? Were the twine binders fought
for two years by McCormick's wire binder defeated by it? Was
every step in the development of harvesting machinery that was
almost universally a step of several years in advance of the machines
put out by the McCormick Harvesting Machine Co. and its predecessors, defeated?

Cyrenus Wheeler   Obed Hussey   John H. Manny
David M. Osborne George Easterly
John H. Appleby   George H. Spaulding
William Deering Cyrus H. McCormick
William W. Marsh   William H. Jones
John P. Adriance Asa L. Bushnell
Lewis Miller   Byron Hembley   Walter A. Wood

CHAPTER XXIV.

Some Deering Contributions Displayed.

The correct history of every great art should be accessible and the credibility of those writing upon the subject is always a proper matter for consideration. The author, having found the greater part of his effort necessary to the correction of the history of harvesting machines, as it is popularly understood, finds it necessary to correct some further misapprehensions and show how they have been created.

The reader to judge for himself the facts in regard to a bit of work for which the author of this book has received high praise and a medal, at the Paris Exposition of 1900. The following from the introduction to "The Official *Retrospective Exhibit* of the Development of Harvesting Machinery" is self-explanatory:

"The Deering Harvester Company, Chicago, U. S. A., was nominated in Paris in the autumn of 1898 to the French authorities, by the American Commissioner to the Paris Exposition of 1900, the Hon. Ferdinand W. Peck, as having been selected by him as the proper one to make the retrospective and historical exhibition of the art of manufacturing harvesting machinery. The nomination was confirmed by the French authorities, and the exhibit was assigned space by Mr. Charles Richards Dodge, Director of Agriculture of the American Commission, in the American section of the Palace of Agriculture, where it will be found.

"This book is an account of the exhibit, and shows the manner in which the Deering Harvester Company has carried out the responsibility entrusted to it. This work has been one of infinite labor and pains. Every record that could be found has been consulted, and every existing American manufacturer of harvesting machinery has seen and approved the models of machines made by him and his predecessors.

"The illustrations in the book are photgraphed from the models themselves. The number on the illustrations and in the text correspond to the numbers on the models in the exhibit."

The preparation of the exhibit was placed in the hands of the author of this book, and, in order to be fair, he prepared ten models of McCormick machines, including those alleged to have been invented by C. H. McCormick, and the Górham binder, the patents covering that machine, which Mr. McCormick had bought. It resulted in ninety-six operative models of mowers, reapers and automatic binders, placed in aisle cases and wall cases, and in addition thereto one hundred and six large photographs of harvest scenes, of portraits of inventors and manufacturers and mural paintings of ancient and modern methods of harvesting, a total of two hundred and two exhibits. The accompanying illustration shows the arrangement of the aisle cases, the wall cases, only partly seen, extending the entire length.

This exhibit cost many thousand dollars and was prepared at the expense of the Deering Company in an effort to do its part to make the Exposition interesting. The models and paintings may all be found in *Le Conservatoire des Arts et Metiers,* in Paris, to which institution they were donated. A medal was awarded which is here shown:

In the so called Retrospective book, the cut being made before the Exposition, the cases are all shown as fronting the aisle, but this arrangement was changed at Paris and wall cases placed behind those shown. Aisles were also provided.

In the Canadian issue of the "Farmers' Advance," a McCormick publication, for February, 1901, is found the following:

"On the third floor of the Annex is displayed the *major* portion of the retrospective exhibit showing the development of the work of harvesting grain from the earliest period, including the steps connecting the reaper of 1831 to the latest modern self-binding harvester."

and in the same paper are two photo engravings of cases of models. The flexibility of photography is here exercised in an effort to make the exhibit appear extensive, by opposing end views looking through the cases. The facts are that there were two cases and seventeen models. The accompanying photo engraving is copied from a true picture of all the cases, now in possession of the author:

Such alleged facts have grown in number and volume during the development of modern advertising methods; and the disregard for

The large wall cases are not seen, having been placed behind the others.

facts is well shown by many plausible falsehoods of voice and pen at the Paris and other expositions.

The credibility of witnesses being always in order, I here refer to an article emanating from Paris, published in the *Farmers' Advance* (a McCormick publication), dated February 10, 1901:

"In previous letters I have set forth in general terms the character of our agricultural exhibit, but there is one display from our own country involving the interests of the toiling millions of the fields that is of such exceptional character that I cannot in justice neglect to refer to its leading feature. I allude to the magnificent efforts made by the

United States manufacturers of agricultural machinery, and more especially to the great retrospective and contemporary exhibit prepared and installed at the request of the American Commissioner General by the McCormick Harvesting Machine Company, of Chicago. This remarkable presentation rises so far above the plane of exposition displays that it reaches the full dignity of a great educational exhibit of industrial and commercial progress. To my mind it excels in genuine human interest any other single exhibit made by any firm from any land in any section of the entire exhibition."

The present writer is not given to fits of jealousy, but as such talk is the stuff that the history of the art has been so largely made of, he will dwell a moment. The McCormick Company claims to have been appointed by the Commissioner General. The fact is that

William Deering was nominated in Paris in the autumn of 1898 for the task, as already stated. The nomination was confirmed by the French authorities and the exhibit was assigned space by Mr. Charles Richards Dodge, Director of American Agriculture of the Commission in the American Section of the Palace of Agriculture. Upon the appointment having been made, this author was selected to prepare the exhibit, and two years were devoted to making operative models, drawings, preparation of portraits of inventors, manufacturers, etc., with the result that ninety-five models and more than one hundred scenes and portraits were produced. Every model was capable of being operated by the mere pulling of a cord outside of the cases. The full description of the models may be found in a work prepared by the author of this volume entitled "Official Retrospective Exhibition of the Development of Harvesting Machinery for the Paris Exposition of 1900, by the Deering Harvester Company, Chicago, U. S. A."

If the reader will refer to the words of the foreign correspondent above quoted he will find the claims fit well to the large exhibit, but are decidedly overdrawn if referred to the two case exhibit.

Not to be outdone at the Paris Exposition, the McCormick Company, inspired by the fact that the Deering Company, its largest competitor, had sent, for exhibition purposes, an auto mower, "got a move on," to quote a street phrase, and between February and June one was received at Paris. It failed to operate before the Jury of Awards, however, and another was received and tested in mowing with the Deering machine in August, with about equal honors. Much printer's ink was devoted to praise of the McCormick auto mower. It was a quick move, late to begin, however.

The Deering automobile mower is here shown with the author of this work, joint inventor and maker, on the seat, in a field of clover near Paris early in July of 1900:

In 1897 a competitor arranged with two independent inventors for rights to make and sell a rotary corn shocker embodying the inventions of both. It hired one of the inventors and by 1901 had so far perfected the machine as to warrant testing it in farmers' hands; it made fifty and put them out, refusing, however, to sell them. They operated so well that the company which claims that its predecessor

Deering Auto Mower in clover, first made in 1894. This picture is of the Paris Exposition, Machine of 1900.

In 1897 a competitor arranged with two independent inventors for rights to make and sell a rotary corn shocker embodying the inventions of both. It hired one of the inventors and by 1901 had so far perfected the machine as to warrant testing it in farmers' hands; it made fifty and put them out, refusing, however, to sell them. They operated so well that the company which claims that its predecessor invented the reaper, and that its predecessor's efforts ripened the reaper into the modern twine binder, sent men into the fields to photograph and make measurements of the shocker developed by its competitor. A well working copy of the machine resulted. A few changes were made in small details. It put the machines out, although it had had no opportunity to test them, with the usual claims of superiority, the McCormick corn cutter and shocker, and printed matter is at hand stating that the machine had been experimented with for several years, but not saying that such had been done only by its competitor at the expense of very many thousand dollars. The building and marketing of this copy of the patented machine was begun after the patent attorney of that company, himself, had critically examined the patents owned by the competitor and had reported favorably of the patent and of consequent infringement. The fact of copying was known to this writer at the time and the matter of investigating the patents was told him by the patent attorney. The fact as to the building of the machine was frequently admitted after those previously interested in the old companies had been associated in the International Harvester Company.

This matter is cited as another instance of "the sort of good generalship on the part of McCormick that has helped to keep his machine where it has stood for the last thirty-five years—in the lead of all others." McCormick was never credited by other manufacturers, and those in touch with the trade, as having led.

The irresistible conclusion is that no one person deserves exclusive, or even principal credit for inventing the reaper, which was the joint product of many minds, and of all who contributed to its development, clearly Cyrus H. McCormick enjoyed no surpassing precedence over others, certainly not enough to warrant the claims to pre-eminence put forward by himself in his lifetime and by his successors since his death.

INDEX

ADAMS, Augustus, 228, 230
ADAMS & GIFFORD, 247, 256
ADRIANCE, John P., 367
ALBERT, Prince, 120, 170, 171
AMBLER, ..., 140, 213, 260, 263
ANDERSON, Joseph, 84
ANDRIST, Prof. Charles M., 304
APPLEBY, John F., 269, 270, 275, 282-284, 287, 288, 299-306, 308-310, 317-342, 344, 367
ATKINS, J., 336
ATKINSON, F., 168
AULTMAN, Cornelius, 260
AULTMAN & COMPANY, Cornelius, 296, 298, 327
AULTMAN & MILLER, 226, 263
AULTMAN, MILLER & COMPANY, 252, 279, 284, 296, 301, 305, 308-310, 327, 332

BAILEY, ..., 219
BAKER, William R., 225, 273, 291, 334
BALCH, ..., 345
BARNUM, P. T., 346
BARTLETT, S. W., 253, 254
BAWDON, John H., 364
BAYLISS, Edwin, 234, 235
BEALE, ..., 213
BEARDSLEY, ..., 291
BEHEL, Jacob, 268, 270, 282, 283, 304, 306, 309, 311, 317
BELL, George, 47
BELL, Rev. Patrick, 30-33, 42-45, 47, 48, 52, 55, 96, 100, 137, 139, 142, 177, 178, 187, 203, 205, 213, 214, 220, 221, 224, 230, 257
BELL, Solymon, 202
BELLERBY, ..., 163, 164
BISHOP, Dr. E. D., 290, 291, 293, 298, 305-307, 327-329
BLANCHARD & ARNOLD, 322
BOLCKOW & VAUGHAN, 158
BOOTH, John, 155, 160
BRAZEE, ..., 294, 296
BRIDGEPORT BRASS COMPANY, 245

BROWN, ..., 59, 260
BROWN, A. C., 80, 196, 197
BROWN, Joseph, 28, 29
BROWN, Thomas, 28, 29
BUCHANAN, James, 144-146
BULLARD, John, 192
BURGESS, ..., 159-161
BURGESS & KEY, 155
BURKE, Edmund, 144-147
BURSON, William W., 268, 270, 283, 311, 313
BUSHNELL, Asa S. (L.), 351, 367
BUTLER, E. K 293, 356, 357

CARLISLE, ..., 359
CARPENTER, Stephen D., 273, 287, 338, 339
CARTER, Thomas, 167, 310
CARVER, George, 324
CASSON, Herbert N., 124, 126, 127, 133, 280, 292, 293, 334, 335, 337, 338
CHAMBERLIN, G. W., 296
CHAMPION COMPANY, 332
CHAMPLIN & TAYLOR, 255
CHENOWETH, Richard B., 66
CHENOWETH, Sarah A., 66
CHENOWETH, W. H., 66
CHILTON, R., 159
CHURCH, D. A., 186, 205
CLEVELAND, Duke of, 170
COATES, George, 158
COBSON, Christopher, 155
COLAHAN, Charles, 290, 324
COMMON, John, 30
CONGER, H. M., 296
COOK, A. J., 188, 206, 207, 363
COSKILL, ..., 152
COULTON, Joseph, 160
CROOME, Rev. Thomas Boys, 167
CROSSKILL, ..., 30, 43, 45, 47, 89
CROUSE, George W., 296
CUMMIN, ..., 205
CURTIS, George, 186
CUSHING, D., 220

377

DANFORD, E., 262
DAVIS, H. B., 347
DAYTON, ..., 321
DEERING, William, 251, 256, 258, 273, 274, 289-296, 298, 300, 301, 306, 307, 317, 325, 329-331, 336-338, 344, 345, 351, 367, 373
DEERING HARVESTER COMPANY, 255, 256, 332, 336, 337, 368, 369, 373
DENNETT, F. A., 321
DENNETT HARVESTING MACHINE COMPANY, 296
DICKERSON, E. N., 347
DINGES, William, 65
DOBBS, ..., 25, 105, 140, 213
DOBSON, ..., 160
DODGE, Charles 'Richard, 368, 373
DORSEY, Owen, 221, 222, 224, 225
DOUGLAS, ..., 347
DRAY, William, 171, 172
DRAY, William & Company, 155, 158, 161, 162, 168
DRYDEN, C. 158
DUNCAN, ..., 205

EASTER, John D., 241
EASTER, John D. & Company, 305
EASTER & GAMMON, 255
EDISON, Thomas D., 351, 353
EDGAR, J. S., 167
EDWARD, ..., 246
ELLIS, George H., 258, 337
ELLSWORTH, Henry William, 62
EMERSON, Ralph, 241, 271, 338, 351
EMMONS, Judge, ... 235, 236
ERPELDING, Lambert, 273, 279, 334
ESTERLY, George, 6, 200, 221, 257, 290, 297, 319, 323, 367
ESTERLY, George & Son, 296, 324, 329
ETHWAITE, John, 167
EXCELSIOR REAPER WORKS, 323, 324

FALLOWS, W., 159
FALVEY & REILEY, 319
FAWCITT, Robert, 157, 160, 161, 163, 164
FIELD, Heman, 206-208
FISHER, S. S., 205, 208, 209
FITLER, Edwin H., 344, 345
FITZGERALD, W. N. P., 68
FITZHUGH, ..., 225
FLENNIKEN, Theodore M., 267, 287, 310, 311, 314, 315
FOGERTY, Valentine, 320
FOSTER, ..., 205, 206, 208

FOSTER, A. S., 363
FOSTER, Algernon, 77-80
FOSTER, S. F., 79
FOWLER, ..., 160, 265
FOWLER, Melyar, 352
FOWLER, Nettie, 352
FRANKLIN, Benjamin, 353
FULLER, George K., 31

GALE, George, 192
GAMMON, Elijah H., 241, 291, 325
GAMMON & DEERING, 250, 256, 275, 276, 279, 289, 305, 322-325, 328-331, 336
GAMMON & DEERING & STEWARD, 256
GARNHART, ..., 246
GARRET & SON, 155
GEORGE, Elijah, 295
GIBBS, James E. A., 84
GIFFORD, James T, 228, 230
GILLET, R. H., 144-146
GLADSTONE, ..., 20, 45, 93, 135, 206, 219, 226, 260
GLESSNER, John J., 351
GOBLE & STUART, 220
GORDON, James F., 271-273, 276, 280, 281, 306, 315, 339
GORDON, John H., 271-274, 278-280, 286, 304, 306, 310, 336
GORDON BROTHERS, 351
GORE, J. H., 346
GORHAM, Helen M. (Mrs. Marquis L.), 286, 292, 294-296, 298-300, 308
GORHAM, Marquis L., 101, 274, 282, 283, 286, 287, 293-297, 299-301, 303-305, 308-311, 313-315, 318, 327, 328, 334, 338, 369
GORHAM, Orange, 294
GRAY BROTHERS, 323
GRAY & WARNER, 192
GREEN, Henry, 202
GREEN, Jesse, 192
GREENHUT, ..., 203, 308, 309
GREENING, William, 282
GREER, Justice, 139, 204
GREY, ..., 173
GRIFFIN, ..., 208
GRONBERG, ..., 255

HAINES, Jonathan, 221, 257
HAINES, ILLINOIS HARVESTER, 221
HALL, Mary Anna, 347
HALL, Patrick, 347
HALL, Susan McChesney, 347

HARDIN, or HARDING, George, 280, 347
HARLBUT, S. S., 339
HARRIS, John, 252, 336
HARRIS & SON, 252
HARRISON, Mrs. Alice M., 294, 295, 299
HARRISON, George P., 167
HARRISON, Joseph, 161
HARRISON, William, 167
HEATH, John, 248, 266, 281
HEMBLEY, Byron, 367
HENNEMAN, ..., 206
HENRY, A. Horace, 84
HILL, James J., 351
HILL, William, 160
HINDS, Albert, 253, 254
HITE, Isaac Irvine, 197, 205, 207
HITE, Samuel, 115, 129, 141
HITT, N. M., 84, 112
HOGSHEAD, Serena M. C., 84
HOLLINGSHEAD, John S., 148
HOLLISTER, John F., 188, 192, 204, 237, 238, 351
HOLLY, Solomon T., 311
HOLMES, John Dickinson, 167, 328, 344
HOLT, Commissioner, 195, 209
HOOVER, Abel, 305, 306
HOOVER & GAMBLE, 302, 306, 307, 329
HOOVER, ALLEN & GAMBLE, 323
HOPPER, John Mason, 161
HOUGHTON, Horace H., 282, 319
HOYLE, Benjamin, 363
HUNTER, James W., 33
HUNTER, Richard, 33
HURLBURT, ..., 233, 234
HUSSEY, Eunice B. (Mrs. Obed), 353, 362, 363
HUSSEY, Martha, 93
HUSSEY, Obed, 6, 42, 56-81, 92-94, 96-98, 101-103, 105, 107-113, 133, 135, 137, 139, 140, 142-145, 147-149, 151, 152, 155, 157, 159-174, 176, 179, 186-190, 192-195, 198, 200, 204-207, 214, 217, 220, 224, 226, 230, 237, 238, 258, 260-262 334-336, 349, 354, 360, 361, 363-365, 367
HUTCHINSON, ..., 75
HYMERS, Robert, 155

INTERNATIONAL HARVESTER COMPANY, 185, 351, 352, 375

JACKMAN, ..., 265

JACKSON, Judge, ..., 285
JACKSON, Barnard, 80
JACKSON, Howell E., 342
JENKINS, ..., 324
JOHNSON, Senator Reverdy, 347, 351, 355
JOHNSTON, Samuel, 224-226
JOHNSTON HARVESTER COMPANY, 256, 296, 332
JOLIET, ..., 3, 4
JONES, William H., 290, 291, 351, 367
JOUTEL, ..., 3

KAY, Richard, 167
KERR, ..., 24, 89
KETCHUM, ..., 206, 365
KNIGHT, Dr., ..., 96, 97

LAMB, ..., 206
LAMBERTON, Eunice W. (former wife of Obed Hussey), 64
LANE, Clark, 67, 79
LANE, Isaac, 79
LANE, John, 77-79
LANE, Thomas W., 320
LATHROP, William, 294-296, 208, 300
LEGGETT, General ......, 280
LELAND, John M., 363
LE VALLEY, ..., 203
LINCOLN, Abraham, 346, 347, 353
LISTER, William, 155, 160, 168
LOCKE, Gorham, 203
LOCKE, Sylvanus D., 258, 269, 270, 273, 274, 278, 279, 282, 323
LONDONDERRY, Marquis of, 163
LOVEGROVE, Thomas J., 363
LOWE, William R., 242
LOWE & ADAMS, 242, 250
LOWE, ADAMS & FRENCH, 246

McCHESNEY, Zachariah, 11, 84, 131
McCOMAS, Governor ......, 353
McCORMICK, C. R., 84
McCORMICK, Cyrus H., 6, 30, 52, 53, 72, 73, 75, 76, 80, 82-87, 89-95, 97-149, 151-153, 155, 157-163, 165-171, 174, 176-185, 187, 190, 192-194, 196-218, 221, 224, 225, 227, 238, 241, 244, 246, 247, 263, 273, 276, 278-281, 293, 300, 306, 308, 324, 329, 332-338, 346-355, 358-362, 365-367, 369, 375
McCORMICK, Cyrus H., Jr., 329
McCORMICK, Henrietta Hamilton, 84

McCORMICK, Henrietta M., 131
McCORMICK, Leander J., 80, 82, 84, 86, 109, 110, 112, 114-116, 128, 131, 132, 134, 135, 196, 200-241, 273, 276, 293, 334, 353, 361, 362
McCORMICK, Mrs. Leander J., 196, 362
McCORMICK, Mary A., 110, 113
McCORMICK, Medill, 278
McCORMICK, Nettie, 362
McCORMICK, Robert, 52, 75, 80, 82-86, 92, 106, 110, 112, 114-116, 128-134, 196, 200, 334, 347, 348, 353
McCORMICK, Robert Hall, 82, 110, 293
McCORMICK, Robert S., 133
McCORMICK, William, 84, 112
McCORMICK, William Steele, 84, 98, 110, 113, 115, 128-130, 133, 195, 198, 200, 354, 362
McCORMICK HARVESTING MACHINE COMPANY, 244, 274, 279, 290-298, 300-302, 305, 308-311, 317, 324, 327, 332, 356-358, 361, 366, 371, 373
McCOWN, John, 109, 112, 354
McCRACKEN, Chancellor, ..., 133
McGREGOR, William, 267, 287, 305, 310, 327
McGUFFIN, Thomas H., 84
MacKENZIE, D. C., 161
McPHERSON, ..., 273
MAGNESS, John, 80, 197, 198
MANN, ..., 45, 361
MANN, Henry F., 230, 231, 234
MANN, Joseph, 27
MANN & MANN, 230, 231, 233, 235
MANNING, J., 259, 260
MANNING, William, 49, 50, 59, 92
MANNY, John H., 139, 194, 195, 198, 202, 204, 241, 354, 365, 367
MANNY, Mrs. John H., 311
MANNY & COMPANY, 218, 271
MARQUETTE, Father, 3, 4
MARSH, Charles Wesley, 17, 29, 32, 96, 253, 255, 256
MARSH, William Wallace, 238, 246, 251, 252, 367
MARSH BROTHERS, 231, 233, 234, 237-239, 242, 244, 250, 251
MARSH BROTHERS & STEWARD, 256
MARSH HARVESTER, 188, 234, 235, 237-256, 270-276, 279, 280, 285-288, 293, 301, 308, 311, 322, 332-334, 336, 338, 354, 365, 366

MASON, Charles, 144, 148
MASSILLON, ..., 246
MAY, Hon. Henry, 71, 72
MAYER, A. E., 353
MECHI, ..., 151, 164, 171
MEDILL, Joseph, 133
MERRIAM, Governor, ..., 351
MILL, Peter, 290
MILLER, ..., 245
MILLER, Jacob, 296
MILLER, Lewis, 226, 260, 261, 336, 351, 367
MINNEAPOLIS HARVESTER WORKS, 290, 296, 324, 325, 329
MINTERN & ALLEN, 80
MITCHELL, John, 167
MONKHOUSE, J. R., 167
MOORE, Hiram, 139
MOORE & HASKELL (or Hascall), 72, 99, 144, 186, 206, 258
MORGAN, Dayton S., 350
MORLEY, William 160
MULDROW, ..., 75
MURDOCK, S. S., 296

NATIONAL CORDAGE COMPANY, 345
NEAME, Jr., ..., 174
NELSON, Samuel, 167
NESEN, Joseph, 202
NISHWITZ, ..., 334, 336
NORTHUMBERLAND, Duke of, 30
NOYES, L. W., 55

OGDEN, William B., 350
OGLE, Henry, 28-31, 45, 59, 60, 93, 98-100, 205, 219, 220, 224, 259, 260
OSBORNE, David M., 280, 306, 336, 351, 367
OSBORNE & COMPANY, David M., 251, 252, 272, 279, 308, 332
OUTHWAITE, John, 157, 160
OUTHWAITE, Thomas P., 157, 160

PAGE, Charles G., 145-148
PALMER, Aaron, 221
PALMER & WILLIAMS, 184, 224, 226, 336, 365
PARKER, Charles H., 298
PARKER, Holdon, 321
PARKER, L. H., 298
PARKER & STONE REAPER WORKS, 241, 287-289, 298, 301, 305, 306, 321-324, 328, 329
PARKINSON, Joseph G., 294
PARKINSON & PARKINSON, 309

PARRINGTON, John, 155
PARRINGTON, Joseph, 157
PARRINGTON, Thomas, 160
PARSONS, ..., 306
PASCHAL, ..., 308, 310
PATENTS granted: to James
  Plucknett, 20; to George Bell,
  47; to James Ten Eyck, 49; to
  William Manning, 49; to L. W.
  Noyes, 55; to Obed Hussey, 57;
  to Barnard Jackson, 80; to Cyrus
  H. McCormick, 86; to Palmer
  & Williams, 184; to F. S. Pease,
  186; to D. A. Church, 186; to
  Moore & Haskell, 186; to J.
  Read, 186; to F. Woodward, 187;
  to A. J. Cook, 188; to Samuel
  Johnston, 224; to Adams & Gif-
  ford, 228; to Mann & Mann, 230;
  to Hurlburt, 233; to Jonathan
  Haines, 257; to J. Manning, 259
PAXTON, Col. Thomas S., 84, 115,
  130
PAYNE, William H., 274
PEARCE, ... 319
PEASE, F. S., 186, 220
PEASE, Henry, 158
PEASE, J. W., 158
PECK, Ferdinand W., 368
PECK, H. P. K., 363, 365
PENNYMAN, Sir William, 161
PHILLIPS, ..., 160, 205, 208
PHILLIPS, Charles, 140
PHILLIPS, Thomas, 157
PIDGEON, ..., 29, 30
PIERCE, J. A., 73, 159-161, 168
PIERCE & STEVENS, 162
PIERSON, John, 158
PINKHAM, Lydia, 359
PITT, William, 18
PITTS BROTHERS, 255
P L A N O   MANUFACTURING
  COMPANY, 296, 329
PLUCKNETT, James, 20, 28, 45
POE, Edgar A., 64
POOLE, W. H., 364
PRATT, Edwin G., 68, 75, 290,
  291
PRIDMORE, Henry, 291, 292
PUSEY, ..., 158

RANDALL, Abram, 51-53, 89, 137,
  138, 141, 194, 195, 198, 203-208
RANNEY, S. Ellen McCormick,
  84
READ, Jonathan, 182, 184, 186,
  202, 205-207
REED (Reade), George, 157-159

REIFSNIDER, C. K., 357
RENWICK, ..., 248, 249, 273
RENWICK, Edward S., 266, 281
RENWICK, Henry B., 208
REYNOLDS, Jarvis, 68, 77, 281
RICE, Dan, 346
ROANE, ..., 76
ROBINSON, Thomas, 163, 164,
  167, 168
ROBINSON & PERRY, 322
ROCKWOOD, Otis, 189, 192
ROGERS, Henry, 79
RUGG, George, 6, 99, 189, 190, 192,
  193, 238
RUNGER, Fred, 124
RUSH, John H., 84

SAGE, George R., 342
SALMON, ..., 22, 24, 44, 45,
  205, 219
SAMUELSON, ..., 159-161
SANDWICH   MANUFACTUR-
  ING COMPANY, 250
SCAITH, Edward, 167
SCHNEBLEY, ..., 98, 140,
  141, 187, 200, 205-207, 237
SCHNEBLY & SCHNEBLY, 257
SCHULTZ, John H. B., 84
SCOTT, Alexander, 25, 44, 206
SEIBERLING, John F, 220
SEWARD, William H., 104, 203,
  347, 351, 354
SEYMOUR, William H., 171, 350
SEYMOUR & MORGAN, 99, 138,
  139, 141, 197, 201, 202, 207, 208,
  221, 224, 225, 336, 354
SHAVER, Jackson R., 190
SHERWOOD, Allen, 339
SHIELDS, James Hall, 82
SHIELDS, Mary Caroline, 84
SHOGREN, ..., 251
SHUGERT, S. T., 363
SHULTZ, Henry, 84
SMITH, L. J., 24, 25, 45, 48, 79,
  89, 90, 219, 259
SONDES, Lord, 174
SOUTHERN, ..., 152
SPAULDING, George H., 203,
  271-274, 283-286, 302, 304, 305,
  308, 311, 315, 318, 367
STABLER, Edward, 68, 69, 72, 73,
  74, 149
STANTON, Edwin M., 347, 351,
  354
STAPELIN, W. D., 284, 285
STEBBINS, F. S., 296
STEELE, Mrs. E., 109
STEELE, John, 100, 109, 112

STEELE, William, 84
STEELE'S TAVERN, 118
STERRITT & GIBBS, 287
STEVENS, ..., 159-161
STEWARD, ..., 193, 204, 251
STEWARD, George, 255
STEWARD, John F., 252, 255, 323, 362
STEWARD, Lewis, 254, 255
STEWARD, Marcus, 187, 188, 192, 237, 238
STEWARD & GAMMON, 274
STEWARD & MARSH, 238, 256, 276
STONE, Gustavus, 298
STONEBRAKER, John, 64
STOREY, Wilbur F., 352
STORLE, ..., 324
STRAWN, David, 192
SWIFT, R. B., 359, 361, 362, 365
SYLLA, Philo, 228

TALCOTT, ..., 139
TEN EYCK, James, 49
THOMPSON, ..., 160, 162
THOMPSON, Henry Stephen, 155, 168, 169
THOMPSON, Horatio, 84, 115, 131
THOMPSON, M. C., 315, 327
THOMPSON, N. C., 267, 287, 294, 295, 297-300
THOMPSON, P. C., 157
THOMPSON, William, 167, 320
THURSTON, Benjamin F., 280
THWAITES, Reuben Gold, 355
TILGHMAN, Tench, 65, 75
TODD, ..., 46
TODD & RAFFERTY, 345
TOWNSEND, D. I., 192
TROTTER, G. D., 158
TYLDEN, Sir John, 174

VAN VALKENBURGH, ..., 246
VANE, Lord Harry, 167-170
VAUGHAN, John, 158

WAGNER, Ausbert H., 258
WALDRON, John, 284-286, 312
WARDER, Benjamin H., 351
WARDER & MITCHELL, 241

WARSON, ..., 273
WATSON, Peter H., 145, 148, 248, 266, 347
WATSON, William, 167, 266
WATSON & RENWICK, 234, 248, 267, 304
WATSON, RENWICK & WATSON, 339
WEBBER REAPER WORKS, 321
WEMYSS, General, ..., 171
WERNER, ..., 246
WEST, E. A., 296
WETHERELL, William, 155, 160
WHARTON, J. T., 158-160
WHARTON, Rev. W. F., 158, 160, 161, 164, 167-169
WHEELER, Cyrenus, 263, 367
WHITE, D. T., 213
WHITE, George, 168
WHITELY, William, N. or M., 77, 80, 224, 300, 338, 351, 353, 359
WHITELY FASSELER & KELLEY, 218, 325
WHITENACK, Thomas S., 222
WHITFIELD, John, 167
WHITNEY, Newell, 308, 310, 359
WILLIAMS, S. G., 221
WILSON, Isaac, 158, 159
WILSON, Woodrow, 353
WINONA HARVESTER COMPANY, 274, 292
WITHINGTON, Charles B., 273, 277-281, 315, 324, 334, 354
WOOD, Walter A., 226, 246, 266, 274, 323, 336, 351, 367
WOOD MOWING & REAPING MACHINE COMPANY, 218, 273, 275, 279, 304, 306, 328, 332, 337, 344
WOODCROFT, ..., 47, 192, 219
WOODWARD, ..., 141, 189, 204, 205, 221, 237
WOODWARD, F., 187
WOODWARD, William R., 146
WRIGHT, ..., 47

YATES, John B., 32, 220
YOUNG, McClintock, 185, 224, 225, 334, 354

ZETLAND, Earl of, 158, 159